salon FUNDAMENTALS™

Learning is a treasure that will follow its owner everywhere.~ Chinese Proverb

A Resource for Your Skin Care Career

D1478033

salon FUNDAMENTALS™ ESTHETICS

A Resource for Your Skin Care Career

STUDY GUIDE

Clif St. Germain, Ph.D., creator and author

Janet Fisher, developer and author

© 2004 Clif St. Germain

ISBN-13: 978-0-9742723-7-5
ISBN-10: 0-9742723-7-X

2nd Edition
23rd Printing, December 2019
Printed in Hong Kong

Pivot Point International, Inc.
World Headquarters
8725 W. Higgins Road, Suite 700
Chicago, IL 60631 USA

847-866-0500
pivot-point.com

salon FUNDAMENTALS™

Career Essentials

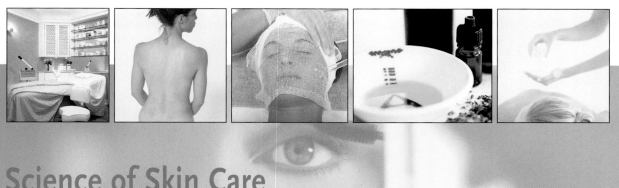

The Science of Skin Care

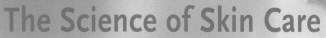

atments and Services

A Resource for Your Skin Care Career

CONTENTS

SALON FUNDAMENTALS™ ESTHETICS STUDY GUIDE

OVERVIEW I

UNIT 1 CAREER ESSENTIALS

CHAPTER 1, PERSONAL DEVELOPMENT 1
  SMART NOTES 2
  BRAIN CONDITIONER 23

CHAPTER 2, PROFESSIONAL DEVELOPMENT 29
  SMART NOTES 30
  BRAIN CONDITIONER 57

CHAPTER 3, BUSINESS BASICS 63
  SMART NOTES 64
  BRAIN CONDITIONER . . . .

UNIT 2 THE SCIENCE OF SKIN CARE

CHAPTER 4, SKIN CARE CENTER ECOLOGY 89
  SMART NOTES 90
  BRAIN CONDITIONER 116

CHAPTER 5, ANATOMY 121
  SMART NOTES 122
  BRAIN CONDITIONER 164

CHAPTER 6, ELECTRICITY AND ELECTRICAL EQUIPMENT . . . 173
  SMART NOTES 174
  BRAIN CONDITIONER 201

CHAPTER 7, CHEMISTRY 211
  SMART NOTES 212
  BRAIN CONDITIONER 230

CHAPTER 8, SKIN PHYSIOLOGY 237
  SMART NOTES 238
  BRAIN CONDITIONER 262

UNIT 3 TREATMENTS AND SERVICES

CHAPTER 9, CLIENT CARE 267
  SMART NOTES 268
  BRAIN CONDITIONER 269

CHAPTER 10, FACIALS 291
  SMART NOTES 292
  BASIC FACIAL RUBRIC 305
  BASIC FACIAL WITH MULTIFUNCTION
    MACHINE RUBRIC 307
  BASIC FACIAL WITH GALVANIC/
    DESINCRUSTATION RUBRIC 309
  BASIC FACIAL WITH GALVANIC/
    IONTOPHORESIS RUBRIC 311
  BASIC FACIAL WITH INDIRECT
    HIGH FREQUENCY RUBRIC 313
  BASIC FACIAL WITH DIRECT
    HIGH FREQUENCY RUBRIC 315
  BRAIN CONDITIONER 322

CHAPTER 11, HAIR REMOVAL 331
  SMART NOTES 332
  EYEBROW WAXING RUBRIC 344
  UPPER LIP WAXING RUBRIC 346
  UNDERARM WAXING RUBRIC 348
  BIKINI WAXING RUBRIC 350
  LOWER LEG WAXING RUBRIC 352
  BRAIN CONDITIONER 359

CHAPTER 12, MAKEUP 365
  SMART NOTES 366
  BASIC DAYTIME MAKEUP RUBRIC 385
  BASIC EVENING MAKEUP RUBRIC 387
  BRAIN CONDITIONER 393

CHAPTER 13, ADVANCED TREATMENTS 401
  SMART NOTES 402
  BRAIN CONDITIONER 418

CHAPTER 14, ESTHETICIANS IN THE MEDICAL FIELD . . . 428
  SMART NOTES 429
  BRAIN CONDITIONER 445

GLOSSARY . . . .

OVERVIEW

Welcome to the *Study Guide* that accompanies your *Salon Fundamentals Esthetics*™ textbook.

Maybe you wonder why there are two books instead of one. That's easy enough. Your text was written by experts, women and men who have proven their skills in the world you want to enter. Your *Study Guide* will be written by YOU. It is the place where learning will become your own. **Everything you need to know to be successful in** *Salon Fundamentals Esthetics*™ **is included in your Study Guide.** It is designed to boost your learning potential and take the fear and confusion out of your professional preparation.

Because everyone learns in different ways, it is reasonable to expect parts of this *Study Guide* to be easy for you and others difficult. Most of your life you have practiced certain ways of learning and avoided others. Take a moment now to think of some ways of learning that you avoid whenever you can. Over the next few days, talk with a few other people and find out what ways of learning they avoid.

Guess what? Most of those preferred and avoided ways of learning will be included in this *Study Guide* in order to make your learning more complete. You can gain confidence by thinking of your *Study Guide* as a jigsaw puzzle. Each piece involves a special way of learning, of using brainpower. Put the easiest pieces together first. (Remember that the easiest pieces for you may be hardest for someone else.) That way you will have more experience when you attempt the more difficult pieces. The more you practice the difficult parts, the easier they will become and the **smarter your brain becomes**. Successful students are not born after all. They evolve by developing a diverse set of learning tools that help them connect new information to what they already know. This *Study Guide* aims to help you build as diverse a set of learning tools as you possibly can.

The **Salon Fundamentals™ Esthetics Study Guide** groups many of these learning puzzle pieces into **MINDFRAMES**. Each MINDFRAME is a specific way of using your brainpower to make you smarter. Your *Study Guide* is organized around seven different MINDFRAMES or puzzle pieces: PREVIEWING, NAMING, CONNECTING, SELF-CHECKING, APPLYING, SELF-TESTING and JOURNALING. We don't mean to suggest that each MINDFRAME is completely separate from the others. They overlap in rich and rewarding ways just the way your mind itself does. One MINDFRAME flows into another.

To help you identify the specific MINDFRAME each activity requires, an icon is placed at the bottom of every *Study Guide* page. That way you know what kind of brainpower you will be using most on that page. The MINDFRAME you need on each page is highlighted in pink. On some pages, two MINDFRAMES are suggested. The following information introduces you to each MINDFRAME and shows how it works in your *Study Guide*.

MINDFRAME 1: PREVIEWING

Previewing sets the stage for purposeful learning. It enables you to get the big picture, the overall design of what you will study before you turn your attention to the details.

Research tells us that 80% of what you need to learn is contained in 20% of the material you study. Known as the 80-20 rule, this finding supports the importance of knowing what to study before you begin. Your *Study Guide* aims to take the mystery out of what's important by showcasing the most important material on the first page or two of each chapter. It gives you a sneak preview of the whole chapter.

Let's see how it works. Here is a sample of what you will see on the first page of each *Study Guide* chapter. The VALUE

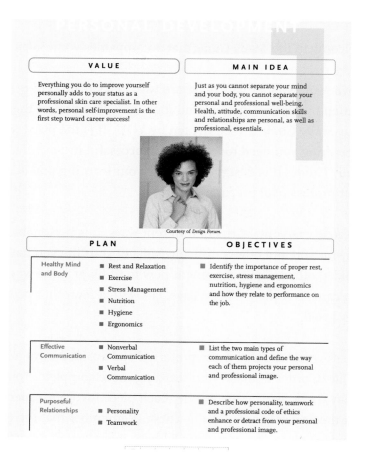

states why this material is important to you personally. The MAIN IDEA states the fundamental message of the chapter. The PLAN gives a preview of the general content of the chapter. The OBJECTIVES communicate the expectations you will be prepared to meet once you successfully complete the chapter. The OBJECTIVES identify each new section of the **Smart Notes**. Together these pieces represent the "warm-up" stages of learning. Can you imagine an athlete entering a competition before warming up? A student needs warm-up time as well! You can warm-up by surveying the chapter and generating a few insights and questions before beginning. Such a warm-up will greatly improve your concentration, memory and learning.

If you've already looked at a chapter in your *Salon Fundamentals* textbook, this first page lineup in your *Study Guide* will look familiar. You have a VALUE, a MAIN IDEA, a PLAN and OBJECTIVES there as well. That's because we want to make sure that you focus on these four important areas:

- Its importance to you personally (VALUE)
- Its major message (MAIN IDEA)
- The way the ideas in the chapter will be developed (PLAN)
- The expected outcomes of your learning (OBJECTIVES)

MINDFRAME 2: NAMING

Once you've seen the big picture, your MINDFRAME shifts. You begin NAMING what you are coming to know, putting it into your own words, arranging the material in a form that makes sense to you.

Some years ago, Dr. Walter Paulk, from Cornell University, developed an excellent system of note-taking. This second MINDFRAME is modeled on his system and is called **SmartNotes**™. Look at a sample page of **SmartNotes**. What do you see? Take a moment to identify how these pages are built and how many ways they offer clues for your learning.

The top of each **SmartNotes** page identifies the Chapter name, the Section—the main topic for **SmartNotes** and the corresponding page numbers in the textbook to consult for additional information.

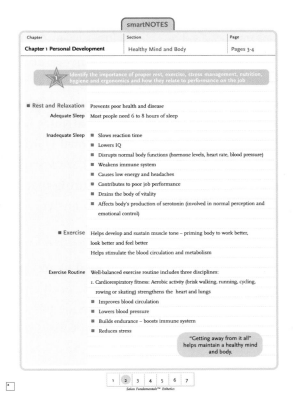

Accustom yourself right away to referring to those pages in the text whenever you have questions or want clarification. That simple practice will deepen your learning and save you time. Instead of searching aimlessly for answers, you will know right where to go. Notice also that the Sections correspond to the main divisions of the PLAN and that the smaller note sections reflect the OBJECTIVES.

The rest of the page is divided into two columns. Key terms and ideas are listed in the smaller left column. They are presented in an order that you can use eventually to tell a story about what you are learning. "Story" in this sense does not mean necessarily the "Once upon a time" variety. Instead story means any narrative or organized way of presenting the material that will make sense to you and help you recall it at will.

Here are recommendations for using these pages:

- Pay particular attention to the key terms and ideas in the left column.
- Note your thoughts in the right-hand column while reading your textbook.
- Refer to the **Glossary** at the end of your *Study Guide* for terms that you may need as a quick review.
- Add what you hear during a class discussion to your notes in the right column.
- Try to use your growing set of notes to tell a story (as story is described above).

How exactly do you fill in the right-hand column of your **SmartNotes** using the prompts in the left column? We would like to encourage you to use short phrases, pictures, cartoon-like doodles, symbols or even questions to generate your own definitions and descriptions. Include only the most essential information—in small places, only key words; use pictures or phrases in larger spaces. The spaces have been designed according to the relative importance of the ideas in the text. Many students already have wonderful spatial intelligence. The design of your *Study Guide* encourages you to put that spatial intelligence to work learning the content you are studying. If you need additional note space, a blank **SmartNotes** template page will be included in your teacher's Support Materials. You or your teacher can duplicate that page whenever necessary.

Your notes do not need to make sense to anyone but yourself. **If they help you learn and remember this material, they are indeed SmartNotes because they're helping to make you smarter!** By translating the ideas of the chapter into your own words and images, you are actively processing the material. You are making sense of what you are learning. You are actually rewriting your textbook in ways that make sense to you. The only thing that is not recommended is that you copy answers word for word from your textbook. Copying answers in someone else's words usually makes them more difficult to remember.

SmartNotes contain a running total of all you are learning about a particular idea. Simply completing this section guarantees that you are on the right track to learning the most important ideas. **SmartNotes** also provide a ready-made personal outline for connecting important ideas and building references you will need to deepen your understanding of the material to be learned.

MINDFRAME 3: CONNECTING

Successfully NAMING what you are learning lays the foundation for making connections of all kinds. Your CONNECTING skill rapidly increases your ability to learn and retain what you learn. Sometimes in your *Study Guide*, CONNECTING activities have been inserted within the **SmartNotes**. Other times they have been placed after your **SmartNotes**. The most creative brains are always seeking novelty. For that reason, you will see many different kinds of activities included as connectors. Our hope is that you enjoy them all!

One excellent way for your brain to make connections is by building **Thinking Map**s. **Thinking Map**s create pictures of what you know using shapes, patterns, words, doodles, and connections of all kinds. Once again your spatial intelligence has a chance to shine. **Thinking Maps make your thoughts visible so that you can think about them in different ways.** They promote discussion and help you explore specific topics in creative and organized ways. You can use them as 'roadmaps' to deeper understanding. Because they tap into your ability to create relationships among the concepts you are learning, **Thinking Map**s are powerful memory joggers. Once you can picture how words and ideas fit together, you will remember them more easily.

LEARNING   CONNECTION   Thinking Map

Create a Thinking Map to help yourself make sense of how your SmartNotes fit together. Use all of the words in the Jump-Start Box as well as pictures to make a visual that will help you connect the important ideas in this section to each other. Be creative!

Thinking Maps appeal to the creative side of your intellect as well as to your spatial intelligence. For this reason, they are usually enjoyable for students who are entering a very creative profession. These maps of colors, pictures and symbols, when coupled with words, create powerful associations in your brain that will ensure better understanding and recall.

You're probably wondering: **How do I make a Thinking Map?**

First...   Start with a topic and circle it in the center of your paper. In your *Study Guide*, you'll notice that the easy part has been done for you.

Then...   Add branches to hold key subtopics. Gather subtopics from your memory, your **SmartNotes**, the PLAN or from the **Jump Start Box** of terms and ideas placed for you on each **Thinking Map** page. Branches can also be categories such as who, what, where, when, how or why.

Next...   Use the words in the **Jump Start Box** to explore all the possible links you can create. If you have questions about any words, you may also refer to the **Glossary** that has been included at the end of your *Study Guide*.

Finally...   Share and compare. Let others see your map and gain ideas and connections from you. Add to your map realizations you have while looking at someone else's map. Shared knowledge makes each person better.

As you follow and intermingle these steps, make sure that you personalize your map with your style. Use more than two colors. Doodle. Vary size and shape for effect. Be creative. Your map can continue to grow in extent and interrelationships. You can always add more insights as you discover them. There is no single, correct way to build a **Thinking Map**. In fact, each **Thinking Map** you may make for this *Study Guide* will probably be different from the others. You are not making carbon copies. You are creating original images of your growing understanding of a topic.

MINDFRAME 4: SELF-CHECKING

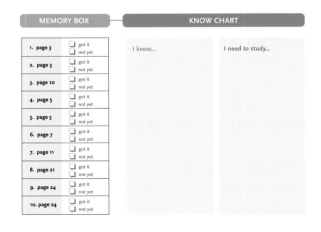

The connections you are making need to stand up to scrutiny, your own first of all. They need to be challenged for accuracy and depth. In the past, you may have regarded that as a job of a teacher or outsider. No longer. That's what your own brain does for you during SELF-CHECKING. Your brain actually doubles back on itself and asks questions: how well am I relating to this new material? Do I know it well enough to advance to the next step in my education and professional development? The more skilled you become at SELF-CHECKING, the more prepared you will be to learn the rest of the information in the chapter. It offers a diagnostic check midway through a chapter to validate and reinforce to yourself that you really are learning, that much of what you need to know is already in place. SELF-CHECKING allows you to tell yourself you're doing fine, to give yourself a pat on the back.

It is also a quick reminder to go back and pick up anything you missed along the way. The better a student you become, the more you will self-check automatically. You will know that before you move forward you need to pause and check your location. You pause to pay attention to certain areas of the text you might ordinarily skip. Remember what we said earlier about ways of learning you avoid? Your natural learning style tends to skip what it considers unpleasant. SELF-CHECKING cues your brain about possible gaps that may exist and gives you time to fill those gaps with new learning.

In this *Study Guide*, your SELF-CHECKING opportunity takes the form of **The Challenge**. You are encouraged to review your *Study Guide* before completing **The Challenge**. The questions represent the most basic ideas in the chapter. You should expect yourself to get at least 80% of these answers correct before you continue on with your work in the rest of the *Study Guide*. If you find **The Challenge** questions too difficult, take time to return to your textbook and your SmartNotes and re-learn the material. You may also wish to review with someone else or approach your teacher for extra help and suggestions.

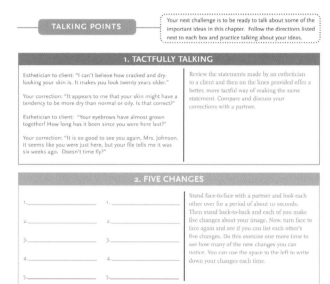

How do you know exactly which answers you have correct? Following every **Challenge** is a **Memory Box**, a self-monitoring activity designed to provide you with immediate feedback about your progress. Study the sample on the previous page. First you use the page references to look up the answers in your textbook. Then check "got it" for all correct answers and "not yet" for all incorrect ones. Next, using the **Know Chart**, record the correct answers in the **I Know** column. Correct the incorrect answers and record the corrected response in the **I Need to Study** column. In this way, you can monitor your progress and clearly determine what you need to study to become more successful.

MINDFRAME 5: APPLYING

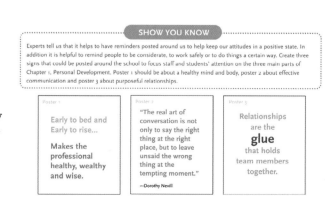

Here is your long-awaited chance to put your knowledge into action. Many of the finest students feel at their best when they are actually doing something. After all, you have the goal of being a skin care specialist because you sense a personal talent for doing creative work with clients and their skin care needs. There are many different activities in the APPLYING sections of your *Study Guide*. Three of these activities are **Talking Point**s, **Show You Know** and the **Rubrics**.

SmartNotes and **Thinking Map**s give you lots to talk about with others. In fact, you really don't 'own' what you learn unless you can talk about it. Part of your reputation will rest on your ability to talk clearly and confidently with your clients. We want you to graduate with that ability and not have to scramble to develop it after you leave school. That's why we created the **Talking Point**s part of your Guide to encourage you to talk about what you know and how you know it. Talking about your ideas is a great way to discover your comfort level with the information. It is another concrete way to monitor your progress and build your skills.

In order to refine your communication skills, you need practice in a non-threatening environment. In your *Study Guide*, each **Talking Point** is placed next to a miniature 'card,' representing an index card. On it you can jot down your key points. You may choose to transfer some **Talking Point**s to real cards and use the cards to role play actual conversations. These practice conversations can be shared with a friend, a parent, classmate or anyone who will listen. The goal of the activity is to learn to explain and communicate your ideas with poise and confidence.

Many chapters have a **Show You Know** project designed to give you the opportunity to be creative and expressive. These activities will reinforce to you that you really do understand and can apply what you are learning. If you devote some time and energy to them, you will begin to realize how smart you really are.

Each **Show You Know** is matched to specific professional guidelines in the esthetics industry. By completing each one, you will gain valuable exposure to our professional ideals and have fun demonstrating that you can apply what you are learning.

In all the practical chapters, your central way of APPLYING what you learn will be through practicing the procedures for that skill. Each procedure has its own evaluation form called a RUBRIC. The word RUBRIC translates "something written in red" from the Latin word for red or red chalk. It means simply a set of standardized directions. Why do you think important directions might be written in red?

In your *Study Guide*, a RUBRIC is a self-assessment tool that will help you gauge your level of performance. It is designed to compare your skill and technique to industry standards. On the following page is a sample of a RUBRIC. Look at the page and see what you can learn immediately about how RUBRICS are set up. You see under the directions the name of the procedure you will be practicing. Then you see a bulleted list of steps under "Preparation," "Procedure" and "Completion." Each bulleted item is followed by three purple boxes, Levels 1, 2 and 3. For each RUBRIC form you complete, you will be asked to check for each item your level of accomplishment at that time.

RUBRIC

This rubric is designed to compare your skill to industry expectations. Indicate your present level of performance by checking the appropriate box. Your teacher will direct you in the completion of this rubric.

Rubric Assessment

Industry Standard – to meet entry level proficiency, industry standards require that you:
- Provide and conduct basic manicure and pedicure services in a safe environment, free from disease.

	Level 1	Level 2	Level 3	To Improve, I Need To:	Teacher Assessment
PREPARATION					
	☐	☐	☐		⬚
PROCEDURE					
	☐	☐	☐		
COMPLETION					
	☐	☐	☐		⬚
	☐	☐	☐		⬚
	☐	☐	☐		⬚

Total = Addition of all Teacher Assessment Boxes ⬚

Percentage = Student Score Divided by 81 (Highest Possible Score)   **Percentage**   _____ %

Here's how you will know one level from another:

Level 1 means you're still "In Progress"
You complete the task with assistance and/or prompting.
You complete the task with inconsistent quality.
You perform the task with several errors evident in technique.
You describe the technique with vague understanding.

Level 2 means you're "Getting Better."
You complete the task alone.
You complete the task approaching the industry standard.
You perform the task with occasional errors evident in technique.
You describe the technique with prompting

Level 3 means you've reached "Entry-Level Proficiency" for the beginning professional.
You complete the task alone.
You complete the task and meet the industry standard described in the text.
You perform the task with very few errors evident in technique.
You communicate and reflect upon the technique to others.
You complete the entire procedure in accordance with required timing.

Next to the boxes is a line on which you can jot down some area in which you wish to improve. Finally, when you are ready, you can ask your teacher to complete a RUBRIC form for you. The teacher will assess your level of competence and place a 1, 2 or 3 in each "Teacher Assessment" box, total your score and determine your percentage for that procedure.

As you use the RUBRIC, remember that some tasks will be easier for you than others. On these tasks you will achieve "Entry-Level Proficiency" sooner. For more difficult tasks, your RUBRIC – no matter in what color you write it – will remind you of the areas in which you need to practice your technique.

MINDFRAME 6: SELF-TESTING

The **Salon Fundamentals Esthetics™ Study Guide** is devoted to taking the mystery and fear out of tests for students. That's why SELF-TESTING is so important. If you practice enough by testing yourself, your actual licensure exam will not seem as threatening. Our aim is to have you prepared, competent and confident from the time you walk into the examining room through the rest of your professional life.

The activity designed for SELF-TESTING is called a **Brain Conditioner**. The **Brain Conditioner** is a test-event designed to simulate your certification test. Why would we put you through something like this? Isn't one test at the end bad enough? Well, guess what. Practice really does make perfect. If you practice the actual test-event, you will learn many valuable things like:

- How to relax enough to deal with test anxiety
- How to skip hard questions until later
- How to space your energy and brainpower over the entire test so that you have as much energy at theend of the test as you had the beginning
- How to avoid discouragement if you don't know every answer
- How to read each question calmly and understand what it is asking
- How to stay in the flow state (a positive place) as long as you can

Although the **Brain Conditioner** is an actual test-event, it is also a learning activity. For that reason, you should use your **Memory Box** just as you did after **The Challenge** to gather information you still need to review a bit more.

MINDFRAME 7: JOURNALING

True learning is a deeply personal experience. It engages the person you are and begins your transformation into the person you wish to become. As this growth is happening in you, you need some kind of record of what is going on with your feelings as well as in your thinking. **SmartNotes** and other activities here in the *Study Guide* give you records of your thinking. This final MINDFRAME, JOURNALING, offers the opportunity to honor what you are feeling and realizing and questioning at levels even deeper than thought.

At the end of each chapter, it is important to jot down your feelings about what you have just studied. Especially important to note are things that surprised you, learning tasks that you found difficult and how you dealt with those difficulties. Also helpful to record are suggestions you received from friends or others that might help you enjoy learning more. You will be surprised how your comments change as you go through the chapters of your *Salon Fundamentals* textbook, giving your energy to each MINDFRAME in its turn.

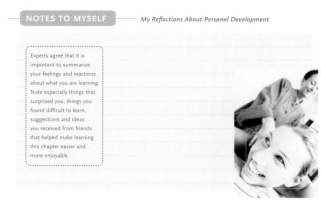

Now you have an overview of this entire book, your book, the place where the knowledge of the experts takes on personal meaning. Everyone's textbook is identical. Everyone's Study Guide, if done correctly, will be unique. Your mind will frame the material to suit your specific learning preferences and needs. You have just received the 'guided tour' of seven of the most common MINDFRAMES you'll be using throughout this Study Guide. In addition, pages 453-490 hold a quick reference Glossary of important terms from your textbook.

You can make your Study Guide a real part of your professional journey by adding to it and improving it every day. If you do, new possibilities for creativity and opportunity will appear in your work. **As you improve your Study Guide**, **you improve yourself.** It is designed to be a developing picture, a portfolio, of what you can do and your commitment to your future. Before you begin ask yourself: Am I ready to step into a fascinating future? Let's go...

Best wishes,

The staff of *Salon Fundamentals Esthetics*

VALUE

Everything you do to improve yourself personally adds to your status as a professional skin care specialist. In other words, personal self-improvement is the first step toward career success!

MAIN IDEA

Just as you cannot separate your mind and your body, you cannot separate your personal and professional well-being. Health, attitude, communication skills and relationships are personal, as well as professional, essentials.

Courtesy of *Design Forum*.

PLAN

Healthy Mind and Body
- Rest and Relaxation
- Exercise
- Stress Management
- Nutrition
- Hygiene
- Ergonomics

Effective Communication
- Nonverbal Communication
- Verbal Communication

Purposeful Relationships
- Personality
- Teamwork
- Ethics

OBJECTIVES

- Identify the importance of proper rest, exercise, stress management, nutrition, hygiene and ergonomics and how they relate to performance on the job.

- List the two main types of communication and define the way each of them projects your personal and professional image.

- Describe how personality, teamwork and a professional code of ethics enhance or detract from your personal and professional image.

Chapter	Section	Page
Chapter 1 Personal Development	Healthy Mind and Body	Pages 3-4

1 Identify the importance of proper rest, exercise, stress management, nutrition, hygiene and ergonomics and how they relate to performance on the job

■ **Rest and Relaxation**

Adequate Sleep

Inadequate Sleep ■

■

■

■

■

■

■

■

■ **Exercise**

Exercise Routine   Well-balanced exercise routine includes three disciplines:

1.

■

■

■

■

"Getting away from it all" helps maintain a healthy mind and body.

Exercise Routine

Three disciplines of a well-balanced exercise routine, cont'd.:

2.

3.

- ■
- ■
- ■
- ■

■ **Stress Management**

Stress

Round out exercise program by exercising your mind

smartNOTES

Chapter	Section	Page
Chapter 1 Personal Development	**Healthy Mind and Body**	**Pages 5-7**

■ Nutrition

"You are what you eat."

Calories used by body to:

■

■

■

RDA Guidelines

RDA = Recommended Dietary Allowances (appropriate nutrient intakes)

■ Calories:

■ Carbohydrates

■ Protein:

■ Fat:

Calories

Carbohydrates

Proteins

smartNOTES

Chapter	Section	Page
Chapter 1 Personal Development	**Healthy Mind and Body**	**Page 7**

Fats

Other Essential Nutrients

Water

Primary functions:

- ◼
- ◼
- ◼

Lack of sufficient water can cause:

- ◼
- ◼
- ◼
- ◼
- ◼

Mayo Clinic recommends 12 cups per day for men and 9 cups for women. This total includes water from all sources, even food!

Sodas, juices, coffee and caffeinated teas cannot replace water

Vitamins and Minerals

Chapter	Section	Page
Chapter 1 Personal Development	Healthy Mind and Body	Pages 7-9

■ Hygiene

PERSONAL HYGIENE	PUBLIC HYGIENE
■	■
■	■ 4 primary health hazards:
■	-
■	-
	-
■	-
	■

> **Halitosis = bad breath**
> Brush teeth 2-3 times per day

Body Odor Prevention

Prevent offensive body odors by:

■

■

■

■

■

■

■

Image

Hair Care

Guideline If your hair touches your face when you tilt your head forward, it should be pulled back.

| 1 | 2 | 3 | 4 | 5 | 6 | 7 |

smartNOTES

Chapter	Section	Page
Chapter 1 Personal Development	Healthy Mind and Body	Pages 9-11

Skin Care

Makeup

Hands

Feet

Clothing

Jewelry

Chapter	Section	Page
Chapter 1 Personal Development	Healthy Mind and Body	**Pages 11-12**

Posture

POSTURE DOs	POSTURE DON'Ts
■	■
■	
	■
■	■
■	

■ **Ergonomics**

Neck and Back

Foot and Leg

Hand and Wrist

Shoulder

Preventative
Measures

Neck and Back ✓

✓

✓

✓

✓

✓

✓

✓

✓

✓

✓

Feet and Legs ✓

✓

✓

✓

✓

✓

Chapter	Section	Page
Chapter 1 Personal Development	Healthy Mind and Body	Page 14

Preventative Measures ✓

Hands and Wrists

✓

✓

✓

✓

Shoulders ✓

✓

✓

✓

✓

What are the first 5 things you notice when meeting someone for the first time?
1. _____
2. _____
3. _____
4. _____
5. _____

What are the first 5 impressions someone meeting you for the first time might have?
1. _____
2. _____
3. _____
4. _____
5. _____

LEARNING CONNECTION — Image Points

This quick and easy exercise is designed to be a fun, interactive way to determine an uncluttered, understated appearance.
An "eye-arresting" feature is considered a point. Fashion experts have established 14 points or less as the median to be considered well-dressed. Calculate your points using the chart shown here to see where you score in relation to 14.

___COLOR	Each color in a costume equals 1 point.
___SHOES	Plain, simple shoes are 1 point each; add extra points for "eye-arresting" details on shoes, including open toes, open heels, bows, large buckles, chains, rope or multi-colored shoes
___STOCKINGS	1 point only if they are a color different from natural leg color.
___JEWELRY	All jewelry, except wedding rings, counts as 1 point each, including watches, chains, bracel etc. If jewelry is multi-colored, count each color as a point.
	Two earrings equal 1 point if they are simple.
___GLASSES	1 point, if simple.
___HANDBAGS	1 point, if simple. Add extra points for chains, buckles, extra colors, etc.
___NAIL POLISH	1 point. Add an extra point if toenails have polish.
___BUTTONS	1 point each if they are not the same color as garment.
___ACCESSORIES	1 point for bows, ruffles, contrasting belts, scarves, etc.
___HAIR	1 point for red hair.
___MAKEUP	1 point for eyeliner with more than 3 shades of eye shadow.

Total Points

1	2	3	4	5	6	7

Chapter	Section	Page
Chapter 1 Personal Development	Effective Communication	**Pages 15-17**

2 List the two main types of communication, and define the way each of them projects your personal and professional image

Communication

■ Nonverbal Communication

Body language – messages exchanged without speaking

✓ ✓ ✓

✓ ✓ ✓

✓ ✓

■ Verbal Communication

Voice and Tone –

Grammar

Chapter	Section	Page
Chapter 1 Personal Development	Effective Communication	**Pages 17-20**

Two-Way
Communication

Steps to Becoming a Better Communicator

1.

2.

3.

4.

5.

6.

7.

8.

Active/Reflective
Listening

Active Listening:

■

■

■

■

Reflective Listening:

■

■

■

Successful
Communication

Chapter	Section	Page
Chapter 1 Personal Development	Effective Communication	**Pages 15-20**

Successful
Communication

What causes communication to break down?
(For possible answers direct students to pages 15-20.)

LEARNING **CONNECTION**

Listening Cue

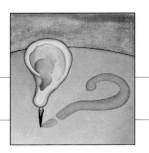

Listening is one of the easiest skills to perform, but the most difficult for most people to remember to do. Sometimes, when first building a skill or habit, it is good to have a 'cue' that can serve as a reminder. For this Learning Connection on listening, complete the cue card below and place it close to you as you work to serve as a reminder.

1	2	3	4	5	6	7

Chapter	Section	Page
Chapter 1 Personal Development	Healthy Mind and Body	**Pages 21-24**

3 Describe how personality, teamwork and a professional code of ethics enhance or detract from your personal and professional image

■ **Personality**

Winning Personality Traits

Attitude

Essential Elements of Purposeful Relationship:

1.

2.

3.

4.

Habits

■ **Teamwork**

■ **Ethics**

Chapter	Section	Page
Chapter 1 Personal Development	Healthy Mind and Body	**Pages 24-25**

Professional Code of Ethics

Code of Ethics

★

★

★

★

★

★

★

★

★

Before you can care for others, you must first care for yourself

Have you known someone that has made a personality change?

How did that person achieve the desired change?

Use this fun Lipstick Personality Indicator to see if the lipstick you use
is a true indicator of your personality.

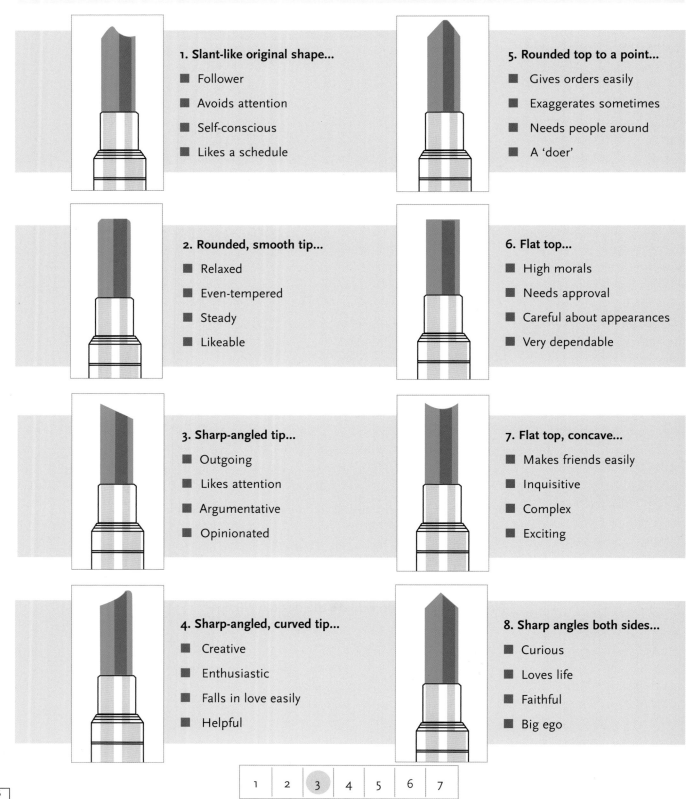

1. Slant-like original shape...
- Follower
- Avoids attention
- Self-conscious
- Likes a schedule

2. Rounded, smooth tip...
- Relaxed
- Even-tempered
- Steady
- Likeable

3. Sharp-angled tip...
- Outgoing
- Likes attention
- Argumentative
- Opinionated

4. Sharp-angled, curved tip...
- Creative
- Enthusiastic
- Falls in love easily
- Helpful

5. Rounded top to a point...
- Gives orders easily
- Exaggerates sometimes
- Needs people around
- A 'doer'

6. Flat top...
- High morals
- Needs approval
- Careful about appearances
- Very dependable

7. Flat top, concave...
- Makes friends easily
- Inquisitive
- Complex
- Exciting

8. Sharp angles both sides...
- Curious
- Loves life
- Faithful
- Big ego

| 1 | 2 | 3 | 4 | 5 | 6 | 7 |

In many cases in order to fully understand a topic, it is important to know its cause, what the effect of that cause is and what the solution could be. A C.E.S (Cause – Effect – Solution) Chart is designed to help you collect information for your review of these three important components. Complete the chart below by filling in the missing information. An example is shown in the first row.

CAUSE	EFFECT	SOLUTION
3 hours of sleep for 4 nights in a row	Lack of energy, slowed reaction time, headaches	Get 6 to 8 hours of sleep per night
	Weak circulation, low muscle tone and agility, muscle spasms, high blood pressure	
		Bring moderation and balance to your life
Female calorie count of 3,000 calories per day		
Drinks one 8-ounce glass of water per day and weighs 150 pounds		
Wears soiled clothes three days in a row without laundering, but adds extra fragrance to compensate		
	Oily hair hangs forward and covers face while esthetician works	
	Makeup runs down face in dark streaks while esthetician works	
Wears long, artificial nails		
Wears pointed-toe, uncomfortable shoes during work hours		
Wears tight-fitting slacks, low-cut, scoop neck tops with long dangling earrings that jingle when esthetician walks		

Match the term from Column A with the corresponding description in Column B by placing the letter of the term in the box provided in front of the description.

Column A		Column B
A. Habits		Appropriate nutrient intakes established by U.S. Government
B. Vertebrae		Swollen veins
C. Tendonitis		Condition that numbs and weakens hand and can eventually affect career and ability to work
D. Ruptured disc		"Learned" behaviors reinforced through events in your environment
E. RDA		Bend your knees slightly and pull in your abdominal muscles when you have to reach up
F. When lifting objects		Bones of the back
G. Ergonomics		Located between each pair of vertebrae in the neck and back to offer flexibility
H. Varicose veins		Pain in the neck, back, arms or legs caused from leaking jelly
I. To prevent shoulder problems		Inflamed tendons
J. To prevent hand and wrist problems		Being truthful without being offensive
K. To prevent foot and leg problems		Science used to study the relationship between people and their work environment
L. Pelvic tilt		Tilt the client's head to a position that is comfortable for you
M. Carpal Tunnel Syndrome		Use strength of arms during massage, not hands or wrists
N. Tact		Keep back erect and bend at the knees, using muscles of the thighs
O. Joints and discs		Wear comfortable, rubber-soled shoes with good arch support

Now it's time to see how well you know your new material. First answer these questions. Then use the Memory Box that follows to check yourself. Look up each answer on the corresponding page in the *Salon Fundamentals™ Esthetics* textbook. Check "got it" for all correct answers and "not yet" for all incorrect responses. Using the "Know Chart," record all of your correct responses in the "I Know" column. After correcting incorrect answers, record all of your corrected responses in the "I Need to Study" column. That way you know exactly what to review before continuing in this Guide.

Directions: Identify whether questions 1 and 2 are True or False by circling TRUE or FALSE. You can earn an extra point for each false statement you appropriately correct. Question 3 requires you to write in an answer in the blank provided. Answers to the questions found in 4 through 10 may be selected by circling a, b, c or d below each statement to indicate your choice.

1. TRUE FALSE   Ten to twelve hours of sleep per night are recommended to avoid fatigue.

   _____

2. TRUE FALSE   Staying out late can have a detrimental effect on job performance.

   _____

3. Another name for a podiatrist, or foot doctor, is _____

4. **The term RDA stands for:**
   a. required dairy allotment
   b. required dietary allowances
   c. requested daily allowances
   d. recommended dietary allowances

5. **What is the RDA of proper daily portions for carbohydrates (complex)?**
   a. 45 – 65 percent
   b. 70 – 75 percent
   c. 80 – 85 percent
   d. 90 – 95 percent

6. **An excellent source for essential fatty acids is:**
   a. milk
   b. apples
   c. fatty fish
   d. wheat bread

7. **The science that studies relationships between people and their work environment:**
   a. ecology
   b. workology
   c. ergoscience
   d. ergonomics

8. **The outward reflection of inner feelings, thoughts, attitudes and values is called:**
   a. habit
   b. ethics
   c. chameleon
   d. personality

9. **Which of the following statements identifies the "Golden Rule"?**
   a. do unto others before they do unto you
   b. do unto others like they did to you before
   c. do unto other like you plan to treat them in the future
   d. do unto others as you would have them do unto you

10. **The study of human conduct is known as:**
    a. professional loyalty
    b. professional ethics
    c. professional dealings
    d. professional precautions

1. page 3	☐ got it ☐ not yet
2. page 3	☐ got it ☐ not yet
3. page 10	☐ got it ☐ not yet
4. page 5	☐ got it ☐ not yet
5. page 5	☐ got it ☐ not yet
6. page 7	☐ got it ☐ not yet
7. page 11	☐ got it ☐ not yet
8. page 21	☐ got it ☐ not yet
9. page 24	☐ got it ☐ not yet
10. page 24	☐ got it ☐ not yet

I know...

I need to study...

SHOW YOU KNOW

Experts tell us that it helps to have reminders posted around us to help keep our attitudes in a positive state. In addition it is helpful to remind people to be considerate, to work safely or to do things a certain way. Create three signs that could be posted around the school to focus staff and students' attention on the three main parts of Chapter 1, Personal Development. Poster 1 should be about a healthy mind and body, poster 2 about effective communication and poster 3 about purposeful relationships.

Poster 1

Poster 2

Poster 3

| 1 | 2 | 3 | 4 | 5 | 6 | 7 |

TALKING POINTS

Your next challenge is to be ready to talk about some of the important ideas in this chapter. Follow the directions listed next to each box and practice talking about your ideas.

1. TACTFULLY TALKING

Esthetician to client: "I can't believe how cracked and dry-looking your skin is. It makes you look twenty years older."

_____

_____

Esthetician to client: "Your eyebrows have almost grown together! How long has it been since you were here last?"

_____

_____

Review the statements made by an esthetician to a client and then on the lines provided offer a better, more tactful way of making the same statement. Compare and discuss your corrections with a partner.

2. FIVE CHANGES

1._____   1._____

2._____   2._____

3._____   3._____

4._____   4._____

5._____   5._____

Stand face-to-face with a partner and look each other over for a period of about 10 seconds. Then stand back-to-back and each of you make five changes about your image. Now, turn face to face again and see if you can list each other's five changes. Do this exercise one more time to see how many of the new changes you can notice. You can use the space to the left to write down your changes each time.

3. EFFECTIVE LISTENING SKILLS

A   B

Practice your listening skills by sitting back to back with a partner as each of you, in the box to the left labeled A, draws a design using only 3 circles, 2 triangles, 1 rectangle and 1 square. Each of you will have your own unique drawing. Remaining back-to-back, one partner will describe his/her drawing as the other partner listens and tries to replicate the drawing in the box labeled B. Only the partner describing the drawing is allowed to talk. Switch tasks and see how close both of you come to replication and mastering communication.

KNOWLEDGE GRID

Start at the top of the Knowledge Grid and work your way down, answering each question to check your understanding of Chapter 1, Personal Development. The questions found here will help you deepen your understanding, build self-confidence and increase your awareness of different ways of thinking about a subject.

KNOW

Identify the three major energy-producing nutrients and describe their importance to personal health.

COMPREHEND

Summarize the negative effects of exhaustion and lack of rest.

APPLY

Give several examples of nonverbal communication (body language).

ANALYZE

Distinguish between public and personal hygiene.

SYNTHESIZE

In your own words, generate a simple code of ethics for skin care professionals.

As skin care professionals, we will:

- ■
- ■
- ■
- ■

- ■
- ■
- ■
- ■

EVALUATE

Evaluate the ergonomic recommendations for improved posture, better work habits and proper use of equipment listed in this chapter by selecting the most practical and useful recommendation in each of the four areas discussed.

The 4 most practical and useful ergonomic recommendations include:

1.

2.

3.

4.

Multiple choice. Circle the correct answer.

1. **Which of the following helps stimulate blood circulation in the body?**
   a. exercise
   b. watching TV
   c. listening to music
   d. reading a good book

2. **The process of converting raw materials in the form of carbohydrates, fats and proteins into energy is known as:**
   a. exercise
   b. nutrition
   c. hygiene
   d. ergonomics

3. **The energy found in food is measured in:**
   a. degrees
   b. calories
   c. fat content
   d. protein content

4. **The energy in food can be stored in the body as:**
   a. fat
   b. protein
   c. minerals
   d. carbohydrates

5. **The applied science that deals with healthful living is:**
   a. physics
   b. hygiene
   c. philosophy
   d. engineering

6. **The practice of good ventilation, proper lighting, disinfection and storage of food to promote and preserve the health of the community is referred to as:**
   a. oral hygiene
   b. client hygiene
   c. public hygiene
   d. personal hygiene

7. **Bathing regularly with soap, using deodorant and washing clothes when soiled are examples of:**
   a. oral hygiene
   b. public hygiene
   c. personal hygiene
   d. excessive grooming

8. Halitosis means:
    a. bad breath
    b. poor posture
    c. poor nutrition
    d. poor public hygiene

9. Which type of shoes are recommended to reduce the fatigue from standing all day?
    a. tennis shoes
    b. high-heeled shoes
    c. low, broad-heeled shoes
    d. old, comfortable, stretched-out shoes

10. A foot doctor is called a:
    a. podiatrist
    b. pediatrician
    c. orthodontist
    d. psychologist

11. When sitting in a chair, it is important to:
    a. keep feet apart
    b. keep knees apart
    c. sit forward in chair
    d. sit squarely in chair

12. Facial expressions, posture and poise are examples of:
    a. hygiene
    b. personality
    c. non-hygienic communication
    d. nonverbal communication

13. The skill that requires learning to be truthful and to say the proper thing to a person without being offensive is called:
    a. tact
    b. attitude
    c. consulting
    d. personality

14. Which of the following statements about communication is true?
    a. know the importance of your ideas
    b. be prepared to talk about yourself a lot
    c. be prepared to talk about politics with your client
    d. don't think before you talk because it slows down the conversation

15. **When having a conversation with a client, it is recommended that you focus your conversation on:**
    a. the weather
    b. other clients
    c. famous personalities
    d. your client's lifestyle and skin care needs

16. **The act of repeating out loud what you heard, processed inside your head and reported is referred to as:**
    a. active listening
    b. reflective listening
    c. whole body listening
    d. nonverbal communication

17. **The outward reflection of inner feelings, thoughts, attitude and values is known as:**
    a. humor
    b. posture
    c. hygiene
    d. personality

18. **A feeling or emotion toward something or someone is referred to as:**
    a. ethics
    b. habits
    c. attitude
    d. philosophy

19. **Which of the following statements is true about attitudes?**
    a. attitudes cannot be changed
    b. attitudes are easy to change
    c. attitudes, like habits, can be changed
    d. people are born with all the attitudes they will have through life

20. **Proper conduct in relationships with employers, co-workers and clients is referred to as:**
    a. public hygiene
    b. personal image
    c. personal hygiene
    d. professional ethics

Write Your Own Ticket! For numbers 21, 22, and 23, write your own questions and answer them. Your questions can be true/false, multiple choice or fill-in-the-blank. The only parameter is that your questions cannot already be found on this test. Earn one point each for writing and correctly answering your questions.

21. Q: _____

A: _____
_____
_____
_____
_____
_____

22. Q: _____

A: _____
_____
_____
_____
_____
_____

23. Q: _____

A: _____
_____
_____
_____
_____
_____
_____

BONUS QUESTION!
Question 24 is the ultimate question. To earn two points, design a question for your class. If you stump the class and no one can answer the question within an agreed upon time (between you and the teacher), you earn a BONUS OF FIVE ADDITIONAL POINTS!

24. Q: _____

ESSAY QUESTION

A maximum of five additional points is possible if you answer one of the following essay questions.

25a.   In your judgment, what are the three most important points made in this section of your text about communication? Please support your selections with a brief description of why you made the choices you did.

25b.   Explain what the Golden Rule means to you and list at least two ways it played a role in your life this week.

25c.   In your opinion, what are two difficult things you might need to talk to a client about that would require the use of tact? Please list support for your decisions.

Check your answers as you did before. Place a check mark next to the page number for any incorrect answer. On the lines to the right, jot down topics that you still need to review.

1.   page 4

2.   page 5

3.   page 5

4.   page 6

5.   page 7

6.   page 7

7.   page 8

8.   page 8

9.   page 10

10.   page 10

11.   page 13

12.   page 15

13.   page 18

14.   page 18

15.   page 19

16.   page 19

17.   page 21

18.   page 21

19.   page 22

20.   page 24

NOTES TO MYSELF — *My Reflections About Personal Development*

Experts agree that it is important to summarize your feelings and reactions about what you are learning. Note especially things that surprised you, things you found difficult to learn, suggestions and ideas you received from friends that helped make learning this chapter easier and more enjoyable.

| 1 | 2 | 3 | 4 | 5 | 6 | 7 |

PROFESSIONAL DEVELOPMENT

VALUE

An ongoing commitment to professional development will help you excel in your career, become a valued asset to your clients and colleagues and help you achieve financial rewards and personal growth.

MAIN IDEA

A professional is someone who commits to high standards of performance and continually seeks to improve. Professionals are rarely satisfied with their present level of knowledge, skill or expertise. In this chapter on professional development, you will examine trends in the esthetics industry, practice job search skills and explore techniques for promoting yourself and your services. Learning to be a professional may start in school but continues throughout your lifetime.

PLAN

Job Quest
- Market Trends
- Goal Setting
- Finding a Job

Career Building
- Networking
- Building a Clientele
- Selling
- Lifelong Learning

OBJECTIVES

- Survey trends in the beauty industry and document recent changes that have a positive impact upon the demand for skin care services

- Establish a process for setting short- and long-range professional goals

- Refine job search preparation skills to include resumé and cover letter development, job interviewing skills, work environment evaluations and familiarity with performance review strategies

- Give examples of strategies that can be used to help you introduce yourself to other professionals within the esthetics industry

- Describe strategies for building professional relationships with clients and staff

- Summarize techniques for successfully promoting services and recommending products to clientele

- Formulate a lifelong learning plan to continue career and professional development

Chapter	Section	Page
Chapter 2 Professional Development	Job Quest	**Pages 29-31**

1 Survey trends in the beauty industry and document recent changes that have a positive impact upon the demand for skin care services

■ **Market Trends**

Statistics

Stay Informed

What do you think your clients in the future will be like? What will be their demographics? Will they be young, middle age, older, female, male, business worker, factory worker, athletic, academic, single, married, etc.? The list goes on and on. List 10 descriptive words that might describe your clients of the future.

Look into the Future

1. _____
2. _____
3. _____
4. _____
5. _____
6. _____
7. _____
8. _____
9. _____
10. _____

2 Establish a process for setting short- and long-range professional goals

■ **Goal Setting**

4-Step Process for Determining Goals

1.
  ■
  ■
  ■

2.
  ■

3.
  ■
  ■
  ■

4.

Successful Business Strategies

Sometimes fads are confused with trends. A fad is short-lived and generally applies to a particular segment of people. Trends are longer lasting, apply to the majority of people within many varied groups and have more impact on business. Look at the list of items below and place 'T' next to an item you feel represents a trend and place 'F' next to the item you feel is a fad.

_____ Large handbags	_____ Short skirts	_____ Dangling earrings
_____ Body piercing	_____ Mini-vans	_____ Saving money
_____ Aromatherapy services	_____ Acupuncture	_____ Seaweed wraps

smartNOTES

Chapter	Section	Page
Chapter 2 Professional Development	Job Quest	Pages 32-35

3 Refine job search preparation skills to include resumé and cover letter development, job interviewing skills, work environment evaluations and familiarity with performance review strategies

■ **Finding a Job**

Methods
- ■
- ■
- ■
- ■
- ■

■
■
■
■
■

Resumé

Resumé Components

➤ _____
➤ _____
➤ _____
➤ _____
➤ _____

➤ _____
➤ _____
➤ _____
➤ _____

Resumé Guidelines

| 1 | 2 | 3 | 4 | 5 | 6 | 7 |

Chapter	Section	Page
Chapter 2 Professional Development	Job Quest	**Pages 35-37**

Resumé Design
Features

- ▪
- ▪
- ▪
- ▪
- ▪

Acceptable colors for resumé papers

White
Pale Blue
Creme/Beige
Pale Gray

Cover Letters

- ▪
- ▪
- ▪
- ▪

Cover Letter Checklist

- ✔ _____
- ✔ _____
- ✔ _____
- ✔ _____
- ✔ _____

- ✔
- ✔
- ✔
- ✔
- ✔

Guidelines for
Writing a
Cover Letter

1.
2.
3.
4.
5.
6.

Job Interview

When interviewing:
- Make eye contact
- Smile
- Shake hands
- Be positive
- Listen
- Ask questions

Personal Appearance

-
-
-
-
-
-

Application Process

Application includes:

✔
✔
✔

Punctuality

Technical and Communication Skills

Interviewer may determine level of technical skills by:

-
-
-

Chapter	Section	Page
Chapter 2 Professional Development	Job Quest	Pages 40-42

Personal Qualities

-
-
-
-
-
-

Work Environments

Evaluate workplace in terms of advantages and disadvantages

-
-
-

Job Benefits

Components of a Total Benefit Package

- _____   - _____
- _____   - _____
- _____   - _____
- _____   - _____
- _____   - _____

Your New Job

Information sources:

-
-
-

Chapter	Section	Page
Chapter 2 Professional Development	Job Quest	Pages 42-43

■ Performance Review

If YOU were the employer, what would be the most important question you would ask a potential employee interviewing for a job in your organization?

_____

LEARNING — **CONNECTION** —— Trust Your Instinct

There are times when you just need to trust your best instinct or intuition. Read the questions below that an employer might ask you during an interview. Trust your instinct and draw a line through two of the questions that would indicate to your instinctive side that this might not be the employer for you.

1. What amount of time would you need to wax a lower leg area?

2. What is your religious background?

3. What would you say is your strongest professional characteristic in dealing with people?

4. Do you live with someone of the same sex?

| 1 | 2 | 3 | 4 | 5 | 6 | 7 |

Chapter	Section	Page
Chapter 2 Professional Development	**Career Building**	**Pages 44-48**

4 Give examples of strategies that can be used to help you introduce yourself to other professionals within the esthetics industry

■ **Networking**

Client Relationships

Staff Relationships

Communication

Sharing Knowledge

Common Goals

Helping Others

5 Describe strategies for building professional relationships with clients and staff

■ **Building a Clientele**

Marketing

Chapter	Section	Page
Chapter 2 Professional Development	**Career Building**	**Pages 48-50**

Word-of-Mouth Advertising/Referrals

Business Cards

Rebooking

Promotional Literature

Guest Appearances

Correspondence

Your Personal Touch

Which client-building strategy do you feel will be most effective for you?

LEARNING **CONNECTION** — Design A Card

Your business card in the future will be a valuable asset to you. Use this space to design a card that will help all the people you meet remember who you are and where you work. Be creative, yet tasteful. Compare your card with others and see if there is any additional information you should add.

| 1 | 2 | 3 | 4 | 5 | 6 | 7 |

Chapter	Section	Page
Chapter 2 Professional Development	Career Building	Pages 50-51

6 Summarize techniques for successfully promoting services and recommending products to clientele

■ **Selling**

Steps for Successful

Selling

> _____

> _____

> _____

> _____

> _____

> _____

> _____

Retailing

Persuading Clients   1.

through Retailing   2.

                        3.

Professional

Recommendation

smartNOTES

Chapter	Section	Page
Chapter 2 Professional Development	**Career Building**	**Pages 51-53**

Retailing
Knowledge
& Confidence

Stay informed of latest developments:

- ■
- ■

Professional Products

Features and Benefits

Customize products to the needs of the client for success in recommendation

- ■
- ■

Involve Clients

WHEN SAMPLING:

- ➤
- ➤
- ➤
- ➤

Chapter	Section	Page
Chapter 2 Professional Development	**Career Building**	**Pages 53-56**

Retailing

Suggest New Products

Cross-selling

Closing the Sale

Written Instructions

Written instructions promote the sale of products to:

- ◼
- ◼
- ◼
- ◼
- ◼
- ◼
- ◼

Phone Calls

Follow-up calls provide the opportunity to:

- ➤ _____
- ➤ _____
- ➤ _____
- ➤ _____
- ➤ _____

Record Keeping

smartNOTES

Chapter	Section	Page
Chapter 2 Professional Development	**Career Building**	**Pages 56-57**

Motivating Buyers

NEED

> _____
> _____
> _____

DESIRE

> _____
> _____

PROFIT

> _____
> _____
> _____

IMPULSE BUYING

> _____
> _____

Chapter	Section	Page
Chapter 2 Professional Development	**Career Building**	Page 58

The Ready Buyer ➤

Esthetician needs to ➤

The Logical Buyer ➤

Esthetician needs to ➤
➤
➤

The Emotional Buyer ➤
➤

Esthetician needs to ➤
➤

The Bargain Buyer ➤

Esthetician needs to ➤
➤

The Stubborn Buyer ➤

Esthetician needs to ➤
➤

Chapter	Section	Page
Chapter 2 Professional Development	Career Building	Pages 58-61

Sales Promotions

-
-
-
-

GIFT-WITH-PURCHASE	HOLIDAY & SEASONAL PROMOTIONS

REFERRAL PROMOTIONS	CO-OP PROMOTIONS

Monthly Promotions

Effective Displays

Selling

Stock and Stock

Inventory

Chapter	Section	Page
Chapter 2 Professional Development	**Career Building**	**Page 61**

Retail Display
Guidelines

Organize Stock

- ◾
- ◾
- ◾
- ◾
- ◾
- ◾
- ◾

Ensure Quality Control

- ◾
- ◾
- ◾
- ◾

Create Promotional Displays

- ◾
- ◾

Maintain Inventory Control

- ◾
- ◾
- ◾

Chapter	Section	Page
Chapter 2 Professional Development	**Career Building**	**Page 61**

Retail Display
Guidelines

Learn from Display Experts

■

■

Price the Merchandise

■

■

■

What invites you to buy skin care products? List at least three reasons why you have purchased particular products in the past.

1. _____ 2. _____ 3. _____

LEARNING **CONNECTION** — Create A Shelf Talker

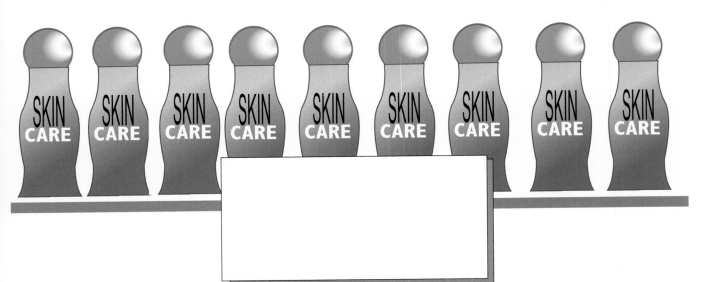

A shelf talker is a product identification card. Design a shelf talker for the products displayed above.
A blank shelf talker has been provided for your promotional message.

| 1 | 2 | 3 | 4 | 5 | 6 | 7 |

Chapter	Section	Page
Chapter 2 Professional Development	Career Building	Pages 62-64

7 Formulate a lifelong learning plan to continue career and professional development

■ **Lifelong Learning**

Why is it important
to stay current? ➤

➤

➤

Seminars and Classes

Trade Shows

Current Periodicals

Local Newspaper

Fashion & Beauty
Magazines

Comparison
Shopping

Visit competitors to

Engage in a

Chapter	Section	Page
Chapter 2 Professional Development	Career Building	**Pages 64-65**

Internet Resources   Excellent way to find info of all sorts:

-
-
-
-
-
-
-
-

Path to Success   No limit to your success if you are willing to invest the time and energy

Are you familiar with the major periodicals published for the skin care industry? List the names of three informative publications.

1. _____ 2. _____ 3. _____

LEARNING ─ CONNECTION ─ Lifelong Learning

It is wise for you to plan ahead for your educational needs. Answer the questions below to help you allocate your time.

1. How many hours of education will your state require in order to renew your license? _____

2. How many hours of education will a professional organization you might join require? _____

3. How many hours of education do you think an employer might require you to attend? _____

4. How many hours of education beyond the required do you feel you might want to attend? _____

Total Hours of Education   _____

Match the term from Column A with the corresponding description in Column B by placing the letter of the term in the box provided in front of the description.

Column A		Column B
A. Professional		One- or two-page outline that lists your educational history, work experience, additional skills and achievements
B. Long-range goal		Involves filling out forms for employment before the interview process begins
C. Resumé		Arriving on time for an interview
D. Cover letter		The amount of money earned, insurance, paid sick or vacation time and educational reimbursements
E. Application process		Someone who commits to higher standards of performance and continually seeks to improve
F. Punctuality		This buyer puts up a struggle and enjoys debating with you
G. Personal qualities		An open-minded person that tends to take chances on new products without hesitation
H. Work environment		The "personality piece" that introduces you to your prospective employer
I. Job benefits		This buyer bases purchases more on personal reasons than facts
J. Performance review		Identifies where you want your career to be in five years
K. Ready buyer		The physical surroundings and emotional "vibe" from employees currently employed
L. Logical buyer		Sincerity and honesty, enthusiasm and charisma, dependability and loyalty, good work ethics and punctuality, flexibility and team spirit, organization and efficiency
M. Emotional buyer		This person wants to save money and concentrates more on price than quality
N. Bargain buyer		This buyer wants to know all the facts about a product and thinks carefully before buying
O. Stubborn buyer		An opportunity to discuss your job performance with your manager

Your next challenge is to be ready to talk about some of the important ideas in this chapter. Follow the directions listed next to each box and practice talking about your ideas.

1. FIVE QUESTIONS

1.
2.
3.
4.
5.

Write 5 questions you would ask someone during an interview if you were an employer.

2. FIVE QUESTIONS—NOTES

1.
2.
3.
4.
5.

Ask a partner the five questions you just created in step 1 of the Talking Points. Play the role of the employer as you ask your questions. Take notes as your partner responds.

Then reverse roles as you answer the five questions your partner created.

3. FIVE QUESTIONS—FEEDBACK

Partner's Strong Points:

Areas of Improvement:

Offer encouragement to your partner by identifying what you felt were strong points in the responses given to your questions. Also, identify areas of improvement your partner could make in the responses given.

Your Strong Points:

Areas of Improvement:

Ask your partner to do the same for you by identifying your strong points and areas of improvement for the responses you gave to questions.

| 1 | 2 | 3 | 4 | 5 | 6 | 7 |

RETAIL DISPLAY GUIDELINES

Organize Stock

REMEMBER:

Use imagination! Keep all displays updated and interesting.

In the boxes provided on these two pages, summarize the material found on page 61 of Chapter 2 in your text.

Maintain Inventory

Learn from Display Experts

RETAIL DISPLAY GUIDELINES

Price the Merchandise

Create Promotional Displays

Ensure Quality Control

REMEMBER:

Selling is an
opportunity waiting
to happen.

Each of the following ads is designed to target one of the specific buyer types. Place the letter of the ad on the blank next to the corresponding buyer type.

A

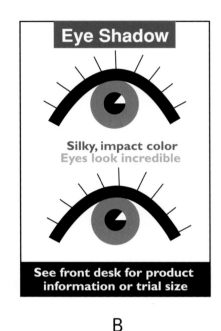

B

Ready Buyer
_____

Logical Buyer
_____

Emotional Buyer
_____

Bargain Buyer
_____

Stubborn Buyer
_____

Skin Cream

✳ Elevates skin's potential for repair

✳ Defuses the look of lines and wrinkles

✳ Creates even-toned and perfectly moisturized skin

TRY
A
SAMPLE!!!

C

5th Anniversary
Sale

Save 25% to 75% on
**ALL
MERCHANDISE!**

**Purchase 3 products,
get the 4th FREE!**

D

BRAND NEW!

SKIN
CARE

New product created using
revolutionary beauty technology

E

Now it's time to see how well you know your new material. First answer these questions. Then use the Memory Box that follows to check yourself. Look up each answer on the corresponding page in the *Salon Fundamentals™ Esthetics* textbook. Check "got it" for all correct answers and "not yet" for all incorrect responses. Using the "Know Chart," record all of your correct responses in the "I Know" column. After correcting incorrect answers, record all of your corrected responses in the "I Need to Study" column. That way you know exactly what to review before continuing in this Guide.

Directions: Identify whether questions 1 and 2 are True or False by circling TRUE or FALSE. You can earn an extra point for each false statement you appropriately correct. Question 3 requires you to write in an answer in the blank provided. Answers to the questions found in 4 through 10 may be selected by circling a, b, c or d below each statement to indicate your choice.

1. TRUE   FALSE   **Market trends help you focus and define what path your career will take.**

     _____

2. TRUE   FALSE   **The opportunity to discuss job performance with the manager is called performance review.**

     _____

3. _____ **means creating an awareness of a product or service, usually striking an emotional chord.**

4. **Building on a sale by recommending a product that complements another product the client has already purchased is known as** _____

5. **Which of the following is essential for evaluating a client's reaction to a product and progression through a treatment?**
     a. organizing stock
     b. effective displays
     c. pricing merchandise
     d. good record keeping

6. **Which of the following percents of all purchases stem from impulse buying?**
     a. 25-30%
     b. 35-40%
     c. 45-65%
     d. 70-75%

7. **Which buyer type has an open mind and tends to take chances on new products without hesitation?**
     a. ready buyer
     b. logical buyer
     c. stubborn buyer
     d. emotional buyer

8. **Which of the following sales promotions offers clients a free gift or service when they purchase a treatment or product at full price?**
     a. co-op promotions
     b. gift-with-purchase
     c. referral programs
     d. holiday and seasonal

9. **Which of the following sales promotions offer your existing clientele a discount if they refer a friend who actually comes in for a treatment?**
     a. co-op promotion
     b. gift-with-purchase
     c. referral programs
     d. holiday and seasonal

10. **The practice of visiting competitors to compare their business practices to your own is called:**
     a. co-op promotions
     b. referral programs
     c. monthly promotions
     d. comparison shopping

1	2	3	4	5	6	7

1. page 31	☐ got it ☐ not yet	
2. page 42-43	☐ got it ☐ not yet	
3. page 48	☐ got it ☐ not yet	
4. page 54	☐ got it ☐ not yet	
5. page 56	☐ got it ☐ not yet	
6. page 57	☐ got it ☐ not yet	
7. page 58	☐ got it ☐ not yet	
8. page 59	☐ got it ☐ not yet	
9. page 59	☐ got it ☐ not yet	
10. page 64	☐ got it ☐ not yet	

I know...

I need to study...

SHOW YOU KNOW

The most common errors in resumé development include spelling, spacing and missing information. On the next page a sample resumé has been provided for you to show you know the appropriate grammar, punctuation and general information found on a resumé. Challenge yourself to find the 12 errors on the resumé.

1.
2.
3.
4.
5.
6.
7.
8.
9.
10.
11.
12.

BAD RESUME

The following resumé contains a minimum of 12 errors in spelling, grammar, formatting and/or style. **Can you find all 12?** Make any corrections necessary in order to create a quality resumé.

---

232 South Winchester
Denver, CO 55959
Fax 232-222-4646
E-mail clrichter@mail.com

Objective   I would like to work in a salon.

Education   1999-2000   ABC Beauty College St. Louis, MO
Degree in cosmetology with emphasis in customer
service

■ 3.8 GPA in College

Work experience   1998-Present   Applebee's   St. Louis, MO
Waitress
■ Escorted customers to their seats
■ Waitd on tables

1995-199   Denver, CO
Checker
■ Worked the cash register
■ Employee of the month for December, 1997

Awards received   I have received many awards. I had a 3.8 GPA while at
college graduating at the top of my class, while working for Hy-Vee,
I was named employee of the month.

Special skills   i am a good comunicator and a very social person. I feel I
would help build your business with my good social skills. I work very well with other
people and can carry on conversations all ages.

References   Janell Fareely
3233 South Branch

Denver, CO 55898
Matty Jacobse

999 Park Avenue
St. Louis, MO

KNOWLEDGE GRID

Start at the top of the Knowledge Grid and work your way down, answering each question to check your understanding of Chapter 2, Professional Development. The questions found here will help you deepen your understanding, build self-confidence and increase your awareness of different ways of thinking about a subject.

KNOW
Locate the section in your textbook on finding a job and list at least three methods you might use when interviewing for a future position.

COMPREHEND
Explain how you would evaluate a typical work environment.

APPLY
Give examples of several strategies for building a clientele. Select the strategy that is considered to be most effective and explain why.

ANALYZE
Specify the seven steps for successful selling.

SYNTHESIZE
Design a promotional campaign that would attract all five buyer types.

EVALUATE
Justify why the following statement is true: "At no other time in history has a career in the field of esthetics been more attractive or lucrative than it is today."

Multiple choice. Circle the correct answer.

1. **What helps you focus and defines what path your career will take?**
   a. a goal
   b. a cover letter
   c. a record book
   d. a business card

2. **Short-range goals identify where you would like your career to be in the next:**
   a. year
   b. three years
   c. seven years
   d. twenty years

3. **Creating a plan to achieve your goals includes:**
   a. establish alternate plans
   b. considering your budget
   c. creating a specific set of objectives and tasks
   d. all of the above

4. **An individual should maintain a current, thorough, error-free:**
   a. photo
   b. resumé
   c. objective
   d. application

5. **What colors are recommended for resumés?**
   a. blue or a shade of pink
   b. red or pale shades of green or blue
   c. yellow or pale shades of red or yellow
   d. white or pale shades of beige, blue or gray

6. **What font size do professional resumé writers recommend?**
   a. 4-5 pt. font
   b. 7-8 pt. font
   c. 10-11 pt. font
   d. 15-17 pt. font

7. **A necessary companion to the resumé is the:**
   a. internet
   b. objective
   c. application
   d. cover letter

| 1 | 2 | 3 | 4 | 5 | 6 | 7 |

8. Which of the following is the basis upon which you create a first impression?
    a. application
    b. punctuality
    c. personal qualities
    d. personal appearance

9. What is the "personality piece" that introduces you to your prospective employer?
    a. resumé
    b. application
    c. cover letter
    d. performance review

10. Which of the following is a personal quality that might be evaluated in an interview?
    a. age
    b. honesty
    c. religious beliefs
    d. health conditions

11. Which of the following is probably the least important factor in deciding whether to accept a position in a skin care center?
    a. benefits
    b. types of clientele
    c. goals of the business
    d. size of the skin care center

12. Salaries, sales commission and paid holidays are all examples of which of the following?
    a. resumé
    b. job benefits
    c. retirement plan
    d. insurance benefits

13. A program to familiarize the new employee with the work habits and standards of the skin care center is called:
    a. apprenticeship
    b. general orientation
    c. performance review
    d. educational seminar

14. Which of the following is a discussion of job performance that occurs at regular intervals with management?
    a. referral
    b. classified review
    c. performance review
    d. cultivating relationships

15. Which of the following is probably the most effective way to build clientele?
    a. advertisement
    b. word-of-mouth
    c. business cards
    d. guest appearances

16. Creating awareness of a product or service is called:
    a. surveying
    b. training
    c. recruiting
    d. marketing

17. Which of the following is the foundation of good salesmanship?
    a. skill
    b. knowledge
    c. self-confidence
    d. personal recommendation

18. Characteristics or specific ingredients of a skin care product are called its:
    a. listing
    b. benefits
    c. features
    d. character

19. Improvements a product will make to enhance the appearance or condition of a client's skin are called:
    a. benefits
    b. features
    c. enhancers
    d. characteristics

20. Which type of buyer wants to know all the facts about a product before buying it?
    a. the ready buyer
    b. the logical buyer
    c. the bargain buyer
    d. the emotional buyer

21. Which type of buyer bases purchases more on personal reasons than facts?
    a. the ready buyer
    b. the logical buyer
    c. the bargain buyer
    d. the emotional buyer

22. **A buyer that has an open mind and tends to take a chance on new products without hesitation is known as:**
    a. the ready buyer
    b. the logical buyer
    c. the bargain buyer
    d. the emotional buyer

23. **Which type of buyer wants to save money and concentrates more on price than quality?**
    a. the ready buyer
    b. the logical buyer
    c. the bargain buyer
    d. the emotional buyer

24. **A buyer who puts up a struggle and enjoys debating with the salesperson is known as:**
    a. the logical buyer
    b. the bargain buyer
    c. the stubborn buyer
    d. the emotional buyer

25. **Which of the following is perhaps the easiest buyer motivation to recognize in the skin care center?**
    a. need
    b. profit or gain
    c. desire to look good
    d. desire to keep up with current trends

Write Your Own Ticket!

For questions 26, 27, and 28, write your own question and answer it. Your question can be true/false, multiple choice or fill-in-the-blank. The only parameter is that your questions cannot already be found on this test. Earn one point each for writing your way to success.

26. Q: _____
    A: _____

27. Q: _____
    A: _____

28. Q: _____
    A: _____

BONUS QUESTION!
Question 29 is the ultimate question. To earn two points, design a question for your class.
If you stump the class and no one can answer the question within an agreed upon time
(between you and the teacher), you earn a *BONUS OF FIVE ADDITIONAL POINTS!*

29. Q:

ESSAY QUESTION

A maximum of five additional points is possible if you answer one of the following
essay questions.

30a. In your judgment, what will be the most difficult aspect for you when finding a job?

30b. Listed below in box A are the six selling strategies. Choose one selling strategy and list the
strengths in box B and weaknesses in box C.

A	B. Selling Strategy – strengths	C. Selling Strategy – weaknesses
■ Ask questions	Ask questions -	Ask questions -
■ Observe and listen	Observe and listen -	Observe and listen -
■ Identify and create the need	Identify and create the need -	Identify and create the need -
■ Recommend products	Communicate while performing services -	Communicate while performing services -
■ Communicate while performing services	Recommend products -	Recommend products -
■ Educate	Educate -	Educate -
■ Demonstrate	Demonstrate -	Demonstrate -

30c. Offer 3 reasons to support why the word-of-mouth strategy is among the most effective methods
to build clientele.

I.

2.

3.

FINAL REVIEW

Check your answers as you did before. Place a check mark next to the page number for any
incorrect answer. On the lines to the right, jot down topics that you still need to review.

1.	page 31	14.	page 42
2.	page 31	15.	page 48
3.	page 31	16.	page 48
4.	page 35	17.	page 51
5.	page 35	18.	page 52
6.	page 35	19	page 52
7.	page 35	20.	page 58
8.	page 38	21.	page 58
9.	page 35	22.	page 58
10.	page 40	23.	page 58
11.	page 41	24.	page 58
12.	page 41	25.	page 57
13.	page 42		

NOTES TO MYSELF — *My Reflections About Professional Development*

Experts agree that it is
important to summarize
your feelings and reactions
about what you are
learning. Note especially
things that surprised you,
things you found difficult
to learn, suggestions and
ideas you received from
friends that helped make
learning this chapter easier
and more enjoyable.

BUSINESS BASICS

VALUE

The more you know about the business aspects of a skin care center, the better prepared you are to take advantage of future career opportunities.

MAIN IDEA

Starting, operating and building an efficient and profitable skin care center requires specialized knowledge and skills. Learning the operational, financial and management needs of a skin care center will improve your professional status and prepare you for business ownership, should you choose this career option.

PLAN

Starting a Business	■ Self-Appraisal
	■ Finance
	■ Business Essentials
	■ Plans for a Successful Skin Care Center
Operating a Business	■ Expenses and Income
	■ Hiring
	■ Skin Care Center Philosophy, Policies and Procedures

OBJECTIVES

■ Describe the financial and legal requirements for starting a business

■ List the skills required for any employer:
- Paying taxes
- Managing inventory and setting prices
- Business administration
- Hiring and other employee issues
- Advertising
- Public relations
- Promotion calendar

■ Define advertising and promotion techniques that will increase sales

smartNOTES

Chapter	Section	Page
Chapter 3 Business Basics	**Starting a Business**	**Pages 69-71**

1 Describe the financial and legal requirements for starting a business

■ **Self-Appraisal**
➤
➤
➤
➤
➤
➤
➤
➤

■ **Finances**

Business Plan

Business Plan Essentials
■
■
■
■
■
■
■

Personal Financial Statement

Assets =   Liabilities =

Net Worth =

smartNOTES

Chapter	Section	Page
Chapter 3 Business Basics	**Starting a Business**	**Pages 72-75**

■ **Business Essentials**

Types of Business Ownership

1. **Sole Proprietorship**
➤
➤
➤

2. **Partnership**
➤
➤
➤

3. **Corporation**
➤
➤
➤

4. **Franchise**
➤
➤

Expert Advice

Any serious future skin care center owner will need the advice of four key experts:

1.

2.

3.

4.

■ **Plans for a Successful Skin Care Center**

LOCATION

MARKET NEED

COST OF NECESSARY IMPROVEMENTS

Chapter	Section	Page
Chapter 3 Business Basics	**Starting a Business**	**Pages 76-78**

Space Requirements

1

Two Primary Goals

2

Space per Esthetician

Other Requirements ➤

➤

➤

➤

➤

➤

Floor Plan

Equipment

The Basics ■

■

■

■

■

Chapter	Section	Page
Chapter 3 Business Basics	**Starting a Business**	**Pages 78-79**

Borrowing Money

Operating Capital

Track Record

Line of Credit

Rental Agreements

Basic Landlord Services:

- _____
- _____
- _____

Types of Rental
Agreements

Fixed

Variable

Chapter	Section	Page
Chapter 3 Business Basics	**Starting a Business**	**Pages 79-80**

Insurance

Malpractice

Property or Premise

Product Liability

Worker's Compensation

LEARNING **CONNECTION** — Personal Financial Statement

Fill in the information for the personal financial statement found below. You can elect to use your personal information or list amounts from a fictional source you name. This exercise is designed to help you become familiar with the key components of a personal financial statement used to determine net worth.

PERSONAL FINANCIAL STATEMENT

Assets	Asset Value	Liability	
House		Mortgage on House	
Car		Loan for Car	
Savings Account Balance		Loan for School	
Checking Account Balance		Credit Card Balance	
Savings Bonds		Money Owed to Doctor	
Personal Jewelry		Money Owed to Creditor	
Household Contents		Money Owed to Family or Friends	
Other		Other	
Total Assets		*Total Liabilities*	
	Assets minus Liabilities = Net Worth		

Chapter	Section	Page
Chapter 3 Business Basics	**Operating a Business**	**Pages 81-84**

2 List the skills required for any employer: paying taxes, managing inventory and setting prices, business administration, hiring and other employee issues, advertising, public relations, promotion calendar

■ **Expenses and Income**

Profit ➡   Loss ➡

Income

Operating Expenses (OE)

Fixed	Variable

Revenue Projection

Expenses

Taxes

Withholding Tax

Social Security

W-2 Form

Chapter	Section	Page
Chapter 3 Business Basics	**Operating a Business**	**Pages 84-86**

Taxes

Sales Tax

Income Tax

■ Hiring

Interview Criteria

➤   ➤

➤   ➤

➤   ➤

➤   ➤

Compliance Issues

Compensation

$$$	$$$	$$$
COMMISSION	SALARY	SALARY PLUS COMMISSION

smartNOTES

Chapter	Section	Page
Chapter 3 Business Basics	**Operating a Business**	**Pages 86-89**

■ Skin Care Center Philosophy, Policies and Procedures

Record Keeping

By maintaining daily and analyzing regularly weekly and monthly appointment and sales records, you will be able to:

■

■

■

■

Inventory and Product Control

Inventory

Inventory Control

Pricing

smartNOTES

Chapter	Section	Page
Chapter 3 Business Basics	**Operating a Business**	**Pages 89-91**

Receptionist Duties

Primary Functions
- ■
- ■
- ■
- ■
- ■
- ■
- ■
- ■
- ■
- ■
- ■
- ■

Telephone Techniques

Phone creates first impression for many clients

1.
2.
3.
4.
5.
6.

> **Ask**
>
> your clients if they are satisfied.

Unhappy clients often do not complain, they just don't return.

How would you handle a client complaint over the phone?

_____

_____

_____

_____

Scheduling Appointments

Important Information ➤ ➤

➤ ➤

Codes for Client Types

"W"

"R"

"O"

"N"

LEARNING — **CONNECTION** — Schedule of Appointments

Appointment 1:

Mary Wilson, phone number 555-7780 has called in and wants to request an appointment with Frances at 10:30 on Tuesday, July 15, for a facial.

Appointment 2:

Wendy Jones would like to come for a facial with makeup sometime in the afternoon. This is a practice session for her wedding in two weeks.

Appointment 3:

Ann Downey would like to change her appointment for a leg waxing from Becky to Frances on Tuesday afternoon at 1:30.

Appointment 4:

Olivia Jackson would like an appointment for a facial on Tuesday afternoon. She would like to schedule it so she can ride home with Mrs. Wilke. She will take a cab to the appointment.

Appointment 5:

Elaine Johnson wants to schedule an eyebrow, underarm, bikini and leg wax and, if time permits, a facial on Tuesday afternoon.

Below you will find an appointment sheet for Tuesday, July 15th. Some of the appointments have been identified on the schedule already. Challenge yourself to place the five additional appointments found in the column to the left of the appointment sheet.

Tuesday, July 15	Rhonda	Frances	Tamika	Becky	Sue
9:00	Smith W	Engstrom T			
9:30	EW	MU	Davis R	Off	Off
10:00			LW/F/MU		
10:30					
11:00					
11:30	Lunch	Lunch	Lunch		
12:00					
12:30					
1:00					Baker R
1:30			Mitchel R		Facial
2:00	Myers T		EALW/F		Williams R
2:30	LW/F				Facial
3:00		Mino			Donnelly O
3:30	Renge R	R			EW
4:00	F/MU	Trt - A			
4:30					Menke R
5:00	Wilke R				EALW/F
5:30	EABLW/F				
6:00					

1	2	3	4	5	6	7

Chapter	Section	Page
Chapter 3 Business Basics	Operating a Business	Pages 92-95

3 Define advertising and promotion techniques that will increase sales

Handling Money

Advertising ➤

➤

➤

➤

➤

➤

➤

➤

Public Relations

Plan of Action

Promotion Calendar

Think of a company that has great public relations. Why do you think this company is accepted within the community?

Which of the following two advertisements professionally represents this skin care center? Discuss with a partner and list at least three specific reasons that led you to choose one advertisement over the other.

A

Selenas Skin Care Ctr.
Located in dwtne. Milfred

Featuring:

- Mud packs
- The best facials in the state
- Great retail Products
- Walkins acceptable
- Open 5 days a week

Call Today for Your appointment.
Visit us at ww.selenasctr.com

We accept major credit cards
Unattended children not allowed
Parking available

B

Selenas Skin Care Center
Located at 110 Pleasant St., Milfred

Featuring

- Exclusive treatments and services
- Full product line to meet skin care needs
- 4 well-trained, licensed estheticians
- Appointments and walk-in sessions are available from 9 am to 8 pm

Call Today for an Appointment
Phone 566-555-5555
Visit us at www.selenasctr.com

VISA, MasterCard and
American Express accepted
Plan ahead for a stress-free appointment
Park free in ramp across the street

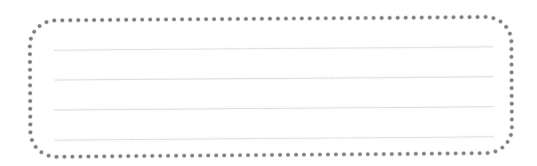

OWNERSHIP

- 2-Person Split
- Owned by Shareholders
- Has a Parent Corporation

FINANCIAL

- Operating Capital

RENTAL

- Fixed Rent
  - Building Changes
  - Set Dollar Plus % of Income

INSURANCE

- Protection from Employee Negligence
  - Protection from Client Misuse
- Property Insurance

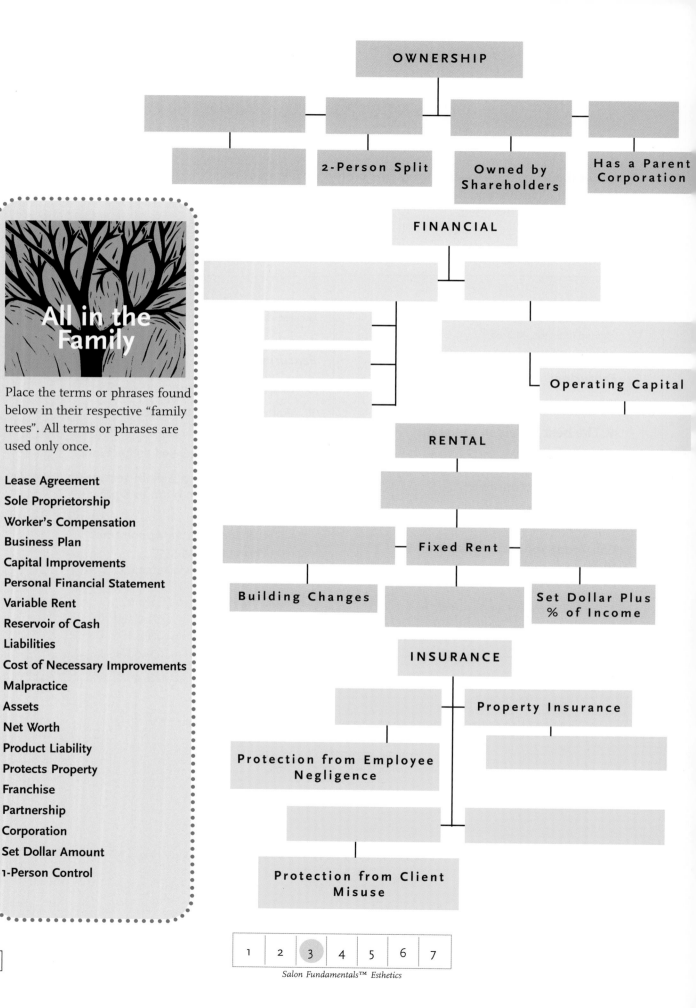

All in the Family

Place the terms or phrases found below in their respective "family trees". All terms or phrases are used only once.

- Lease Agreement
- Sole Proprietorship
- Worker's Compensation
- Business Plan
- Capital Improvements
- Personal Financial Statement
- Variable Rent
- Reservoir of Cash
- Liabilities
- Cost of Necessary Improvements
- Malpractice
- Assets
- Net Worth
- Product Liability
- Protects Property
- Franchise
- Partnership
- Corporation
- Set Dollar Amount
- 1-Person Control

Match the term from Column A with the corresponding description in Column B by placing the letter of the term in the box in front of the description.

Column A		Column B
A. Corporation		Reservoir of cash needed to stay ahead of your creditors
B. Fixed rent		Set dollar amount paid per month plus a percentage of the total monthly income
C. Malpractice Insurance		Assets minus liabilities
D. Franchise		Legal entity, separate from its shareholders, formed under legal guidelines
E. Operating cash		Person with low personal net worth that is borrowing money
F. Annual W-2		Dollar amount paid per month to the lessor; allows you to predict monthly expenses
G. Inventory		Income minus operating expenses
H. Variable rent		An operating agreement in which a fee is paid to a parent corporation
I. Social Security		Protects the owner from financial loss that can result from employee negligence
J. Inventory Control		Money you owe
K. Salary		Stock in quantity
L. "High risk"		Planned savings/retirement fund for every worker in the U.S.
M. Net worth		Procedures used to ensure that products are accounted for from purchase through sale
N. Liabilities		Form given to an employee by the employer that indicates all taxes paid for the past year
O. Profit		Compensation that guarantees a set income on a weekly or monthly basis

Your next challenge is to be ready to talk about some of the important ideas in this chapter. Follow the directions listed next to each box and practice talking about your ideas.

1. CALCULATING COMPENSATION

	Tues.	Wed.	Thurs.	Fri.	Sat.	Total
Service Total	$200	$100	$200	$300	$400	$1200
Retail Total	$100	$ 50	$100	$200	$300	$ 750

State Tax = $60
Federal Tax = $80
Social Security = $44

With a partner, use the information found in box 1 to calculate the compensation that would be earned by this employee. The compensation rate is a guaranteed salary of $250.00, plus 50% of the service amount over $500 for the week. A commission of 10% is paid for retail sales.

Discuss the calculation process and results with your partner.

2. CALCULATING PROFIT MARGIN

	Income	Expenses	Profit
Skin Care Center A	$100,000	$88,000	$12,000
Skin Care Center B	$200,000	$185,000	$15,000

Discuss with a partner the differences between skin care centers A and B shown in box 2.

Which of the skin care centers shows the largest profit margin?

3. THIRD QUARTER PROMOTIONS

JUL AUG SEP

Imagine that you have just started a new job and have been informed that you are a part of the 3rd quarter (July, Aug. and Sept.) promotion group.

The meeting is next week and you want to share some of your promotion ideas. Jot down your ideas in the space provided to the left and be prepared to explain them to the class.

Now it's time to see how well you know your new material. First answer these questions. Then use the Memory Box that follows to check yourself. Look up each answer on the corresponding page in the *Salon Fundamentals™ Esthetics* textbook. Check "got it" for all correct answers and "not yet" for all incorrect responses. Using the "Know Chart," record all of your correct responses in the "I Know" column. After correcting incorrect answers, record all of your corrected responses in the "I Need to Study" column. That way you know exactly what to review before continuing in this Guide.

Directions: Identify whether questions 1 and 2 are True or False by circling TRUE or FALSE. You can earn an extra point for each false statement you appropriately correct. Question 3 requires you to write in an answer in the blank provided. Answers to the questions found in 4 through 10 may be selected by circling a, b, c or d below each statement to indicate your choice.

1. TRUE   FALSE   Asset is the term used to identify an amount you owe.

   _____

2. TRUE   FALSE   A partnership is a business owned by two or more persons.

   _____

3. _____ is a set dollar amount paid per month plus a percentage of the total monthly income for rent.

4. Which of the following insurance types is used to protect the owner from financial loss that can result from employee negligence while performing services on clients?
   a. product liability
   b. premise insurance
   c. property insurance
   d. malpractice insurance

5. When operating expenses are subtracted from income, what term describes the amount of money that remains?
   a. profit
   b. credit
   c. turnover
   d. liabilities

6. Which of the following percentages represents a typical percent of income paid out for rent for a skin care center?
   a. 12%   b. 25%   c. 45%   d. 60%

7. Which of the following is the best determining factor upon which to establish service prices for your skin care center?
   a. results of a national marketing survey
   b. prices charged in a city two times larger than your city
   c. prices charged in a city two times smaller than your city
   d. results of a market survey conducted within the targeted area of your skin care center

8. What is the term used to describe the amount of time it takes to sell the product once it is on the shelf?
   a. guides
   b. monitors
   c. controllers
   d. turns or turnovers

9. A suggested telephone answering tip is to answer the phone within how many rings?
   a. one ring
   b. two rings
   c. four rings
   d. six rings

10. Which of the following statements best describes the order in which to count back change to a client?
    a. bills first, then coins
    b. coins first, then bills
    c. dollars first, then quarters
    d. quarters first, then pennies

| 1 | 2 | 3 | 4 | 5 | 6 | 7 |

1. page 71	☐ got it ☐ not yet
2. page 72	☐ got it ☐ not yet
3. page 79	☐ got it ☐ not yet
4. page 79	☐ got it ☐ not yet
5. page 81	☐ got it ☐ not yet
6. page 83	☐ got it ☐ not yet
7. page 88	☐ got it ☐ not yet
8. page 88	☐ got it ☐ not yet
9. page 90	☐ got it ☐ not yet
10. page 92	☐ got it ☐ not yet

I know...

I need to study...

SHOW YOU KNOW

Design a promotional contest that could be offered in the salon that would encourage retail sales. Be creative and innovative. Think of an idea that will gain the attention of the clients and still be exciting for the employees. Your theme (idea) might include a seasonal or community event or focus on wellness or personal development. Include incentives, goals, time frames, motivators (spirit builders or "rah, rah" rallies) or decorating ideas you have that will support this promotional contest.

Contest Theme (Name):

Promotion:

Goals:

Time Frames:

Motivators:

Decorating Ideas:

KNOWLEDGE GRID

Start at the top of the Knowledge Grid and work your way down, answering each question to check your understanding of Chapter 3, Business Basics. The questions found here will help you deepen your understanding, build self-confidence and increase your awareness of different ways of thinking about a subject.

KNOW

Define the four major types of business ownership

COMPREHEND

Summarize the general duties of a business accountant.

APPLY

Make a list of the basic equipment needed to operate a Skin Care Center.

ANALYZE

Distinguish between withholding and sales taxes.

SYNTHESIZE

Design an advertisement for your Skin Care Center.

EVALUATE

Justify owning your own business by comparing its advantages and disadvantages.

ESSAY WIZARD

Writing doesn't have to be a chore. Here's how to make it easy! Just use the Essay Wizard boxes provided on this and the following page to write your thoughts.

Explain, describe or refute the theme of the essay.

"Why Will the Esthetics Industry Be Better Because I Am a Part of It?"

NEXT

Write it!

THEN

Summarize your ideas.

BRAIN	CONDITIONERS

Multiple choice. Circle the correct answer.

1. Which of the following describes an essential ownership skill necessary for skin care center owners?
    a. ability to do electrical wiring
    b. ability to do their own tax work
    c. ability to excel in every service offered in the skin care center
    d. ability to manage the financial operations of a skin care center

2. What is a list of all the property you own called?
    a. net profit
    b. net worth
    c. total assets
    d. total liabilities

3. What is a list of all the money you owe others called?
    a. assets
    b. net profit
    c. net worth
    d. total liabilities

4. Which of the following formulas best describes net worth?
   a. liabilities plus profit
   b. liabilities minus profit
   c. assets minus liabilities
   d. net worth minus liabilities

5. What would the $3,000 balance you owe on your car be listed as on a financial statement?
   a. an asset
   b. a liability
   c. a net worth
   d. a bad business risk

6. What would the $6,000 your car is actually worth be listed as on a financial statement?
   a. an asset
   b. a liability
   c. a net worth
   d. a franchise

7. What is a business called that is owned by one person who is in complete control of the business?
   a. franchise
   b. partnership
   c. corporation
   d. sole proprietorship

8. What is a business called in which two or more persons share management responsibilities?
   a. franchise
   b. corporation
   c. partnership
   d. sole proprietorship

9. What type of business is owned by its shareholders and is formed under state law?
   a. franchise
   b. corporation
   c. partnership
   d. proprietorship

10. What is the title given to a form of operation in which a fee is paid to a parent corporation?
    a. entity
    b. franchise
    c. partnership
    d. corporation

11. Which type of expert would most likely be of assistance in designing a skin care center layout?
    a. a banker
    b. a lawyer
    c. an accountant
    d. a distributor sales consultant

12. Which of the following is an advisor on the legal obligations of business ownership, borrowing money, signing rental agreements and assuming tax responsibilities?
    a. a banker
    b. a lawyer
    c. an accountant
    d. a distributor sales consultant

13. What is the most important factor in opening a salon?
    a. cost
    b. location
    c. workforce
    d. market need

14. How much room per esthetician is needed to create an efficient working space?
    a. 50 to 75 square feet
    b. 120 to 150 square feet
    c. 200 to 300 square feet
    d. Over 300 square feet

15. What type of insurance do states require employers to carry in order to protect the employee if the employee is injured while working?
    a. premise insurance
    b. property insurance
    c. malpractice insurance
    d. Worker's Compensation insurance

16. Which of the following is the largest expense in operating a skin care center?
    a. rent
    b. utilities
    c. supplies
    d. salaries and commissions

17. Which of the following identifies a form of compensation that guarantees a certain amount of money on a regular basis and allows additional payment based on the number of clients the employee brings into the business?
    a. salary
    b. commission
    c. salary-plus-commission
    d. commission-plus-salary

18. Which of the following is a typical commission rate for an employee to receive when selling retail to a client?
    a. 2% to 5%
    b. 8% to 15%
    c. 35% to 45%
    d 50% to 55%

19. In many cases, who is the first person to greet a client?
    a. owner
    b. manager
    c. esthetician
    d. receptionist

20. Which of the following is usually said to be the best form of advertising?
    a. billboards
    b. pamphlets
    c. television
    d. word of mouth

Write Your Own Ticket! For numbers 21, 22, and 23, write your own questions and answer them. Your questions can be true/false, multiple choice or fill-in-the-blank. The only parameter is that your questions cannot already be found on this test. Earn one point each for writing your way to success.

21.   Q: _____

       A: _____

22.   Q: _____

       A: _____

23.   Q: _____

       A: _____

BONUS QUESTION!

Question 24 is the ultimate question. To earn two points, design a question for your class. If you stump the class and no one can answer the question within an agreed upon time (between you and the teacher), you earn a *BONUS OF FIVE ADDITIONAL POINTS!*

24.   Q: _____

       _____

ESSAY QUESTION

A maximum of five additional points is possible if you answer one of the following essay questions.

25a.   You have been asked to practice your interviewing skills by participating in a role play of a job interview. You have been assigned the role of employer in this role play scenario. Please list at least three questions you will plan to ask as criteria for making your judgment on who to hire.

       1. _____

       2. _____

       3. _____

25b.   In your opinion what is it that really makes a skin care center a profitable, successful business? Please list at least three factors.

       1. _____

       2. _____

       3. _____

Check your answers as you did before. Place a check mark next to the page number for any incorrect answer. On the lines to the right, jot down topics that you still need to review.

1. page 69

2. page 71

3. page 71

4. page 71

5. page 71

6. page 71

7. page 72

8. page 72

9. page 72

10. page 73

11. page 74

12. page 74

13. page 75

14. page 76

15. page 80

16. page 83

17. page 86

18. page 88

19. page 89

20. page 92

NOTES TO MYSELF

My Reflections About Business Basics

Experts agree that it is important to summarize your feelings and reactions about what you are learning. Note especially things that surprised you, things you found difficult to learn, suggestions and ideas you received from friends that helped make learning this chapter easier and more enjoyable.

VALUE

By adhering to rigorous sanitation procedures, skin care professionals can create an attractive and safe environment that will guarantee the health and well-being of clients and enhance the value of the skin care center's services. When it comes to ecology, or the scientific study of the relationship of organisms to each other and to their environment, everything you do to keep your center clean and free of germs will ensure client satisfaction.

MAIN IDEA

Because services that could result in the transmission of infectious diseases are performed in skin care centers, estheticians must maintain stringent infection control standards. These standards, often mandated by law, regulate the ecology of each skin care center. In this chapter you will learn about microbiology, infection control and first aid as they relate to safety and cleanliness in the esthetics environment.

PLAN

Microbiology	■ Bacteria
	■ Growth of Bacteria
	■ Viruses
	■ External Parasites
	■ Infection
	■ Immunity

Infection Control	■ Sanitation
	■ Disinfection
	■ Sterilization
	■ Equipment

First Aid	■ Bleeding and Wounds	■ Choking
	■ Burns	■ Fainting
		■ Eye Injury

OBJECTIVES

■ Identify the microorganisms to which you may be exposed

■ Recognize the structure and function of bacteria and viruses by their types, classifications, growth and reproduction patterns and relationship to the spread of infection

■ Identify the three levels of infection control: sanitation, disinfection and sterilization

■ Explain and demonstrate the procedures and precautions for the infection control used in schools and skin care centers

■ Name two regulating agencies and describe what they do

■ List several types of infection control equipment

■ List simple safety and first-aid applications for minor burns, cuts, choking, eye injury and fainting

Chapter	Section	Page
Chapter 4 Skin Care Center Ecology	Microbiology	Pages 99-101

1 Identify the microorganisms to which you may be exposed

2 Recognize the structure and function of bacteria and viruses by their types, classifications, growth and reproduction patterns, and relationship to the spread of infection

Microbiology

■ Bacteria

Pathogenic	Nonpathogenic
▪	▪
▪	▪
	▪
▪	▪
▪	▪
▪	▪

Pathogenic

Nonpathogenic

Cocci

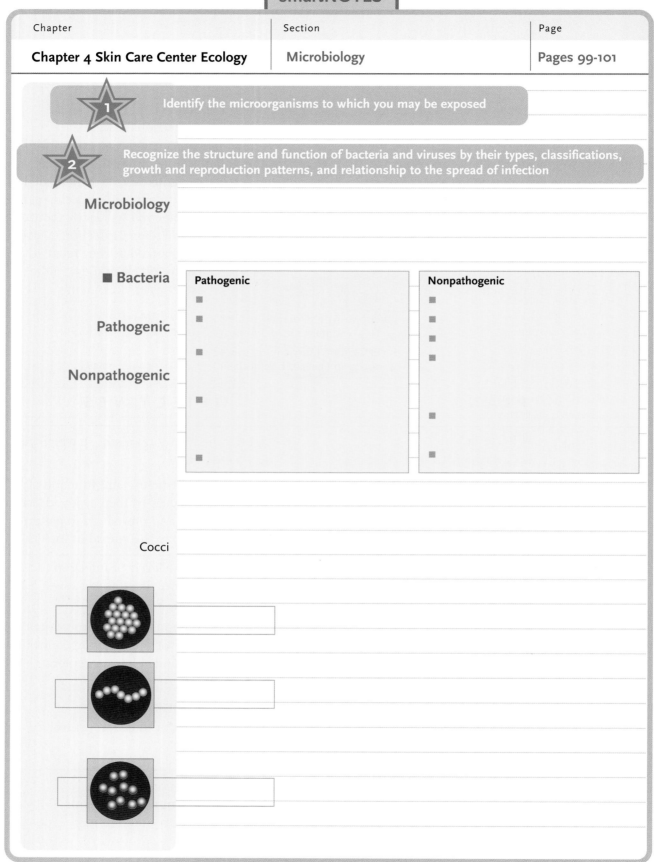

Chapter	Section	Page
Chapter 4 Skin Care Center Ecology	Microbiology	Pages 101-102

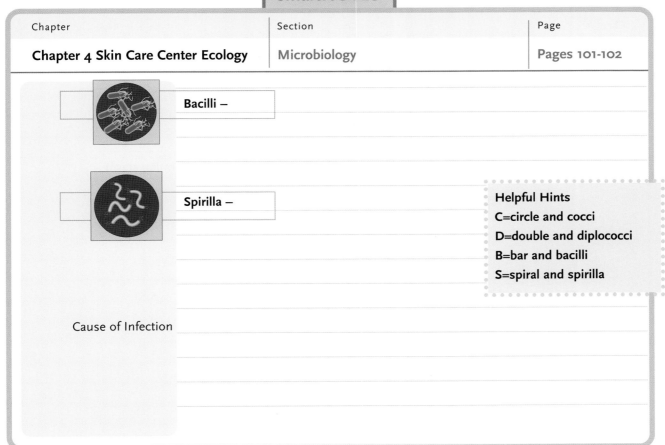

Bacilli —

Spirilla —

Helpful Hints
C=circle and cocci
D=double and diplococci
B=bar and bacilli
S=spiral and spirilla

Cause of Infection

LEARNING CONNECTION — Alias Terms

What if the terms in pathogenic bacteria were given creative, fun names? Would you be able to recognize them? Below is a list of "alias" names and their descriptions. See if you can determine the term that matches the description or "alias" and then draw a picture of it in the frame provided.

My name is Curly. I am very "coiled" and curvy! My real name is

_____

My name is Phyl. I hang out with a "bunch" of guys and sometimes we "boil" up lots of trouble. My real name is

_____

My name is Pearl. I come from a long "chain" of hot oysters, so hot we bring a "fever"! My real name is

_____

Our names are Arnold and Danny. We are a "pair" and when we are around everyone starts coughing! Our real name is

_____

My name is Rodney. I'm a tough guy with lots of muscle. I have the power to lock your jaw! My real name is

_____

| 1 | 2 | 3 | 4 | 5 | 6 | 7 |

Chapter	Section	Page
Chapter 4 Skin Care Center Ecology	Microbiology	Pages 102-103

■ **Growth of Bacteria**

Active Stage (vegetative stage)	Inactive Stage (spore-forming stage)
■	■
■	
	■
■	
	■

Movement of Bacteria

■ **Viruses**

> Since you will be exposed to openings in the skin during the extraction process of most facial procedures, you should consider being inoculated as a preventative measure. Gloves and eye protection are essential during the extraction process to protect yourself from exposure to client's blood or body fluids.

Life-threatening Viruses

HBV

AIDS

Chapter	Section	Page
Chapter 4 Skin Care Center Ecology	**Microbiology**	**Pages 104-105**

■ **External Parasites**

■ **Infection**

Bloodborne Pathogens

Common means of spreading infection in a skin care center include:

■

■

■

■

■

■

Infectious disease –

Contagious/communicable disease –

Contagious Diseases

Disease	Infectious	Contagious
AIDS	X	
Chickenpox	X	X
Common Cold	X	X
Hepatitis B	X	
Herpes	X	X
Influenza	X	X
Legionnaire's Disease	X	
Lyme Disease	X	
Measles	X	X
Tuberculosis	X	X

Tuberculosis Prevention

Tuberculosis – contagious, potentially _____ infection caused by _____ _____ that first affect the lungs

Use _____ disinfectants for equipment and implements as an effective preventative measure in the _____ of tuberculosis

Infections can also be _____ by good personal hygiene, public awareness and following _____ procedures in the skin care center

Chapter	Section	Page
Chapter 4 Skin Care Center Ecology	Microbiology	**Pages 106-107**

Universal Precautions

Local Infection	General Infection (Systemic)
■	■
■	
■	■

Defense Mechanism

Asymptomatic Carrier

■ Immunity

Natural Immunity	Passive Immunity
■	■
■	■
■	
■	

smartNOTES

Chapter	Section	Page
Chapter 4 Skin Care Center Ecology	Infection Control	**Pages 107-108**

★ **3** Identify the three levels of infection control: sanitation, disinfection and sterilization

General Practices

Glove Regulations

Common Types of Gloves

Efficacy

Important Vocabulary

- **Infection control** –

- **Sanitation, Disinfection and Sterilization** –

- **Sanitation** –

- **Disinfection** –

- **Sterilization** –

- **Antiseptics** –

- **OSHA's Bloodborne Pathogen Standard** –

Chapter	Section	Page
Chapter 4 Skin Care Center Ecology	**Infection Control**	**Pages 108-109**

4 Explain and demonstrate the procedures and precautions for the infection control used in schools and skin care centers

Three Levels of
Infection Control

Important Procedures
and Precautions

■ Sanitation

smartNOTES

Chapter	Section	Page
Chapter 4 Skin Care Center Ecology	Infection Control	**Pages 110-111**

Sanitation Guidelines

1. Wash hands with liquid antibacterial soap _____ and _____ each service

2. Sanitize all surfaces _____ and _____ each service

3. Provide _____ and _____ running water at all times

4. Provide clean restrooms with well-stocked liquid soap, toilet tissue and paper towels

5. Provide _____ drinking cups

6. Clean sinks and water fountains regularly

7. Keep the skin care center free from _____ and _____

8. Empty waste receptacles daily

9. Wear clean, freshly laundered clothing

10. Provide freshly laundered towels for each client

11. Use fresh, clean sheet to cover table, facial bed or chair _____ each service

12. Launder all towels and linens on a regular basis

13. Store soiled towels in a covered receptacle until laundered

14. Avoid touching your face, mouth or eyes during services

15. Wear _____ gloves if performing a service that has _____ to blood or body fluids

16. Never allow pets or animals in service areas - except _____ Animals

17. Provide a new loofah or sponge for each client during a _____ for showering

18. Dispense all semi-fluids and powders with a _____, dispenser pump, spray-type container, spatula or disposable applicator

19. Label all _____ and keep them covered when not in use

20. Use a fresh _____ or applicator stick for every client and every dip in for more product

21. Mix skin care formulations in flexible mixing bowls manufactured with _____ material

22. Dispose of _____ in sealable, rigid container strong enough to protect from _____

23. Discard _____ items, porous implements and sponges after each service

24. Maintain a file of Material Safety Data Sheets for all products used in the skin care center

Proper Handwashing Procedures

1.	4.
	5.
2.	6.
3.	

Chapter	Section	Page
Chapter 4 Skin Care Center Ecology	Infection Control	**Pages 112-113**

Ventilation

■

  ■

  ■

  ■

  ■

■ Disinfection

  ■

  ■

  ■

  ■

  ■

  ■

  ■

⭐ **5** Name two regulating agencies and describe what they do

Regulating Agencies Occupational Safety and Health Administration (OSHA)

  ■

  ■

OSHA

smartNOTES

Chapter	Section	Page
Chapter 4 Skin Care Center Ecology	**Infection Control**	**Pages 113-115**

Material Safety
Data Sheets (MSDS)

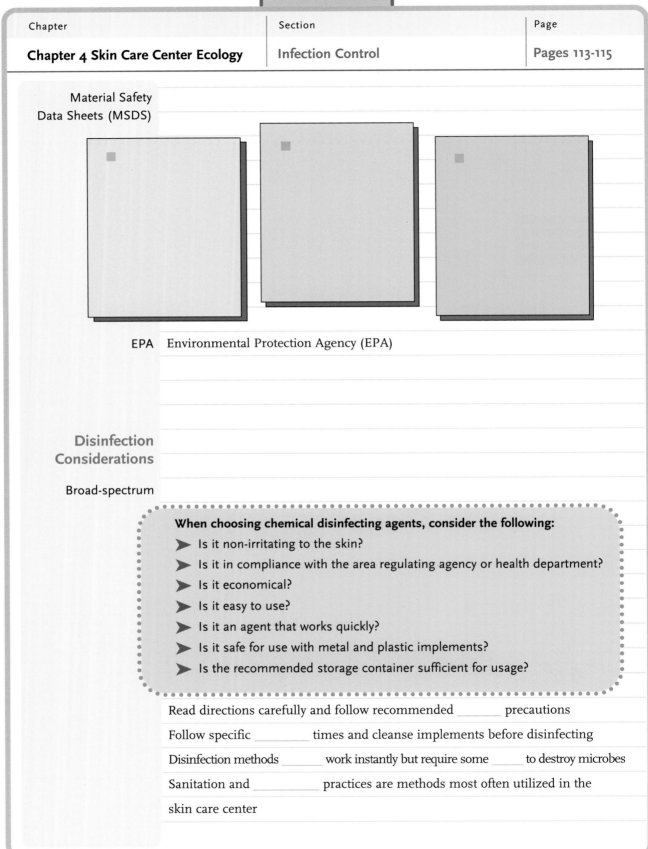

EPA   Environmental Protection Agency (EPA)

**Disinfection
Considerations**

Broad-spectrum

When choosing chemical disinfecting agents, consider the following:
- ➤ Is it non-irritating to the skin?
- ➤ Is it in compliance with the area regulating agency or health department?
- ➤ Is it economical?
- ➤ Is it easy to use?
- ➤ Is it an agent that works quickly?
- ➤ Is it safe for use with metal and plastic implements?
- ➤ Is the recommended storage container sufficient for usage?

Read directions carefully and follow recommended _____ precautions

Follow specific _____ times and cleanse implements before disinfecting

Disinfection methods _____ work instantly but require some _____ to destroy microbes

Sanitation and _____ practices are methods most often utilized in the

skin care center

Chapter	Section	Page
Chapter 4 Skin Care Center Ecology	Infection Control	Page 116

Disinfection Guidelines

1. Discard or disinfect every _____

2. Remove all debris from non-disposable implements and _____ by washing with soap and _____, by hand or with an ultrasonic cleaner

3. Rinse thoroughly and pat implements dry prior to immersion to avoid _____

4. Completely submerge all non-porous skin care implements in an EPA-registered, hospital-level disinfectant effective against HIV and _____ or tuberculocidal

5. Change chemical solutions in disinfectant containers _____

6. Remove the implement with forceps, tongs or _____, or use a self-draining basket

7. Follow the manufacturer's directions for rinsing and drying

8. Store implements that have been _____ in a clean, dry, covered container or cabinet

9. Never pick up and use an implement or towel that has been _____

10. Use additive that disinfects and sanitizes for towels and body wraps laundered in your facility

11. Keep a first-aid kit on hand

12. Refer to guidelines for _____ for cuts or broken skin exposures

13. Dispose of any material that comes in contact with blood or body fluids in a _____ plastic bag and place inside a covered waste can liner or use appropriate _____ container

Precautions for Mixing Chemicals

1. Tightly cover and _____ disinfecting products and other chemicals for use in skin care center

2. Store in a cool, dry area; air, light and heat can _____ chemicals

3. Purchase chemicals in _____ quantities

4. Do not inhale chemical solutions; avoid contact with skin or eyes; wear protective gloves; refer to _____ for procedures if contact does occur with the skin or eyes

5. Wash hands with a liquid _____ soap and water after handling all chemicals

6. Try to avoid spilling; if you do spill, _____ at once. Refer to MSDS for handling

7. Change chemical solutions in _____ regularly as recommended by manufacturer

8. Always follow _____ instructions

Chapter	Section	Page
Chapter 4 Skin Care Center Ecology	Infection Control	Page 117

Blood Spill Procedure — Treat all blood encountered in workplace as infectious

Blood Spill Procedure

If you are exposed to a client's blood during a procedure, take the following steps:

1.

2.

3.

4.

5.

6.

If you are injured during a service, follow this procedure:

■

■

■ **Sterilization**

■

■

■

■

smartNOTES

Chapter	Section	Page
Chapter 4 Skin Care Center Ecology	Infection Control	**Pages 117-120**

■ **Sterilization**

★6 List several types of infection control equipment

■ **Equipment**

UV Light Sterilizer

Autoclave

Chemiclave

Chapter	Section	Page
Chapter 4 Skin Care Center Ecology	Infection Control	Pages 119-121

Infection Control
Guidelines

Level of Infection Control	
Item	**Procedure**
SANITATION	
DISINFECTION	
STERILIZATION	

Sterilization and
Disinfection
Considerations

*Iodophor Germicidal
Detergent Solution*

*Phenolic Germicidal
Detergent Solution*

| 1 | 2 | 3 | 4 | 5 | 6 | 7 |

smartNOTES

Chapter	Section	Page
Chapter 4 Skin Care Center Ecology	Infection Control	**Page 119**

UV Light Sterilizer

Ethyl(70%) or
Isopropyl(90%) Alcohol

Stabilized Hydrogen
Peroxide (6%)

Quaternary Ammonium
Germicidal Detergent

Glutaraldehyde-Based
Formulations (2%)

Sodium Hypochlorite
(Household Bleach)

Demand-Release
Chlorine Dioxide

Chapter	Section	Page
Chapter 4 Skin Care Center Ecology	Infection Control	Page 119

Heat Sterilization

Ethylene Oxide Gas

Which of the disinfection guidelines do you feel you might have trouble remembering to complete?
Why?

LEARNING — CONNECTION — Infection Control Pyramid

Please identify what each level of the Infection Control Pyramid removes, prevents or kills by placing your answers on the lines to the right.

more

KILLING POWER

STERILIZATION	KILLS
BLOODBORNE PATHOGEN DISINFECTION	KILLS
DISINFECTION	KILLS
ANTISEPTIC	PREVENTS
SANITATION	REMOVES

less

Chapter	Section	Page
Chapter 4 Skin Care Center Ecology	First Aid	**Pages 122-124**

7 List simple safety and first-aid applications for minor burns, cuts, choking, eye injury and fainting

First Aid

■ **Bleeding and Wounds**
-
-

-
-
-
-
-

■ **Burns**

Chemical Burns

Chemical Burns
First Aid
-
-
-
-

Heat Burns
First Aid

-

-

Chapter	Section	Page
Chapter 4 Skin Care Center Ecology	First Aid	**Pages 124-126**

Electrical Burns

First Aid ▪

▪

■ **Choking**

First Aid ▪

▪

▪

▪

▪

▪

▪

First Aid
for Choking ▪
Summary ▪

▪

▪

■ **Fainting**

First Aid ▪

▪

▪

1	2	3	4	5	6	7

Chapter	Section	Page
Chapter 4 Skin Care Center Ecology	First Aid	**Pages 126-127**

■ **Eye Injury**

Cut, Scratch or Embedded Object

First Aid ■

■

■

Chemical Injury ■

■

■

■

■

Which of these procedures do you feel would be the easiest for you to perform? Why?

LEARNING **CONNECTION** — Emergency Windowpanes

A windowpane is a learning strategy that highlights chunking and visual representation. It consists of a series of rectangles, each one holding a quick sketch and no more than three to five words to describe a key phrase or idea from the lesson. The brief phrase chunks the material for recall. The drawing also helps by offering a visual reference for the brain to utilize as it begins the pursuit of understanding and retention. One example of a windowpane has been completed for the emergency choking procedure. Try your skill at windowpanes, by selecting any of the other emergency procedures to complete the remaining set of windows. You may not need to use all of the windows provided.

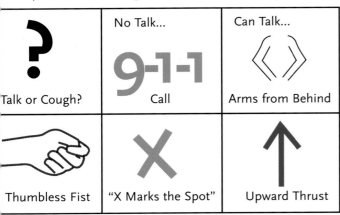

? Talk or Cough?	No Talk... **9-1-1** Call	Can Talk... Arms from Behind
Thumbless Fist	**X** "X Marks the Spot"	↑ Upward Thrust

1 | 2 | 3 | 4 | 5 | 6 | 7

In many cases in order to fully understand a topic, it is important to know its cause, what the effect of that cause is and what the solution could be. A C.E.S (Cause – Effect – Solution) Chart is designed to help you collect information for your review of these three important components. Complete the chart below by filling in the missing information. An example is shown in the first row.

CAUSE	EFFECT	SOLUTION
Esthetician used electrolysis non-disposable needle on client	Needle is considered contaminated	Sterilize needle with a liquid sterilizer and/or moist or dry heat, calibrated to the specified temperatures
Client spilled coffee on counter used to hold makeup displays	Countertop appears dirty and sticky	
Client is ready for a foot treatment	Surface of skin needs to be clean	
Towels were used during a facial for a client	Towels are soiled	
Sponges were used during a facial for a client	Sponges are soiled and contaminated	
Microdermabrasion service was performed on a client	Tip of hand piece of the microdermabrasion machine is contaminated	
Comedone extractor has come into contact with blood during an extraction	Comedone extractor is contaminated	
Esthetician wears excessive makeup	Makeup runs down face in dark streaks while esthetician works	
Esthetician wears long, artificial nails	Scratches a client and, in the process, loses an artificial nail	
Your next client has just arrived for a facial and you have just walked your last client to the desk	You are ready to begin your next appointment	

Match the term from Column A with the corresponding description in column B by placing the letter of the term in the box provided in front of the description.

Column A		Column B
A. Disinfection		Prevention of the spread of infectious agents to you and your clients
B. AIDS		Eliminates all living organisms on non-porous surfaces, including bacterial spores that adhere to surgical instruments in medical rooms
C. External parasites		Using the same infection control practices on all clients
D. Natural immunity		One-celled microorganisms that are either disease-producing or nondisease-producing
E. Communicable disease		Comprised of bacteria or viruses that flow through the blood or body fluids and cause infectious diseases
F. HBV		The low-level destruction of surface bacteria
G. Infection control		Eliminates bacteria, viruses and most organisms on inanimate, non-porous surfaces
H. Passive immunity		Ability to produce results, effectiveness
I. Bacteria		A highly infectious disease caused by HIV, which interferes with the body's natural immune system
J. Sterilization		Partially inherited, natural resistance to disease
K. Sanitation		Organisms that grow and feed on other living organisms
L. Efficacy		Highly infectious disease affecting the liver
M. Bloodborne pathogens		Hair-like projections used by bacilli and spirilla to move
N. Universal precautions		Can be transmitted from one person to another
O. Flagella		Occurs through vaccinations that stimulate the body's immune response

Your next challenge is to be ready to talk about some of the important ideas in this chapter. Follow the directions listed next to each box and practice talking about your ideas.

1. A Touchy Subject

Describe in your own way the most common means of spreading infection in the skin care center.

2. Infection

Make and explain a creative sign depicting how to prevent the spread of infection.

3. Keys to Infection Control Success

Design and share a poster displaying safety precautions for the skin care center.

Now it's time to see how well you know your new material. First answer these questions. Then use the Memory Box that follows to check yourself. Look up each answer on the corresponding page in the *Salon Fundamentals™ Esthetics* textbook. Check "got it" for all correct answers and "not yet" for all incorrect responses. Using the "Know Chart," record all of your correct responses in the "I Know" column. After correcting incorrect answers, record all of your corrected responses in the "I Need to Study" column. That way you know exactly what to review before continuing in this Guide.

Directions: Identify whether questions 1 and 2 are True or False by circling TRUE or FALSE. You can earn an extra point for each false statement you appropriately correct. Question 3 requires you to write in an answer in the blank provided. Answers to the questions found in 4 through 10 may be selected by circling a, b, c or d below each statement to indicate your choice.

1. TRUE   FALSE   Bacteria are two-celled microorganisms.

_____

2. TRUE   FALSE   Nonpathogenic bacteria are harmful and cause infection and disease.

_____

_____

3. _____ live on dead matter, do not produce disease and are considered nonpathogenic bacteria.

4. Cocci appear singly or in groups and their shape is:
   a. spiral
   b. round
   c. rod-like
   d. rectangular

5. Which of the following statements represents a common means of spreading infection?
   a. coughing or sneezing
   b. use of liquid antibacterial soap
   c. use of copper electrolysis needles
   d. disinfection of implements between clients

6. Which of the following terms identifies how the common cold and measles are similar?
   a. beneficial
   b. harmless
   c. communicable
   d. nonpathogenic

7. Which of the following occurs when the circulatory system carries bacteria and their toxins to all parts of the body?
   a. local infection
   b. general infection
   c. natural immunity
   d. passive immunity

8. Which of the following describes what a product is effective in fighting against?
   a. product name
   b. product directions
   c. product bar code
   d. product efficacy label

9. Which of the following identifies where to find key information on a specific product regarding ingredients, associated hazards, combustion levels and storage requirements?
   a. product cap
   b. product label
   c. product MSDS
   d. OSHA comments

10. Which term below identifies that all bacteria have been killed or destroyed?
   a. sanitation
   b. disinfection
   c. ventilation
   d. sterilization

MEMORY BOX

1. page 99	☐ got it ☐ not yet
2. page 100	☐ got it ☐ not yet
3. page 100	☐ got it ☐ not yet
4. page 101	☐ got it ☐ not yet
5. page 104	☐ got it ☐ not yet
6. page 105	☐ got it ☐ not yet
7. page 106	☐ got it ☐ not yet
8. page 108	☐ got it ☐ not yet
9. page 113	☐ got it ☐ not yet
10. page 117	☐ got it ☐ not yet

KNOW CHART

I know...	I need to study...

SHOW YOU KNOW

Experts tell us that it helps to have reminders posted around us to help keep our attitudes in a positive state. In addition it is helpful to remind people to be considerate, to work safely or to do things a certain way. With this chapter in mind, create 3 signs that could be posted around the school to focus staff and student attention on the three main parts of this chapter. Poster 1 should be about microbiology, poster 2 about infection control and poster 3 about first aid.

Poster 1 Microbiology	Poster 2 Infection Control	Poster 3 First Aid

Start at the top of the Knowledge Grid and work your way down, answering each question to check your understanding of Chapter 4, Skin Care Center Ecology. The questions found here will help you deepen your understanding, build self-confidence and increase your awareness of different ways of thinking about a subject.

KNOW

What are the two types of bacteria and how are they different?

COMPREHEND

Explain why viruses are more deadly than bacteria.

APPLY

List the common means of spreading infection.

ANALYZE

Specify the most common procedures for infection control used in a skin care center.

SYNTHESIZE

Compose three sentences that explain the differences among sanitation, disinfection and sterilization.

EVALUATE

Justify why the first-aid procedures for wounds, burns, choking, fainting and eye injury are particularly important for an esthetician.

Multiple choice. Circle the correct answer.

1. Which of the following is the study of small organisms?
   a. ecology
   b. science
   c. bacteriology
   d. microbiology

2. Which of the following do not produce disease?
   a. diplococci
   b. streptococci
   c. saprophytes
   d. staphylococci

3. Which of the following identifies the most common form of bacterial cells?
   a. cocci
   b. bacilli
   c. spirilla
   d. streptococci

4. Which type of bacterial cell is a coiled, corkscrew-shaped organism that can cause highly contagious diseases?
   a. bacilli
   b. spirilla
   c. streptococci
   d. staphylococci

5. The size of viruses in relation to bacteria is:
   a. the same size as bacteria
   b. much larger than bacteria
   c. impossible to determine
   d. much smaller than bacteria

6. A virus does not cause:
   a. mumps
   b. measles
   c. smallpox
   d. strep throat

7. Plants or animals that live on or obtain nutrients from another organism are called:
   a. fungus
   b. vaccinations
   c. external parasites
   d. internal parasites

8. What is developed through the injection of antigens that stimulate the body's immune response?
   a. active immunity
   b. natural immunity
   c. parasitic immunity
   d. passive immunity

9. The low-level destruction of surface bacteria is called:
   a. sanitation
   b. disinfection
   c. sterilization
   d. microdermabrasion

10. The second level of infection control is:
    a. sanitation
    b. disinfection
    c. inoculation
    d. sterilization

11. The OSHA Bloodborne Pathogen Standard requires the use of an EPA-registered tuberculocidal disinfectant or an EPA-registered disinfectant labeled as effective against:
    a. HBC
    b. HIV
    c. HBV
    d. both b and c

12. Which of the following is the regulating agency under the Department of Labor that enforces safety and health standards in the workplace?
    a. EPA
    b. MSDS
    c. USDA
    d. OSHA

13. Which of the following groups approves the efficacy of disinfectants?
    a. EPA
    b. MSDS
    c. USDA
    d. OSHA

14. Implements that come in contact with the client must be:
    a. discarded or disinfected
    b. disinfected on a weekly basis
    c. sanitized at the end of each day
    d. sanitized at the beginning of each day

15. When disinfecting an implement, it is important to:
    a. let the implement air dry
    b. pre-clean the implement
    c. store disinfected items in an open container
    d. partially submerge the implement in solution

16. When using chemical disinfecting agents, it is important to:
    a. store the agent in a warm, moist area
    b. smell the chemical to see if they are potent
    c. remember it takes time to destroy microbes
    d. not put the lid back on the chemicals right away

17. What is the first step to take when exposed to a client's blood during a procedure?
    a. stop the service and wash your hands
    b. cover your hands with protective gloves
    c. supply the injured party with styptic powder or spray
    d. disinfect the station with a broad-spectrum disinfectant

18. Which of the following is NOT an example of a disposable item?
    a. sponge
    b. cotton
    c. UV sterilizer
    d. tongue depressor

19. A bleeding wound should be treated by:
    a. applying a tourniquet
    b. applying cold water to the wound
    c. applying hot water to the wound
    d. applying pressure with gauze and a gloved hand

20. What is the first course of action taken if it is suspected that a person is choking?
    a. make a thumbless fist with one hand
    b. determine if the victim can talk or cough
    c. wrap your arms around the victim's stomach
    d. perform an upward thrust by pulling the client quickly toward you

Write Your Own Ticket! For numbers 21, 22, and 23, write your own questions and answer them. Your questions can be true/false, multiple choice or fill-in-the-blank. The only parameter is that your questions cannot already be found on this test. Earn one point each for writing your way to success.

21.   Q: _____   A: _____

22.   Q: _____   A: _____

23.   Q: _____   A: _____

BONUS QUESTION!

Question 24 is the ultimate question. To earn two points, design a question for your class. If you stump the class and no one can answer the question within an agreed upon time (between you and the teacher), you earn a BONUS OF FIVE ADDITIONAL POINTS!

24. Q: _____

ESSAY QUESTION:

A maximum of five additional points is possible if you answer one of the following essay questions.

25a. Summarize the various levels of infection control as they apply to your specific needs. The three levels of infection control are sanitation, disinfection and sterilization. List here a description of each of these three areas, along with how you use them on a daily basis.

1. Sanitation _____

_____

2. Disinfection _____

_____

_____

_____

_____

3. Sterilization _____

_____

_____

_____

25b. In your opinion what do you think would be the client's biggest infection control concern during an appointment for a service at the skin care center?

_____

_____

_____

_____

Check your answers as you did before. Place a check mark next to the page number for any incorrect answer. On the lines to the right, jot down topics that you still need to review.

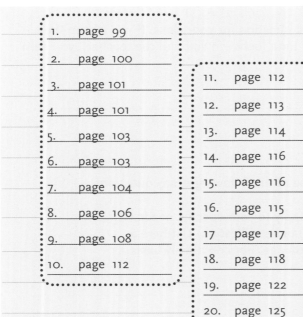

1.   page 99

2.   page 100

3.   page 101

4.   page 101

5.   page 103

6.   page 103

7.   page 104

8.   page 106

9.   page 108

10. page 112

11. page 112

12. page 113

13. page 114

14. page 116

15. page 116

16. page 115

17   page 117

18. page 118

19. page 122

20. page 125

NOTES TO MYSELF — *My Reflections About Skin Care Center Ecology*

Experts agree that it is important to summarize your feelings and reactions about what you are learning. Note especially things that surprised you, things you found difficult to learn, suggestions and ideas you received from friends that helped make learning this chapter easier and more enjoyable.

ANATOMY

VALUE

Only a select group of professionals is licensed to touch people in ways that promote health and well-being. This licensure carries with it an expectation that these professionals understand the human body and its functions. As an esthetician, this understanding is a fundamental part of your preparation for a career as a skin care specialist.

MAIN IDEA

This chapter involves the careful study of the human body, progressing from the simplicity of the single cell to the wondrous organization of each body system. Of particular importance to the esthetician will be the skeletal, muscular, circulatory and nervous systems. As you deepen your understanding of the human body, you will also enhance your capacity to touch your clients in ways that enrich health and well-being.

PLAN

Building Blocks of the Human Body
- ■ Cells
- ■ Organs
- ■ Tissues
- ■ Body Systems

Basic Body Systems
- ■ The Skeletal System
- ■ The Muscular System
- ■ The Circulatory System
- ■ The Nervous System
- ■ The Digestive System
- ■ The Excretory System
- ■ The Respiratory System
- ■ The Endocrine System
- ■ The Reproductive System
- ■ The Integumentary System

OBJECTIVES

- ■ Explain the relationship and function of cells, tissues and primary organs within the human body.

- ■ Identify the structure and function of the ten major body systems.

Chapter	Section	Page
Chapter 5 Anatomy	Building Blocks of the Human Body	Pages 131-133

Why Estheticians Study Anatomy and Physiology

1.

2.

3.

Categories of the Study of the Human Body

Anatomy	Gross Anatomy

Physiology	Histology

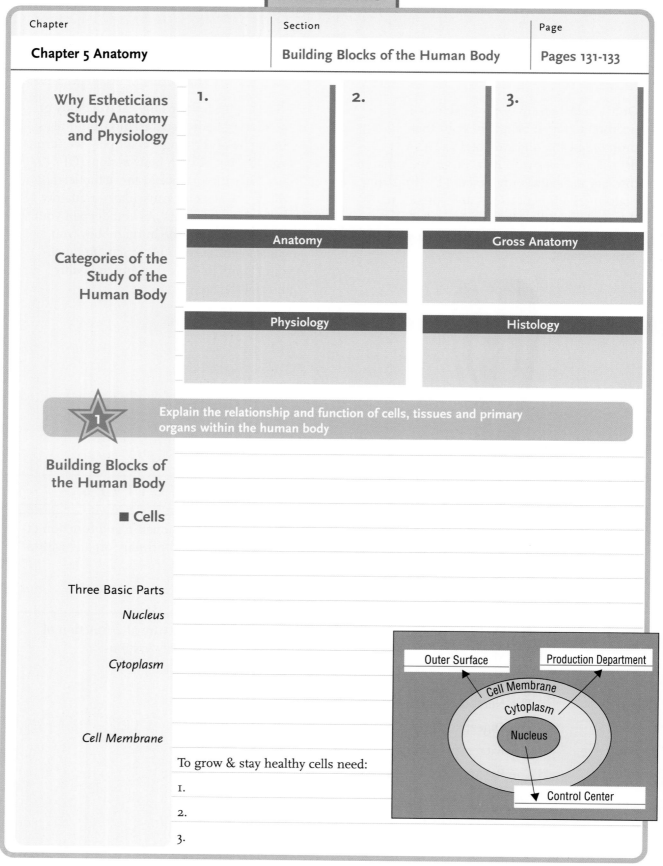

⭐ 1 — Explain the relationship and function of cells, tissues and primary organs within the human body

Building Blocks of the Human Body

■ **Cells**

Three Basic Parts

Nucleus

Cytoplasm

Cell Membrane

To grow & stay healthy cells need:

1.

2.

3.

Outer Surface

Production Department

Cell Membrane

Cytoplasm

Nucleus

Control Center

Chapter	Section	Page
Chapter 5 Anatomy	**Building Blocks of the Human Body**	**Pages 133-134**

Mitosis

Metabolism

Anabolism

Catabolism

■ **Tissues**

5 Primary
Types of Tissues

1.

2.

3.

4.

5.

■ **Organs**   Separate body structures that perform specific functions

Controls all body functions	**Digest food**
Provide vision	**Removes toxic by-products of digestion**
Circulates the blood	**Eliminate water & waste products**
Supply blood with oxygen	**Forms body's external protective layer** **Body's largest organ**

smartNOTES

Chapter	Section	Page
Chapter 5 Anatomy	**Building Blocks of the Human Body**	**Page 135**

2 Identify the structure and function of the ten major body systems

■ **Body Systems**

Vital Functions

Skeletal

Muscular

Circulatory

Nervous

Digestive

Excretory

Respiratory

Endocrine

Reproductive

Integumentary

CELLS
make up
▼
TISSUES
make up
▼
ORGANS
make up
▼
SYSTEMS

Did you know that your eye is the same size at birth as it is now?

What other interesting fact about the human body do you know?

| 1 | 2 | 3 | 4 | 5 | 6 | 7 |

Shown below are two separate Learning Connections. The first one is titled Acrostic Memory and it asks you to create a name that will help you remember the body systems. The second Connection is titled Humorous Paragraph and it asks you to write a creative paragraph using the names of the eight organs. You can elect to do both Connections or work with a partner and share your results. You'll be surprised at how easy it becomes to remember these 18 terms!

Acrostic Memory
The word acrostic can be simply defined as a series of letters from a poem or rhyme that when joined together form a name or motto. Using the first letter of each of the body systems listed below, see if you can come up with an acrostic that can be used to help you remember the names of the body systems.

Skeletal Muscular	Circulatory Respiratory	Nervous Endocrine	Digestive Reproductive	Excretory Integumentary

Humorous Paragraph
Using the names of the eight primary organs write a brief humorous paragraph. Experts say that it helps the brain make associations when there is a story format to the learning and/or when a creative approach is taken to add variety or uniqueness. Try your hand at making a humorous memory. The eight primary organs include the brain, eyes, heart, lungs, stomach, liver, kidneys and skin.

Chapter	Section	Page
Chapter 5 Anatomy	**Basic Body Systems**	**Pages 136-137**

■ **The Skeletal System**

Osteology

3 Types of Bones

Bone Composition

Bone Functions
1.
2.
3.
4.
5.
6.

Skull ➤

➤

➤

Describe in Your Own Words

The Cranium

Frontal

Parietal

Occipital

Temporal

Sphenoid

Ethmoid

Why didn't the skeleton go to the dance?

He didn't have the guts.

1	2	3	4	5	6	7

Chapter	Section	Page
Chapter 5 Anatomy	**Basic Body Systems**	**Pages 137-138**

Label the
Bones of the
Cranium

1.

2-3.

4.

5-6.

7.

8.

Facial Skeleton

14 bones compose the facial skeleton

9 bones involved in massage

Mandible

Maxillae

Zygomatic

Lacrimal

Nasal

Label the
Bones of the
Facial Skeleton

1.

2.

3.

4.

5.

Chapter	Section	Page
Chapter 5 Anatomy	**Basic Body Systems**	**Pages 139, 142**

Neck Bones

Cervical Vertebrae

Hyoid

Label the Neck
Bones

1-7.

8.

8

Back, Chest and
Shoulder Bones

Thorax

Thoracic Vertebrae

Clavicle

Décolleté

Scapula

**Why are
skeletons usually
so calm?**

Nothing gets under their skin.

Chapter	Section	Page
Chapter 5 Anatomy	**Basic Body Systems**	**Page 142**

Label the Back, Chest and Shoulder Bones

Arm, Wrist and Hand Bones

Humerus

Radius

Ulna

Carpals

Metacarpals

Phalanges

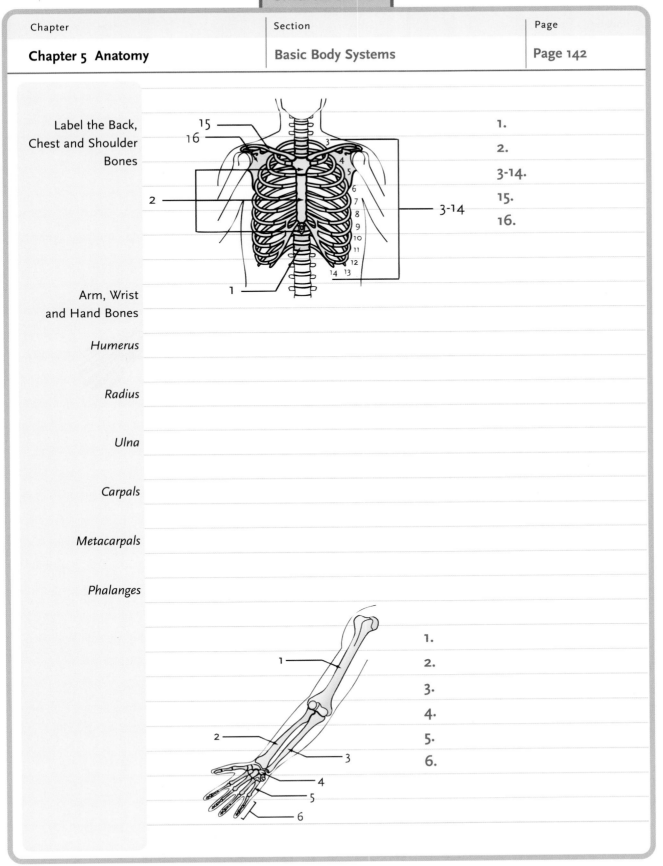

1.

2.

3-14.

15.

16.

1.

2.

3.

4.

5.

6.

■ Skeletal
System
(Anterior)

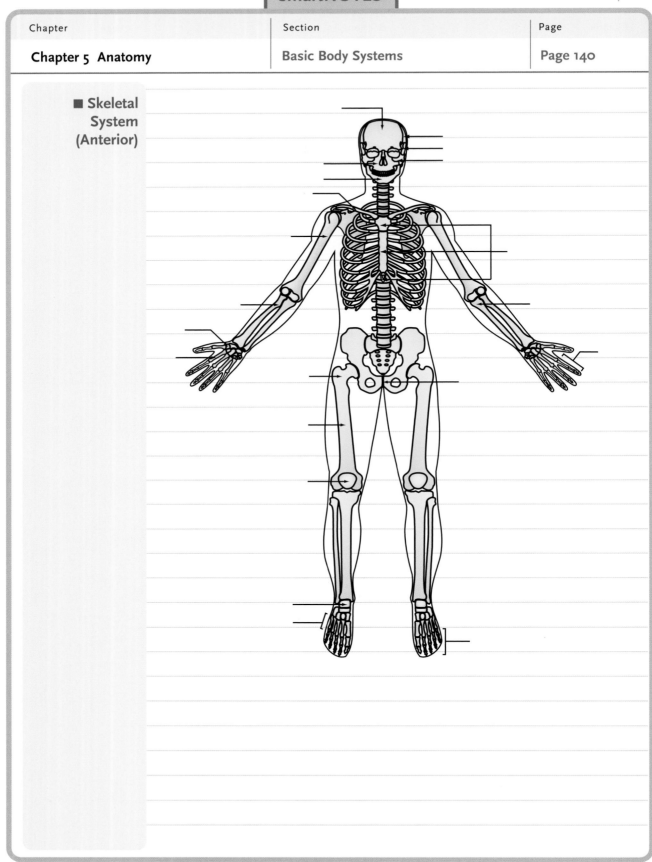

Chapter	Section	Page
Chapter 5 Anatomy	Basic Body Systems	Page 141

■ Skeletal
System
(Posterior)

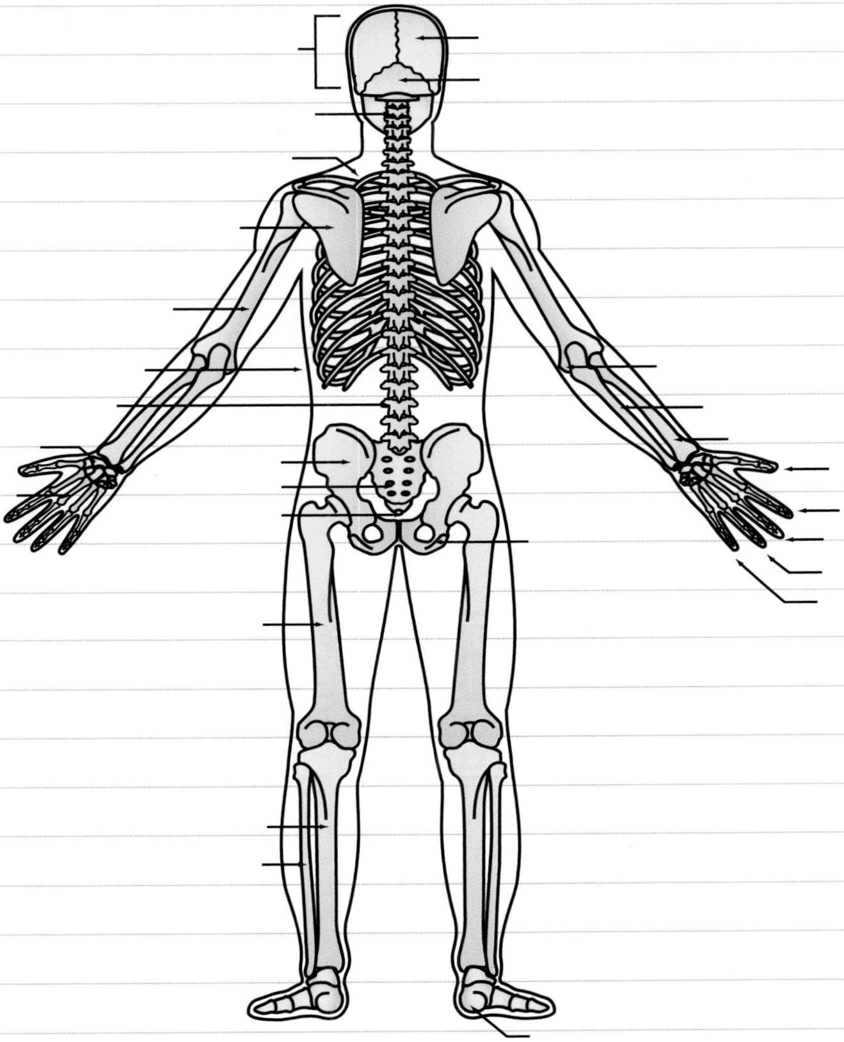

■ **Muscular System**

Muscles

Myology

Muscular Functions

M

A

P

S

3 Types of Muscle Tissue

STRIATED

NON-STRIATED

CARDIAC

Some muscles may function as voluntary and involuntary (e.g. eye blinking)

Esthetician's Primary Concern

■ anterior

■ levator

■ superioris

■ dilator

■ posterior

■ depressor

■ inferioris

Chapter	Section	Page
Chapter 5 Anatomy	**Basic Body Systems**	**Pages 143-144**

3 Parts of a Muscle

  Origin

  Belly

  Insertion

Label the
3 Parts of
a Muscle

1.

2.

3.

Muscle Movement

  Tendons

  Ligaments

Methods of
Muscular
Stimulation

Chapter	Section	Page
Chapter 5 Anatomy	**Basic Body Systems**	**Pages 144-145**

Scalp and Face Muscles

Scalp Muscles

Epicranius

Frontalis

Occipitalis

Label the Scalp Muscles

1.

2.

Ear Muscles

Auricularis Anterior

Auricularis Superior

Auricularis Posterior

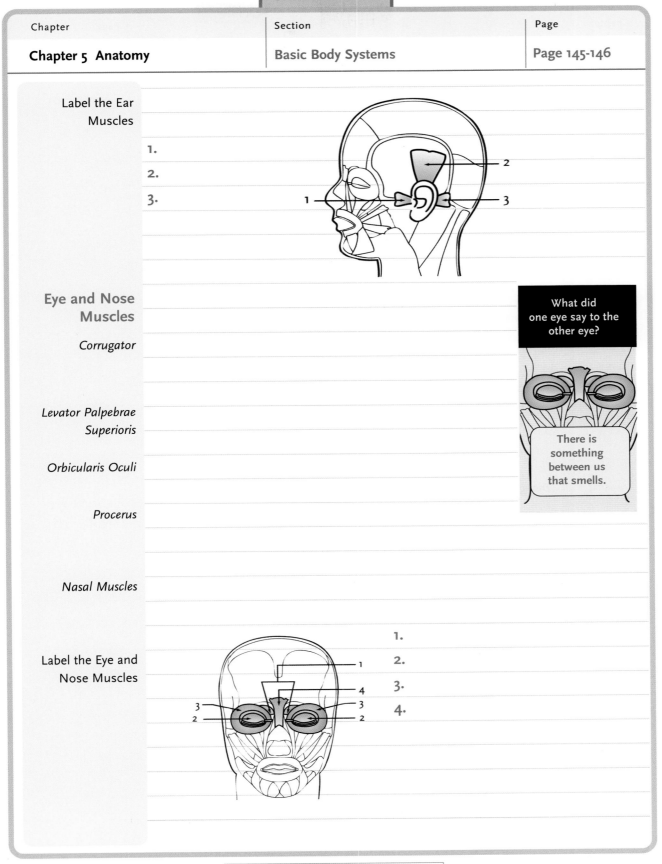

Label the Ear Muscles

1.

2.

3.

Eye and Nose Muscles

Corrugator

Levator Palpebrae Superioris

Orbicularis Oculi

Procerus

Nasal Muscles

Label the Eye and Nose Muscles

1.

2.

3.

4.

What did one eye say to the other eye?

There is something between us that smells.

Mouth Muscles

Oris Obicularis

Quadratus Labii Superioris

Quadratus Labii Inferioris

Mentalis

Risorius

Caninus

Triangularis

Zygomaticus

Buccinator

Mouth Muscles

Label the Mouth Muscles

1.

2.

3.

4.

5.

6.

7.

8.

9.

Chapter	Section	Page
Chapter 5 Anatomy	**Basic Body Systems**	**Pages 148-149**

Mastication, Neck and Upper Back Muscles

Mastication Muscles

Temporalis

Masseter

Neck and Upper Back Muscles

Platysma

Sternocleido Mastoideus

Trapezius and Latissimus Dorsi

Label the Mastication, Neck and Upper Back Muscles

1.

2.

3.

4.

5.

5a.

5b.

Shoulder, Chest and Arm Muscles

Pectoralis Major and Pectoralis Minor

Serratus Anterior

Chapter	Section	Page
Chapter 5 Anatomy	**Basic Body Systems**	Page 149

Deltoid

Bicep

Tricep

Supinator

Pronator

Flexor Ulnaris

Extensor

Label the Shoulder, Chest and Arm Muscles

Anterior View

1a

3

5

4

1b

6

7

Posterior View

2

8

9

1a.

1b.

2.

3.

4.

5.

6.

7.

8.

9.

Chapter	Section	Page
Chapter 5 Anatomy	Basic Body Systems	Page 150

Muscular
System
(Anterior)

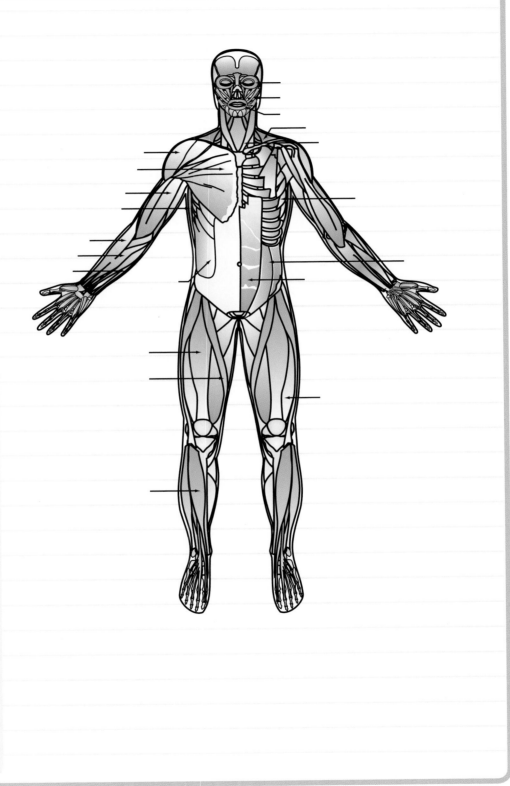

Chapter	Section	Page
Chapter 5 Anatomy	Basic Body Systems	Page 151

Muscular
System
(Posterior)

| 1 | 2 | 3 | 4 | 5 | 6 | 7 |

Chapter	Section	Page
Chapter 5 Anatomy	**Basic Body Systems**	**Pages 152-153**

Hand Muscles

Abductors

Adductors

Opponens

Label the Hand
Muscles

Palm Down

Palm Up

1.

2.

3.

■ The Circulatory System

Cardiovascular
System

Lymph Vascular
System

The Heart

Pericardium

Left Atrium

Right Atrium

Left Ventricle

Right Ventricle

Chapter	Section	Page
Chapter 5 Anatomy	Basic Body Systems	Pages 153-154

Label the Parts of the Heart

1.

2.

3.

4.

5.

Normal Heart Beat

Vagus

The Cardiovascular System

Blood

Erythrocytes

Hemoglobin

Leucocytes

Chapter	Section	Page
Chapter 5 Anatomy	**Basic Body Systems**	**Pages 154-156**

Thrombocytes

Plasma

Blood Vessels
Arteries

Veins

Capillaries

Blood Flow Through The Heart

Systematic or General Circulation

Basic Process:

-
-
-
-
-
-
-
-

-
-

Arteries and Veins of the Face, Head and Neck

Common Carotid Arteries

Internal Carotid Artery

External Carotid Artery

Internal Jugular

External Jugular

Occipital Artery

Posterior Auricular

Superficial Temporal

-
-
-
-
-

External Maxillary

Breaks down into smaller branches with specific destinations as follows:

-
-
-
-

Chapter	Section	Page
Chapter 5 Anatomy	**Basic Body Systems**	**Pages 163-164**

Nerves and Massage

Methods to Stimulate Nerve Tissues
- ■
- ■
- ■
- ■
- ■
- ■
- ■

Face, Head and Neck Nerves

Trifacial Nerve

Ophthalmic Branch

Supraorbital

Supratrochlear

Nasal

Maxillary Branch

Zygomatic

Infraorbital

Mandibular Branch

Auriculo Temporal

Mental

Facial Nerve

Posterior Auricular

Temporal

Zygomatic

Buccal

Mandibular

Cervical

Greater Occipital

Lesser Occipital

Greater Auricular

Cervical Cutaneous

Chapter	Section	Page
Chapter 5 Anatomy	Basic Body Systems	Pages 164-165

Label the Face,
Head and
Neck Nerves

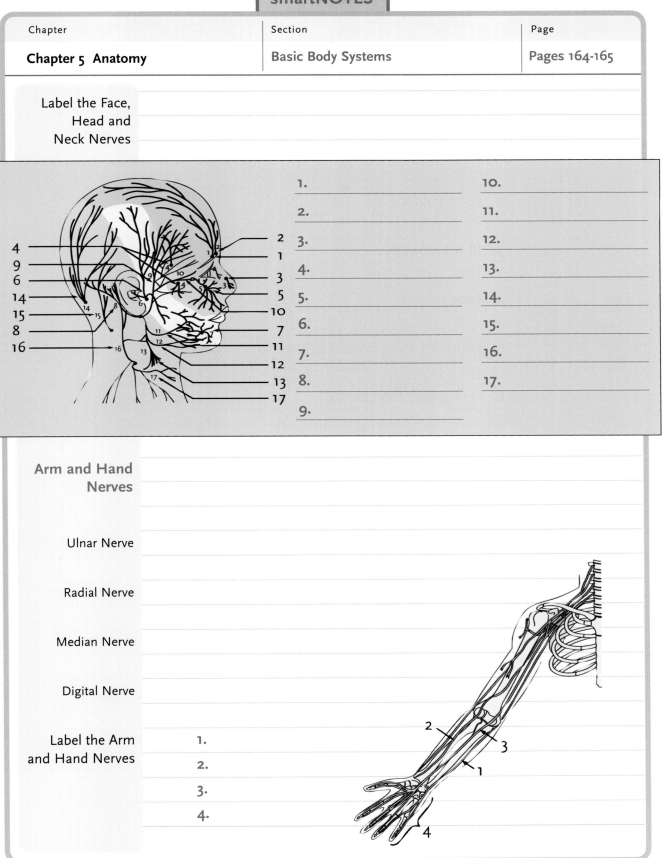

1. _____

2. _____

3. _____

4. _____

5. _____

6. _____

7. _____

8. _____

9. _____

10. _____

11. _____

12. _____

13. _____

14. _____

15. _____

16. _____

17. _____

**Arm and Hand
Nerves**

Ulnar Nerve

Radial Nerve

Median Nerve

Digital Nerve

Label the Arm
and Hand Nerves

1. _____

2. _____

3. _____

4. _____

Chapter	Section	Page
Chapter 5 Anatomy	**Basic Body Systems**	**Pages 166-167**

■ **The Digestive System**

Digestion Process

1. Food is ingested;

2. Food travels

3. In the stomach,

4. Food passes

5. Nutrients are absorbed by the villi

6. Undigested food passes

Salivary Glands

Pharynx

Esophagus

Stomach

Small intestine

Large Intestine

Digestion Time

Label the Parts of the Digestive System

1.

2.

3.

4.

5.

6.

Chapter	Section	Page
Chapter 5 Anatomy	**Basic Body Systems**	**Pages 167-169**

■ **The Excretory System**

    Skin

    Liver

    Kidneys

    Nephrons

■ **The Respiratory System**

Primary Functions ■

      ■

Upper Respiratory Tract

Larynx

Lower Respiratory Tract

Trachea

Bronchi

Lungs

Diaphragm

Chapter	Section	Page
Chapter 5 Anatomy	**Basic Body Systems**	**Pages 169-171**

Label the Parts of
The Respiratory
System

1.

2.

■ **The Endocrine System**

■ **The Reproductive System**

Pregnant Clients

Chloasma

■ **The Integumentary System**

Two Primary Glands

1.

2.

"OLOGY"	is the study of something. Define the following ologies.
PHYSIOLOGY	
HISTOLOGY	
OSTEOLOGY	
MYOLOGY	
NEUROLOGY	
DERMATOLOGY	

FUNCTION — *FOLLOWS* — FORM

In this chapter several important terms describe major functions of the human body. Can you identify the "action" these terms describe?

FORM	FUNCTION
CELLS	
TISSUES	
ORGANS	
BODY SYSTEMS	
CRANIUM	
THORAX	

FORM	FUNCTION
LEUCOCYTES	
THROMBOCYTES	
ARTERIES	
VEINS	
CAPILLARIES	
CAROTID ARTERIES	
LYMPH SYSTEM	
CENTRAL NERVOUS SYSTEM	
PERIPHERAL NERVOUS SYSTEM	
TRIFACIAL NERVE	
AUTONOMIC NERVOUS SYSTEM	
DIGESTIVE SYSTEM	
ENZYMES	
EXCRETORY SYSTEM	
SKIN	
LIVER	
KIDNEYS	
RESPIRATORY SYSTEM	

1. page 131	☐ got it ☐ not yet	
2. page 133	☐ got it ☐ not yet	
3. page 136	☐ got it ☐ not yet	
4. page 142	☐ got it ☐ not yet	
5. page 152	☐ got it ☐ not yet	
6. page 154	☐ got it ☐ not yet	
7. page 154	☐ got it ☐ not yet	
8. page 158	☐ got it ☐ not yet	
9. page 159	☐ got it ☐ not yet	
10. page 169	☐ got it ☐ not yet	

I know...

I need to study...

SHOW YOU KNOW...

Using 20 of the terms found in this chapter and a minimum of 10 sentences, write a short story that includes your newly understood terms. Be creative and at the same time make sure everyone will understand the area of the body to which you might be referring. An example sentence is shown below to help spark your creativity. When you have completed your story, share it with a partner and see if he or she can interpret it back to you with a full understanding.

Sample: As I combed my hair over my temporalis, I realized the incident of hitting the door jam of the car had left a large bump on my frontalis that extended to my parietal.

_____

_____

_____

_____

_____

_____

| 1 | 2 | 3 | 4 | 5 | 6 | 7 |

Start at the top of the Knowledge Grid and work your way down, answering each question to check your understanding of Chapter 5, Anatomy. The questions found here will help you deepen your understanding, build self-confidence and increase your awareness of different ways of thinking about a subject.

KNOW

State the seven methods for stimulating muscle tissue.

Answer:
1. _____ 3. _____ 5. _____ 7. _____

2. _____ 4. _____ 6. _____

COMPREHEND

Explain the different functions of erythrocytes, leucocytes and thrombocytes.
Include their common names in your explanation.

Answer:

Blood Cell	Common Name	Function

APPLY

Label a sketch of the muscles of the Shoulder, Chest and Arm to include the following:
pectoralis(major and minor), serratus anterior, deltoid, bicep, tricep, supinator and pronator.
Include a description of the function of each muscle.

Answer:

Anterior View

Muscle	Function
1a.	
1b.	
2.	
3.	
4.	
5.	
6.	
7.	

KNOWLEDGE GRID

ANALYZE

Distinguish the functions of cells, tissues, organs and body systems.

Answer:

SYNTHESIZE

Construct a 3-column chart summarizing the primary function of the skeletal, muscular, circulatory and nervous systems. Include in your chart an explanation of why these systems are especially important to estheticians.

System	Function	Importance

Answer:

EVALUATE

Support the teaching of anatomy to estheticians. Suggest changes you would make to this chapter to help students understand anatomy better.

Answer:

Multiple choice. Circle the correct answer.

1. The study of the organs and systems of the body is called:
   a. biology
   b. anatomy
   c. physiology
   d. microbiology

2. What are the basic units of life?
   a. cells
   b. nerves
   c. organs
   d. tissues

3. Cells vary in size, shape, structure and:
   a. color
   b. location
   c. function
   d. distribution

4. What is the control center of the cell's activities?
   a. nucleus
   b. cytoplasm
   c. protoplasm
   d. cell membrane

5. The process by which cells reproduce, dividing in half, is called:
   a. mitosis
   b. anabolism
   c. catabolism
   d. metabolism

6. A body's metabolic rate or speed is dependent upon:
   a. exercise
   b. eating habits
   c. hereditary factors
   d. all of the above

7. The process of building up larger molecules from smaller ones is called:
   a. mitosis
   b. anabolism
   c. catabolism
   d. indirect division

8. Which type of tissue covers and protects body surfaces and internal organs?
   a. nerve tissue
   b. liquid tissue
   c. muscular tissue
   d. epithelial tissue

37. What controls all three subsystems of the nervous system?
    a. brain
    b. cerebrum
    c. cerebellum
    d. medulla oblongata

38. The portion of the brain that is responsible for motor function, muscle movement and balance is the:
    a. pons
    b. cerebrum
    c. cerebellum
    d. medulla oblongata

39. Which type of nerve determines our senses of smell, sight, touch, hearing and taste?
    a. motor nerves
    b. efferent nerves
    c. sensory nerves
    d. sensory-motor nerves

40. How many pairs of nerves originate in the brain?
    a. 11
    b. 12
    c. 13
    d. 14

41. What continues to break down food once it has entered the stomach?
    a. villi
    b. saliva
    c. hydrophilic acid
    d. hydrochloric acid

42. Where does the undigested food pass for eventual elimination?
    a. liver
    b. colon
    c. stomach
    d. small intestine

43. What is the function of the excretory system?
    a. eliminates toxins from the body
    b. eliminates solid, liquid and gaseous waste from the body
    c. recycles solid, liquid and gaseous waste throughout the body
    d. all of the above

44. The liver converts and neutralizes ammonia to:
    a. urea
    b. urine
    c. nephrons
    d. carbon dioxide

45. What are the primary functions of the respiratory system?
    a. inhalation and exhalation
    b. purification and excretion
    c. inhalation and purification
    d. exhalation and purification

46. The muscular organ that contracts and expands, forcing air into and out of the lungs is called the:
    a. larynx
    b. trachea
    c. pharynx
    d. diaphragm

47. Which of the following is the conducting pathway through which air flows?
    a. larynx
    b. bronchi
    c. pharynx
    d. trachea

48. Chemical substances manufactured by the glands of the endocrine system are called:
    a. cilia
    b. enzymes
    c. hormones
    d. amino acids

49. Which system is responsible for the process by which a living organism procreates?
    a. Endocrine System
    b. Circulatory System
    c. Reproductive System
    d. Integumentary System

50. What are the two primary glands of the integumentary system?
    a. pituitary and sebaceous
    b. pituitary and sudoriferous
    c. endocrine and sebaceous
    d. sebaceous and sudoriferous

Check your answers as you did before. Place a check mark next to the page number for any incorrect answer. On the lines to the right, jot down topics that you still need to review.

1. page 131	26. page 144
2. page 132	27. page 144
3. page 132	28. page 144
4. page 132	29. page 145
5. page 133	30. page 157
6. page 133	31. page 154
7. page 133	32. page 154
8. page 134	33. page 154
9. page 134	34. page 154
10. page 135	35. page 159
11. page 136	36. page 160
12. page 137	37. page 158
13. page 138	38. page 158
14. page 138	39. page 161
15. page 139	40. page 162
16. page 142	41. page 166
17. page 142	42. page 167
18. page 142	43. page 167
19. page 142	44. page 167
20. page 143	45. page 168
21. page 143	46. page 169
22. page 144	47. page 169
23. page 144	48. page 170
24. page 143	49. page 170
25. page 143	50. page 171

Experts agree that it is important to summarize your feelings and reactions about what you are learning. Note especially things that surprised you, things you found difficult to learn and suggestions and ideas you received from friends that helped make learning this chapter easier and more enjoyable.

VALUE

Learning to use specialized electrical appliances to treat clients is a critical professional skill and is highly important to the success of any skin care center.

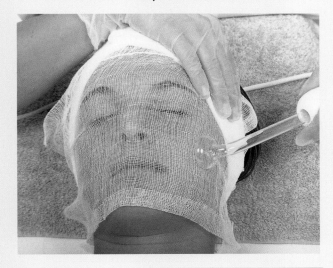

MAIN IDEA

As part of your training as a professional esthetician, you will learn to use electricity to cleanse skin follicles, induce muscle relaxation, increase blood circulation and improve your clients' overall skin and muscle tone. This chapter provides information on the principles of electricity, including safety precautions for using electrical currents to treat clients, and the workings of specialized electrical appliances.

PLAN

Principles of Electricity	■ Electricity Basics ■ Measurements of Electricity ■ Electrical Safety
Electrotherapy in Esthetics	■ Electrical Currents ■ Light Therapy ■ Effects of Electrotherapy ■ Electrotherapy Essentials
Electrical Equipment in Esthetics	■ Skin Analysis Equipment ■ Cleansing and Toning Equipment ■ Exfoliation Equipment ■ Additional Treatment Equipment ■ Infection Control and Safety

OBJECTIVES

■ Define the two forms of electric current.

■ Identify the units used to measure electricity.

■ State in your own words the safety measures to follow when using electrical appliances.

■ Identify the four types of currents (modalities) used in electrotherapy.

■ Explain the three effects achieved by using electricity in esthetic services.

■ List the essentials for performing electrotherapy and light therapy treatments.

■ List and explain the functions of the various types of electrical equipment that may be used to enhance the results of related skin care treatments.

Chapter	Section	Page
Chapter 6 Electricity and Electrical Equipment	**Principles of Electricity**	**Pages 175-177**

■ **Electricity Basics**

⭐ **1**   Define the two forms of electric current

Electricity

Vocabulary of Electricity

Electricity

Electric current

Conductor

Load

Insulator

Amp

Volt

Ohm

Watt

Electrotherapy

Electric Current

Direct Current or DC	Alternating Current or AC

Frequency

Converter

Rectifier

Hertz Rating

Conductor

Chapter	Section	Page
Chapter 6 Electricity and Electrical Equipment	Principles of Electricity	Pages 177-178

Insulator

conductor + insulator = electrical cord

Electric Shock

Generator

■ **Measurements of Electricity**

2 · Identify the units used to measure electricity

Amp

unit of electric

Volt

unit of electric

Ohm

unit of electric

Watt

measure of

UL or Underwriter's Laboratory

Chapter	Section	Page
Chapter 6 Electricity and Electrical Equipment	**Principles of Electricity**	**Pages 179-181**

3 State in your own words the safety measures to follow when using electrical appliances

■ **Electrical Safety**

Circuit

Open Circuit

Rheostat

Load

Overload and Short Circuit

Overload

In the event that a fire results from an overload:

■

■

■

■

■

Short Circuit

Proper procedure to remove an appliance from water:

1.

2.

3.

Power Box

Fuse

Chapter	Section	Page
Chapter 6 Electricity and Electrical Equipment	**Principles of Electricity**	**Pages 181-183**

Circuit Breaker

Grounding Wire

Shock

Electrical Shock

2 Types of Shock

Local Shock	General Shock

Safety

To free someone who is being shocked:

- ▪
- ▪
- ▪

Ground Fault Circuit
Interrupter (GFCI)

Fire

Fire Prevention

- ▪
- ▪
- ▪
- ▪

Chapter	Section	Page
Chapter 6 Electricity and Electrical Equipment	**Principles of Electricity**	**Pages 183-184**

Fire Safety   In event of a fire:

■   ■

■   ■

In the event of being trapped in a smoke-filled
room or building: ■

■   ■

Fire Extinguishers   ■

■

Safety   ■

■

Fire Extinguisher   ■

Inspection   ■

■

■

To Operate Fire   P

Extinguisher   A

S

S

Why is electricity a critical resource in the skin care center?

LEARNING

CONNECTION

Electrical Fill-Ins

Fill in the correct answers in the blank
spaces to complete the sentences.

1. A material that allows electricity to flow through it easily is called a(n) _____

2. A material that does not allow the flow of electric current is called a(n) _____

3. A reusable device that breaks the flow of current when an overload occurs is called
    a(n) _____ .

4. A safety device called a three-wire system is also known a(n) _____

5. Human contact with an electric current causes a(n) _____

| 1 | 2 | 3 | 4 | 5 | 6 | 7 |

Chapter	Section	Page
Chapter 6 Electricity and Electrical Equipment	**Principles of Electricity**	**Pages 185-186**

★ 4 Identify the four types of currents (modalities) used in electrotherapy

Electrotherapy Treatments

■ **Electrical Currents**

Galvanic Current

Phoresis

Anaphoresis

Anaphoresis	
Treatment	
Benefits	■ ■ ■

Cataphoresis

Cataphoresis		
Treatment		
Benefits	■ ■ ■ ■	■ ■

Chapter	Section	Page
Chapter 6 Electricity and Electrical Equipment	Electrotherapy in Esthetics	Pages 187-189

Polarity

Test for Polarity
1.
2.

Electrodes

Use of Electrodes

Active Electrode Held by	**Inactive Electrode** Held by
_____	_____

Cathode

Anode

Polarity Changer

Electrode in Positive Mode = _____ **Reaction**	**Electrode in Negative Mode =** _____ **Reaction**

High Frequency Current

Ozone

Sparking ▪

CAUTION !!!
▪
▪
▪
▪

Chapter	Section	Page
Chapter 6 Electricity and Electrical Equipment	**Electrotherapy in Esthetics**	**Pages 189-191**

Direct High Frequency

Benefits of Using
Direct High Frequency:
■
■
■
■
■
■

Indirect High Frequency

Benefits of Using
Indirect High Frequency
■
■
■

Faradic Current

Benefits of Faradic Current
■
■

Direct Faradic

Chapter	Section	Page
Chapter 6 Electricity and Electrical Equipment	**Electrotherapy in Esthetics**	**Pages 191-193**

Indirect Faradic

Sinusoidal Current

Electrical Current Guidelines

Precautionary measures for use of electrical current:

- ■
- ■
- ■
- ■
- ■
- ■
- ■
- ■
- ■
- ■
- ■
- ■
- ■
- ■
- ■
- ■

Chapter	Section	Page
Chapter 6 Electricity and Electrical Equipment	**Electrotherapy in Esthetics**	**Page 194**

Contraindications for Using Electrotherapy

Do not perform treatments if client has any of the following conditions:

- ▪
- ▪
- ▪
- ▪
- ▪
- ▪
- ▪
- ▪

Imagine you were asked to give a talk about estheticians to a community group. Briefly explain the benefits of electrically induced skin care treatments.

LEARNING — **CONNECTION** — Electrical Fill-Ins

Fill in the correct answers in the blank spaces to complete the sentences.

1. The application of special currents (or modalities) that have certain effects on the skin is called _____.

2. The four types of current you need to be familiar with include Galvanic, High Frequency, Faradic and _____.

3. A current conductor that is used to bring the current from the appliance to the client's skin is called a(n) _____.

4. A special appliance used to convert alternating current to direct current is called a(n) _____.

5. The use of a negative electrode with a negatively charged solution to perform desincrustation is called _____.

6. A procedure used to treat clogged pores and remove blackheads is called _____.

7. The use of a positive electrode with a positively charged solution to perform iontophoresis is called _____.

8. High Frequency Current is also referred to as _____.

9. When the skin care specialist uses an electrode in direct contact with the client's skin, it is referred to as

   _____.

10. The formation of ozone to produce a germicidal effect on the skin is known as _____.

Chapter	Section	Page
Chapter 6 Electricity and Electrical Equipment	**Electrotherapy in Esthetics**	**Pages 194-195**

■ Light Therapy

Radiation

Heat Energy

Electromagnetic Radiation

Wavelength

Electromagnetic Spectrum

Visible Light

White Light

White Light

Fluorescent Light

Fluorescent Light

Incandescent Light

Incandescent Light

smartNOTES

Chapter	Section	Page
Chapter 6 Electricity and Electrical Equipment	**Electrotherapy in Esthetics**	**Pages 195-198**

Invisible Light

Infrared Rays

Ultraviolet Rays

Infrared Light

Benefits of using infrared light:

■

■

■

> Placed 30"
> (76 cm)
> from face

> Exposure time
> 5-15 minutes

> Eye pads must be worn

Ultraviolet Light

3 Types of Rays:
UVC, UVB and UVA

UVC rays

UVB rays

> Place lamp 30" (76 cm) from treated areas

UVA rays

> **UV Light
> Exposure time**
>
> **1 to 5 minutes**
>
> **Up to 15 minutes for larger areas 30" to 36" or 76 to 91 cm**

SAD

Chapter	Section	Page
Chapter 6 Electricity and Electrical Equipment	Electrotherapy in Esthetics	Pages 198-199

5 Explain the three effects achieved using electricity in esthetic services

■ **Effects of** Most common are thermal, mechanical or magnetic and electrochemical
Electrotherapy

Thermal Effects

Thermal or Heating Effects

■

■

■

■

■

Thermal Energy — Can Be Transferred In One of Three Ways

1.

2.

3.

Mechanical Effects

Mechanical or Magnetic Effects

■

■

■

Electrochemical Effects

Electrochemical Effects

■

■

■

6 List the essentials for performing electrotherapy and light therapy treatments

■ **Electrotherapy**
Essentials

Electrode

In your opinion which of the four currents used in electrotherapy treatments will you use most often?

What's the Benefit?

Fill the correct answers in the blank shapes under the title 'Benefit' to identify the benefit of using the various electrodes used by skin care professionals. The first shape in each set represents the name of the electrode, the second shape gives the description of the electrode and the third shape that you will be completing will list the benefit of using the electrode.

NAME	DESCRIPTION	BENEFIT
Metal or Ionto Rollers	Metal rollers, the shape of tiny rolling pins	
Galvanic or Ionto Mask	A soft, sponge type mask that covers the entire face, except the eyes, nose and mouth	
Mushroom	Glass electrode with a long stem and mushroom-like shape at the opposite end	
Metal Ball	Small metal ball that easily fits into smaller facial areas	
Single or Double-Prong Metal	Approximately 4" (10 cm) metal prongs the width of a pinky finger	
Indirect or Spiral	Glass electrode with spiral metal filament visible in the center	

Chapter	Section	Page
Chapter 6 Electricity and Electrical Equipment	**Electrical Equipment in Esthetics**	**Pages 202-203**

★ 7 — List and explain the functions of the various types of electrical equipment that may be used to enhance the results of related skin care treatments

■ **Skin Analysis Equipment**

Magnifying Lamp

Loupe =

Diopter =

> 3 diopter = 30 X magnification
> 5 diopter = 50 x magnification

Wood's Lamp

Black light colorizes skin conditions to indicate:

Blue-white

Bright fluorescent

Light violet

Purple fluorescent

White spots

White fluorescent

Yellow, pink, orange

Brown

CAUTION !!!

When using light and magnification:

■

■

■

Skin Scope (Dermascope)

smartNOTES

Chapter	Section	Page
Chapter 6 Electricity and Electrical Equipment	**Electrical Equipment in Esthetics**	**Pages 204-206**

■ Cleansing and Toning Equipment

Facial Steamer

Facial vaporizer =

> Check water level several times a day

Benefits

Benefits of a Facial Steamer:

➤

➤

> Some machines produce ozone

➤

➤

Precautions

Facial Steamer should be used sparingly if client is experiencing:

■

■

■

■

> When steam flows, place 16" (40 cm) from client's face; position for 3 to 5 minutes

■

■

Suction Machine

Contraindications

Contraindications include:

■

■

> Massage can be eliminated when suction is used

■

■

■

Chapter	Section	Page
Chapter 6 Electricity and Electrical Equipment	**Electrical Equipment in Esthetics**	**Pages 206-207**

Spray Machine

Atomizer =

Typically, the spray machine is used:

- ☐
- ☐
- ☐
- ☐

Face cuvette = face bowl

Electric Pulverizer Spray (Lucas Spray)

Invented by
Dr. Lucas Championniere

Spray is applied 14" to 16"
(35 to 40 cm) from face

Spray no longer than
1 minute

- ☐
- ☐
- ☐

**CAUTION
!!!**

Beaker 1

ingredients to be
pulverized

Beaker 2

dripping
liquid

Chapter	Section	Page
Chapter 6 Electricity and Electrical Equipment	**Electrical Equipment in Esthetics**	**Pages 207-210**

■ **Exfoliation Equipment**

➤

➤

Rotating Brush Machine

➤

➤

➤

Contraindications

■   ■

■   ■

■   ■

       ■

Microdermabrasion Machine

■

■

■

CAUTION !!!

Container 1   Container 2

■ **Additional Treatment Equipment**

Electric Mask

Contraindications   Contraindications include:

■

■

■

■

Chapter	Section	Page
Chapter 6 Electricity and Electrical Equipment	Electrical Equipment in Esthetics	Pages 210-212

Treatment Mittens and Booties

■
■
■

Paraffin Heating Unit

■

■
■

Wax Heating Unit

■
■

Hot Towel Cabinet

■
■

■

Multifunction Machine

■

■

■ **Infection Control and Safety**

Safety

Electrode Guidelines for Infection Control & Safety

■

■

■

Chapter	Section	Page
Chapter 6 Electricity and Electrical Equipment	**Electrical Equipment in Esthetics**	**Page 213**

Safety

Guidelines used for maintaining safe use of electrical equipment:

- ■
- ■
- ■

- ■

- ■

- ■
- ■

Which piece of electrical equipment described in this chapter requires the highest caution level?

LEARNING — **CONNECTION** — Electrical Fill-Ins

Fill in the correct answers in the blank spaces to complete the sentences.

1. The piece of skin analysis equipment that allows things to be seen on the surface of the skin that would otherwise be invisible to the naked eye is the _____.

2. A measurement of the degree of magnification is known as a(n) _____.

3. A type of skin analysis equipment that utilizes violet rays or black light is referred to as the _____.

4. The elaborate magnifying mirror/light that incorporates a black light and allows the client to see his or her reflection is called a(n) _____.

5. The piece of equipment used to soften dead surface skin cells, expand pores and increase product penetration by spraying a vapor mist onto the surface of the skin is called a(n) _____.

6. The handheld appliance that performs superficial exfoliation is called the _____.

7. The apparatus that acts like a miniature vacuum cleaner to help in deep pore cleansing is called the _____.

8. The automated spraying device that is also called an atomizer is referred to as the _____.

9. Facial equipment designed to feature a combination of different electrical units is referred to as a(n) _____.

10. The unique atomizer that allows for the application of various herbs, extracts or astringents in a fine mist is called a(n) _____.

| 1 | 2 | 3 | 4 | 5 | 6 | 7 |

Match the term from Column A with the corresponding description in column B by placing the letter of the term in the box provided in front of the description.

Column A		Column B
A. Amp		A unit of electrical strength
B. Circuit breaker		A unit of electrical pressure
C. Conductor		Material that prevents electrical flow
D. Desincrustation		Material that allows electricity to flow through it
E. Electrotherapy		Equipment used to change alternating current to direct current
F. Galvanic Current		The use of special currents to create certain effects on the skin
G. General shock		A unit of electric resistance
H. Incandescent light		A measure of electrical energy
I. Insulator		A constant, direct current (DC) of low voltage and high amperage
J. Iontophoresis		A reusable safety device that breaks the flow of current in the event of an overload
K. Local shock		Light produced by an ordinary light bulb
L. Ohm		A shock that passes through a small part of the body
M. Phoresis		The process of breaking down blockages in the skin with an alkaline solution
N. Rectifier		A High Frequency Current
O. Tesla Current		The process of forcing beneficial nutrients into the skin with an acidic solution
P. Visible light		The portion of the electromagnetic spectrum that we see with the naked eye
Q. Volt		A shock that passes through the nervous system
R. Watt		The process of forcing a water-based solution into the skin

Modality or Method	Function	Benefits
Galvanic		■ Deeper penetration of product ■ Relaxation
	Uses an alkaline (negative) solution and a negative electrode to break down oil and blockages in the skin	■ ■ ■
Iontophoresis		■ Tightens and firms tissue ■ Contracts walls of pores ■ Constricts blood vessels ■ Decreases blood flow ■ Soothes sensory nerve endings ■ Creates an anti-bacterial effect on skin ■ Aids in calming post-extraction irritation
	Creates heat to stimulate surface tissue and increase circulation; generates ozone gas close to the surface to create germicidal, healing and drying effect	■ Improves blood circulation ■ Increases rate of metabolism and sebaceous glandular activity ■ Generates heat inside tissues ■ Aids in deeper penetration of product ■ Aids in elimination and absorption
Direct High Frequency		■ Stimulates surface tissue ■ Creates heat on surface of skin ■ Increases circulation and blood flow ■ Dries surface of skin and excess sebum ■ Heals existing papules and pustules ■ Delivers a germicidal effect and kills bacteria on the skin
Indirect High Frequency	Utilizes electrical current to relax and sedate client; aids in penetration of product; assists in massage for mature skin	■ ■ ■ ■
Faradic		■ Improves blood circulation ■ Improves muscle tone ■ Increases glandular activity
Indirect Faradic		■ Preserves muscle tone
	Muscle stimulation caused by current traveling through motor nerves between two positioned electrodes	■
Sinusoidal		■ Deeper penetration to treated area ■ Greater stimulation to treated area

Your next challenge is to be ready to talk about some of the important ideas in this chapter. Follow the directions listed next to each box and practice talking about your ideas.

1. Color Psychology

As you have learned in this chapter, color in the skin care treatment room can have a psychological effect. In the box to the left, there are blocks of color. Below each of the colors, write the first word that comes to your mind when you see that color.

2. Electrical Equipment Opinions

1.

2.

3.

Consider the electrical equipment that you reviewed in this chapter and, with a partner, discuss the following questions:

1. Which skin care electrical appliance would you consider the most difficult to operate?

2. Which skin care electrical appliance do you feel you will use most often?

3. About which skin care electrical appliance do you feel clients will ask the most questions?

| 1 | 2 | 3 | 4 | 5 | 6 | 7 |

Now it's time to see how well you know your new material. First answer these questions. Then use the Memory Box that follows to check yourself. Look up each answer on the corresponding page in the *Salon Fundamentals™ Esthetics* textbook. Check "got it" for all correct answers and "not yet" for all incorrect responses. Using the "Know Chart," record all of your correct responses in the "I Know" column. After correcting incorrect answers, record all of your corrected responses in the "I Need to Study" column. That way you know exactly what to review before continuing in this Guide.

Directions: Identify whether questions 1 and 2 are True or False by circling TRUE or FALSE. You can earn an extra point for each false statement you appropriately correct. Question 3 requires you to write in an answer in the blank provided. Answers to the questions found in 4 through 10 may be selected by circling a, b, c or d below each statement to indicate your choice.

1.   TRUE   FALSE   Electricity is a form of energy that produces only light

_____

2.   TRUE   FALSE   An insulator is material that does not allow the flow of electric current.

_____

3.   A _____ is a measure of how much electrical energy is being used.

4.   **What are the two conditions that must exist for electrical current to be produced?**
a. an open and closed path must be present
b. a source and an open path must be present
c. a source and a closed path must be present
d. a closed circuit and an open path must be present

5.   **Human contact with an electric current causes a(n):**
a. shock
b. short circuit
c. use overload
d. overloaded circuit

6.   **Galvanic, High Frequency, Faradic and Sinusoidal are four types of:**
a. electrodes
b. currents
c. applications
d. electrical lights

7.   **Which of the following is the only constant direct current of low voltage and high amperage?**
a. Faradic
b. Galvanic
c. Sinusoidal
d. High Frequency

8.   **Which treatment uses an acidic solution and a positive electrode to nourish deep layers of the epidermis?**
a. phoresis
b. anaphoresis
c. desincrustation
d. iontophoresis

9.   **What term is used when electric current has opposite poles?**
a. anode
b. polarity
c. cathode
d. electrode

10. **What piece of equipment is used in a dark room to provide light and magnification to determine skin type and condition?**
a. facial steamer
b. Wood's Lamp
c. suction machine
d. microdermabrasion machine

1. page 175	☐ got it ☐ not yet	
2. page 177	☐ got it ☐ not yet	
3. page 178	☐ got it ☐ not yet	
4. page 179	☐ got it ☐ not yet	
5. page 182	☐ got it ☐ not yet	
6. page 185	☐ got it ☐ not yet	
7. page 185	☐ got it ☐ not yet	
8. page 186	☐ got it ☐ not yet	
9. page 187	☐ got it ☐ not yet	
10. page 203	☐ got it ☐ not yet	

I know...

I need to study...

SHOW YOU KNOW...

Interview a skin care specialist in your area either by phone or in person. Your goal is to determine which skin care electrical appliance is the most valuable to him or her in the practice of his or her profession.

Compare your finding with others in your class.

1	2	3	4	5	6	7

KNOWLEDGE GRID

Start at the top of the Knowledge Grid and work your way down, answering each question to check your understanding of Chapter 6, Electricity and Electrical Equipment. The questions found here will help you deepen your understanding, build self-confidence and increase your awareness of different ways of thinking about a subject.

KNOW

State how electrical current is produced and define the 4 major measurements of electricity.

COMPREHEND

In your own words, describe the effects of thermal, mechanical and electrochemical currents upon the human skin.

APPLY

Make a 'First Aid for Local Shock' poster that could be displayed in the break area of your skin care center.

ANALYZE

Specify the benefits of using Galvanic, High Frequency, Faradic and/or Sinusoidal electrical currents to perform skin care treatments.

SYNTHESIZE

Design an advertisement describing the benefits of an electrically induced skin care treatment.

EVALUATE

Rate the electrical equipment listed below that is used in skin care centers as (1) essential, (2) supplementary or (3) special-use. Justify your rating.

Equipment	Rating	Justification
Magnification lamp		
Wood's Lamp		
Skin scope		
Facial steamer		
Rotating brush attachment		
Suction machine		
Spray machine		
Electric pulverizer spray		
Carbonic gas spray		
Microdermabrasion		
Electric mask		
Treatment mittens & booties		
Paraffin heating unit		
Wax heating unit		
Hot towel cabinet		
Facial bed		
Facial stool		
Utility table		
Face cuvette		

Multiple choice. Circle the correct answer.

1. Which of the following is the movement of electricity along a path called a conductor?
   a. watt
   b. load
   c. ohm
   d. electric current

2. Which of the following is the technical term for any appliance that requires electricity in order to work?
   a. load
   b. insulator
   c. electrotherapy
   d. electric current

3. Which of the following is a material that allows electricity to flow through it easily?
   a. insulator
   b. generator
   c. conductor
   d. open circuit

4. Material around a conductor that does not allow current to pass through it is called a(n):
   a. insulator
   b. generator
   c. conductor
   d. closed circuit

5. Which of the following indicates the number of electrons flowing through a particular line?
   a. voltage
   b. amp rating
   c. hertz rating
   d. ohm's rating

6. What is referred to as a unit of electric pressure?
   a. volt
   b. amp
   c. ohm
   d. watt

7. Which of the following is the resistance to the motion of the electrons through a conductor?
   a. voltage
   b. amp rating
   c. hertz rating
   d. ohm's rating

| 1 | 2 | 3 | 4 | 5 | 6 | 7 |

8. Since a watt is a small unit of energy, power companies describe watt usage in:
   a. milliamp
   b. kilowatts
   c. milliampere
   d. kilowatt hours

9. Which of the following indicates that the appliance has been certified to operate safely under the conditions specified in the instructions?
   a. volts needed
   b. frequency-hertz
   c. Underwriter's Laboratory
   d. watts consumed per second

10. Which of the following is a rapid oscillating current that alternates back and forth, allowing electrons to flow first in one direction and then in the other?
    a. rectifier
    b. converter
    c. direct current
    d. alternating current

11. Which of the following items is able to change alternating current to direct current?
    a. battery
    b. rectifier
    c. converter
    d. generator

12. Which of the following changes direct current to alternating current?
    a. battery
    b. rectifier
    c. converter
    d. generator

13. An electrical path that is broken is called a(n):
    a. circuit
    b. rectifier
    c. open circuit
    d. closed circuit

14. A path on which the electricity leaves the source and operates an appliance is called a(n):
    a. open path
    b. closed path
    c. series wiring
    d. parallel wiring

15. What can occur any time a foreign conductor comes in contact with a wire carrying current to a load?
    a. volt
    b. open path
    c. closed path
    d. short circuit

16. What is the technical term for any appliance that requires electricity in order to work?
    a. load
    b. open path
    c. closed path
    d. parallel wiring

17. All of the following are true EXCEPT:
    a. A load is the technical term for any appliance
    b. Too many appliances on one circuit could cause an overload
    c. A short circuit occurs when an appliance is dropped in water
    d. Use water to extinguish a fire caused by an overload

18. Which type of shock passes through the nervous system?
    a. total shock
    b. local shock
    c. muscle shock
    d. general shock

19. The application of special currents that have certain effects on the skin is called:
    a. ray therapy
    b. electrotherapy
    c. light therapy
    d. electromagnetic radiation

20. Which of the following is a constant direct current of low voltage and high amperage that produces an electrochemical effect?
    a. Tesla Current
    b. Faradic Current
    c. Galvanic Current
    d. Sinusoidal Current

21. The process of forcing a water-based solution into the skin by applying current to the chemical solution is:
    a. phoresis
    b. ionization
    c. anaphoresis
    d. cataphoresis

22. Which of the following is true about cataphoresis?
    a. increases sensitivity
    b. increases blood flow
    c. tightens and firms the tissue
    d. expands follicle walls

23. The process of breaking down blockages in the skin with an alkaline solution to open the pores and soften blockages is referred to as:
    a. polarity
    b. cataphoresis
    c. iontophoresis
    d. desincrustation

24. The process of forcing a water-soluble acidic product into the skin to nourish deep layers of the epidermis is called:
    a. phoresis
    b. iontophoresis
    c. anaphoresis
    d. cataphoresis

25. A negatively charged ion is referred to as:
    a. anion
    b. anode
    c. cation
    d. cathode

26. A positive electrode is called:
    a. anion
    b. anode
    c. cation
    d. cathode

27. High Frequency Current is also referred to as:
    a. Tesla Current
    b. Faradic Current
    c. Galvanic Current
    d. Sinusoidal Current

28. A gas generated close to the skin's surface that has a germicidal, healing and drying effect is:
    a. oxygen
    b. ozone gas
    c. electric gas
    d. hydrogen gas

29. Tesla Current treatment is sometimes also known as the:
    a. red-ray
    b. violet-ray
    c. infrared-ray
    d. ultraviolet-ray

30. Which of the following are benefits of Direct High Frequency current?
    a. reduces rate of metabolism
    b. improves blood circulation
    c. increases sebaceous glandular activity
    d. blocks penetration of product into skin

31. Which High Frequency method creates an even more powerful ozone effect by slowly lifting the electrode away from the skin?
    a. sparking
    b. sebum gap
    c. argon effect
    d. quartz treatment

32. Which of the following is an alternating current interrupted to produce a mechanical, non-chemical reaction?
    a. Tesla Current
    b. Faradic Current
    c. Galvanic Current
    d. Sinusoidal Current

33. During which type of treatment does the esthetician place both electrodes on the client's skin making certain they never touch?
    a. Sinusoidal method
    b. Viennese massage
    c. Indirect Faradic method
    d. Direct Faradic method

34. Which of the following treatments produce beneficial effects on the body through treatments using light rays or waves?
    a. light therapy
    b. Faradic Current
    c. short-wave treatment
    d. fluorescent light therapy

35. The transfer of heat energy through an empty air space is called:
    a. radiation
    b. wavelength
    c. heat energy
    d. electromagnetic spectrum

36. Which two kinds of light in the skin care center produce a balance of light when used together?
    a. visible and infrared light
    b. invisible and fluorescent light
    c. ultraviolet and incandescent light
    d. fluorescent and incandescent light

37. Any infrared light produces:
    a. heat
    b. black light
    c. discoloration
    d. harmful chemical effects

38. If an individual feels depressed when there are fewer hours of daylight he or she may be experiencing:
    a. Spring fever
    b. Northwest Winter Depression
    c. Southeast Winter Depression
    d. Seasonal Affective Disorder

39. During UV light therapy treatments:
    a. client should wear sunglasses
    b. esthetician should wear sunglasses
    c. client's eyes must be covered with cotton eye pads
    d. both client and esthetician need to wear protective eyewear

40. The transfer of heat via direct contact is:
    a. radiation
    b. conduction
    c. friction heat
    d. thermal heat

41. Which type of equipment utilizes rotating brushes and massagers?
    a. radiation equipment
    b. thermal equipment
    c. conduction equipment
    d. mechanical equipment

42. During a High Frequency treatment, which machine would the esthetician use on a client's neck?
    a. roller electrode
    b. indirect electrode
    c. mushroom electrode
    d. horseshoe electrode

43. What are created when electric current travels through a water-based solution (a liquid conductor) and onto the body?
    a. warm effects
    b. thermal effects
    c. mechanical effects
    d. electrochemical effects

44. When using a Wood's Lamp, what type of skin condition exists when the skin is seen as light violet in color?
    a. hydrated skin
    b. dehydrated skin
    c. normal, healthy skin
    d. oily, sun-damaged skin

45. What type of skin cells are sloughed off during superficial exfoliation?
    a. oily skin cells
    b. thick skin cells
    c. dead skin cells
    d. healthy skin cells

46. Which machine acts like a miniature vacuum cleaner and helps in deep pore cleansing, drawing out dirt, impurities and sebum?
    a. spray machine
    b. suction machine
    c. multifunction machine
    d. rotating brush machine

47. When using light and magnification you need to:
    a. allow the bulb to come in contact with the skin
    b. ask your client to look directly at the bulb
    c. look directly at the bulb
    d. ensure you and your client look away from the light source

48. Which machine serves as an atomizer to refresh the skin?
    a. Wood's Lamp
    b. suction machine
    c. electric pulverizer
    d. microdermabrasion spray

49. Which type of skin is effectively treated by using heated paraffin?
    a. dry skin
    b. oily skin
    c. acne skin
    d. sensitive skin

50. What plays a key role in the successful operation of every skin care center?
    a. the number of facial beds
    b. safe and effective use of electricity
    c. landscaping surrounding the center
    d. the number of paraffin heating units

Check your answers as you did before. Place a check mark next to the page number for any incorrect answer. On the lines to the right, jot down topics that you still need to review.

1. page 175
2. page 175
3. page 175
4. page 175
5. page 177
6. page 178
7. page 178
8. page 178
9. page 178
10. page 176
11. page 176
12. page 176
13 page 179
14. page 179
15. page 180
16. page 180
17. page 180
18. page 182
19. page 185
20. page 185
21. page 185
22. page 186
23. page 186
24. page 186
25. page 187

26. page 187
27. page 188
28. page 189
29. page 189
30. page 190
31. page 189
32. page 191
33. page 191
34. page 194
35. page 194
36. page 195
37. page 196
38. page 198
39. page 197
40. page 198
41. page 199
42. page 201
43. page 199
44. page 203
45. page 204
46. page 205
47. page 203
48. page 207
49. page 210
50. page 213

My Reflections About Electricity and Electrical Equipment

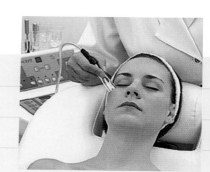

Experts agree that it is important to summarize your feelings and reactions about what you are learning. Note especially things that surprised you, things you found difficult to learn and suggestions and ideas you received from friends that helped make learning this chapter easier and more enjoyable.

VALUE

Chemistry explains how and why products influence the skin. It also helps you choose appropriate client treatment plans and recommend safe and effective skin care products.

MAIN IDEA

Chemistry is responsible for a wide variety of skin and product interactions. In this chapter, you will learn about basic and cosmetic chemistry so you can understand the skin's properties, how it functions, and how skin care and makeup products are formulated to deliver specific results. Knowledge of different ingredient types will help you understand skin care products and their purposes.

PLAN

The Chemistry of Matter
- Classifications of Matter
- Biochemical Components of the Body and Skin

Cosmetic Products and Ingredients
- Understanding pH
- Cosmetic Products
- Cosmetic Ingredients
- Cosmetic Regulations

OBJECTIVES

- Describe the three basic forms of matter and the key differences between elements, atoms, molecules and compounds.
- Identify and describe the three major biochemical components of the body and skin.
- Compare and contrast the acid and alkaline segments of the pH scale.
- List agencies and federal guidelines that regulate cosmetic formulations and claims.
- Specify the defining properties of cosmetic product categories including:
  - Mixture
  - Solution
  - Suspension
  - Gel
  - Powder
  - Ointment
  - Stick
  - Aerosol
  - Emulsion

⭐ 1   Describe the three basic forms of matter and the key differences between elements, atoms, molecules and compounds

Chemistry

Chemists

Biochemistry

Organic Chemistry

Inorganic Chemistry

■ **Classification of Matter**

Matter

3 Distinct Forms of Matter

■ Example -

■ Example -

■ Example -

smartNOTES

Chapter	Section	Page
Chapter 7 Chemistry	**The Chemistry of Matter**	**Pages 219-221**

Changing Matter   Matter can be changed from one form to another in two ways:

Physical Change

Chemical Change

Example:

Example:

Sublimination

Energy

Elements

Periodic Table

Periodic Law

Elements of Interest for Estheticians   (C),   (O),   (H),   (N) and   (S)

Atoms

Three Particles
That Make Up Atoms

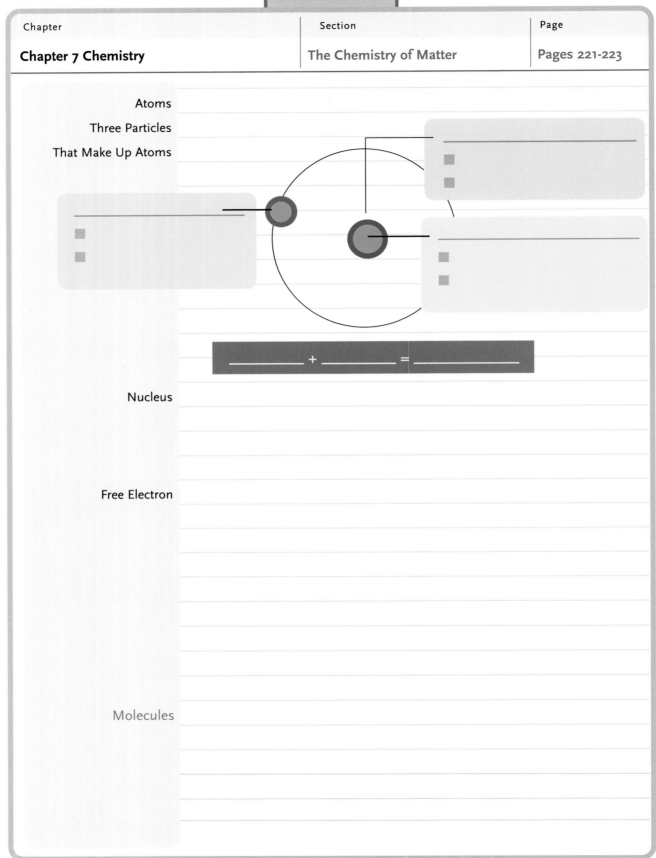

Nucleus

Free Electron

Molecules

Chapter	Section	Page
Chapter 7 Chemistry	**The Chemistry of Matter**	**Pages 223-225**

Compounds

Chemical Reaction

Oxidation _____

Reduction _____

Ions

Ionic Bond

Covalent Bond

Chemical Bonds

LEARNING — **CONNECTION** — Mapping

Map the various forms of matter using the Jump Start Box. Begin with the form of matter, define the form and finally give an example of each form of matter.

Forms of Matter	Definition	Example

Jump Start Box	Gases	Matter with definite weight, volume and shape	Air
	Liquids	Matter with definite weight and volume but no shape	Human Skin
	Solids	Matter with definite weight, but indefinite volume and shape	Skin Care Lotions

1	2	3	4	5	6	7

Chapter	Section	Page
Chapter 7 Chemistry	**The Chemistry of Matter**	**Pages 225-226**

2 Identify and describe the three major biochemical components of the body and skin

■ **Biochemical Components of the Body and Skin**

Biochemistry

3 Major Biochemical Compound Groups

Three major biochemical compound groups in the body:

1.

2.

3.

Proteins

Enzymes

Amino Acids

Monomers

Polymers

Polymers =

Carbohydrates

Chapter	Section	Page
Chapter 7 Chemistry	The Chemistry of Matter	Page 226

Lipids

Examples -

If you were asked to write a 500-word essay on the topic you found most interesting so far in this chapter, what would that topic be?

LEARNING

Word **cbelrsam** Scramble

Listed below you will find scrambled letters that, when unscrambled, will identify some of the key terms found within this portion of the chapter. Challenge yourself to unscramble all 10 words.

> a. **caiedcasdihr**
>
> b. **adcsceriha**
>
> c. **seylmorp**
>
> d. **dipsli**
>
> e. **rnoomesm**
>
> f. **yacspocershaid**
>
> g. **ntorpies**
>
> h. **cityembohsir**
>
> i. **aorsonmaicechd**
>
> j. **rbarcesyodhta**

| 1 | 2 | 3 | 4 | 5 | 6 | 7 |

Chapter	Section	Page
Chapter 7 Chemistry	Cosmetic Products and Ingredients	Pages 228-231

3 Compare and contrast the acid and alkaline segments of the pH scale

■ **Understanding pH**

Acid

Alkaline

The pH Scale

The pH scale is logarithmic, each step or number increases by multiples of 10.

							10X	100X	1000X	10,000X	100,000X	1,000,000X	10,000,000X
1	**2**	**3**	**4**	**5**	**6**	**7**	**8**	**9**	**10**	**11**	**12**	**13**	**14**

A pH of 8 is 10 times more alkaline than 7

pH Balanced or
Acid Balanced

Acid Mantle

Water and the pH Scale

> **Water sent through a water softener has minerals remaining but they are not active!**

Chapter	Section	Page
Chapter 7 Chemistry	**Cosmetic Products and Ingredients**	**Pages 231-233**

4 Specify the defining properties of cosmetic product categories

■ **Cosmetic Products**

Categories	1.	4.	7.
	2.	5.	8.
	3.	6.	9.

Mixture

Solution

Solute = _____ ; Solvent = _____ ; Solution = _____

Saturation point =

Miscible and Immiscible Solvents

Miscible solvents	Immiscible solvents
■	■

Suspension

Gel

Powders

Ointment

smartNOTES

Chapter	Section	Page
Chapter 7 Chemistry	Cosmetic Products and Ingredients	Pages 233-235

Stick

Aerosols

Emulsion

Emulsifiers

Viscosity

Crème and Lotion

Product Profile

- ■
- ■
- ■
- ■

- ■
- ■
- ■
- ■

Active Ingredients

smartNOTES

Chapter	Section	Page
Chapter 7 Chemistry	Cosmetic Products and Ingredients	Pages 235-239

■ **Cosmetic Ingredients**

Labeling

■

■

Water vs. Oil

Humectants

Humectants	Fatty Acids
■	■
	■

Emollients

■

Fatty Acids

Emollients	Fatty Alcohols
■	■
	■

Fatty Alcohols

■

Other Common Ingredients

Surfactants

Surfactants in Cleanser-Type Products

■
■
■

Surfactants Used to Create Emulsions

■
■

smartNOTES

Chapter	Section	Page
Chapter 7 Chemistry	Cosmetic Products and Ingredients	Pages 239-242

Thickeners or
Viscosity Modifiers

Botanicals ▪

▪

▪

Preservatives

Chelating Agents

Coloring Agents

Fragrance Oils	Less expensive, but are artificial	**Essential Oils**	Natural and distilled from plant materials

Fragrance

Antibacterial

pH Adjustors

Active Ingredients

Comedogenicity

Comedogenic	Non-comedogenic

Chapter	Section	Page
Chapter 7 Chemistry	Cosmetic Products and Ingredients	Pages 242-247

Sunscreen

UV Absorbers or Blockers

Antioxidants

Co-Enzyme Q-10

- ■
- ■
- ■
- ■

Silicones

Skin Renewal Agents

Hydroxy Acids

ALPHA	BETA	POLY
■	■	■

Enzymes

Kinetin

Vitamins

Lighteners

Chapter	Section	Page
Chapter 7 Chemistry	Cosmetic Products and Ingredients	Pages 247-248

★ 5 List agencies and federal guidelines that regulate cosmetic formulations and claims

■ **Cosmetic Regulations**

Cosmetics

Drugs

How does knowing about product types and ingredients help you when recommending proper products for your clients to use?

LEARNING ─ **CONNECTION** ─ Create a Label

Create your own label for a product of your choice. List the ingredients and identify the use for each.

| 1 | 2 | 3 | 4 | 5 | 6 | 7 |

MATCHING

Match the term from Column A with the corresponding description in Column B by placing the letter of the term in the box provided in front of the description.

Column A		Column B
A. Water		Categorized as oil-in-water or water-in-oil
B. Emulsion		Makes up the largest portion of most formulations
C. Emulsifiers		Organic ingredients that bind water and deposit it on the skin
D. Humectants		Ingredients that help increase the density in emulsions and gel-type products
E. Fatty Acids		Used to heal the skin
F. Fatty Alcohols		Binding substances used to slow down the destruction of the product
G. Thickeners		Triglycerides that come from either plant or animal sources
H. Preservatives		Ingredients used in skin treatment products in order to bleach or lighten
I. Fragrance		Preserve against microorganisms
J. Sunscreens		General classification of a wide variety of natural or naturally derived ingredients
K. Anti-oxidants		Not listed individually in the ingredient label
L. Antibacterial		Related to the prevention of skin inflammation and damage due to the presence of free radicals
M. Vitamins		Block or absorb UV radiation emitted by the sun
N. Lighteners		Ingredient designed to destroy bacteria that can cause problems such as acne
O. Botanicals		Fatty acids that have been exposed to hydrogen

Now it's time to see how well you know your new material. First answer these questions. Then use the Memory Box that follows to check yourself. Look up each answer on the corresponding page in the *Salon Fundamentals™ Esthetics* textbook. Check "got it" for all correct answers and "not yet" for all incorrect responses. Using the "Know Chart," record all of your correct responses in the "I Know" column. After correcting incorrect answers, record all of your corrected responses in the "I Need to Study" column. That way you know exactly what to review before continuing in this Guide.

Directions: Identify whether questions 1 and 2 are True or False by circling TRUE or FALSE. You can earn an extra point for each false statement you appropriately correct. Question 3 requires you to write in an answer in the blank provided. Answers to the questions found in 4 through 10 may be selected by circling a, b, c or d below each statement to indicate your choice.

1.   TRUE   FALSE   Organic chemistry deals with all matter that is now living or was alive.

_____

2.   TRUE   FALSE   Solids are matter with a definite weight and volume but no shape.

_____

3.   The process of a substance losing an electron is called_____.

4.   What is the branch of science that deals with chemicals and their reactions within the body?
    a. biochemistry
    b. organic chemistry
    c. physical chemistry
    d. inorganic chemistry

5.   The basic material the body uses to construct itself is called:
    a. lipid
    b. oxygen
    c. protein
    d. amino acid

6.   What is a mixture of two or more chemicals in which each component is evenly disperse
    a. gel
    b. solution
    c. mixture
    d. powder

7.   Which of the following may contain salts such as calcium and magnesium?
    a. HCL
    b. soft water
    c. hard water
    d. moisturizers

8.   What is an even dispersion of a solid substance in a liquid base?
    a. sticks
    b. solution
    c. powders
    d. suspension

9.   Which ingredient listed below is compatible with both water and oil?
    a. fatty acid
    b. emulsifier
    c. humectant
    d. surfactant

10. Which item below makes up the largest percentage of many cosmetic skin care products
    a. water
    b. aerosols
    c. emulsions
    d. fragrance

1	2	3	4	5	6	7

1. page 218	☐ got it ☐ not yet	
2. page 218	☐ got it ☐ not yet	
3. page 224	☐ got it ☐ not yet	
4. page 225	☐ got it ☐ not yet	
5. page 225	☐ got it ☐ not yet	
6. page 232	☐ got it ☐ not yet	
7. page 231	☐ got it ☐ not yet	
8. page 232	☐ got it ☐ not yet	
9. page 234	☐ got it ☐ not yet	
10. page 236	☐ got it ☐ not yet	

I know...

I need to study...

SHOW YOU KNOW...

After reading this chapter and becoming familiar with chemistry, it is now your turn to interpret the label from your favorite cosmetic. In this section, list at least three ingredients from the label and state what each ingredient's use is in the product.

Your next challenge is to be ready to talk about some of the important ideas in this chapter. Follow the directions listed next to each box and practice talking about your ideas.

1. VARYING VISCOSITY

_____

_____

_____

List three products that you are familiar with that have varying degrees of viscosity. Discuss your list with a partner.

2. THEY'RE IN THE BOOK!

_____
_____
_____
_____
_____
_____
_____
_____
_____
_____

List the ingredients from a cosmetic product and see how many of the ingredients you can locate in _Salon Fundamentals Esthetics_, Chapter 7.

| 1 | 2 | 3 | 4 | 5 | 6 | 7 |

KNOWLEDGE GRID

Start at the top of the Knowledge Grid and work your way down, answering each question to check your understanding of Chapter 7, Chemistry. The questions found here will help you deepen your understanding, build self-confidence and increase your awareness of different ways of thinking about a subject.

KNOW

Define chemistry.

COMPREHEND

Please describe amino acids, proteins and lipids in your own words.

APPLY

Make a list of the different physical product types and give examples of each type.

PRODUCT TYPE	EXAMPLE	PRODUCT TYPE	EXAMPLE
1.		6.	
2.		7.	
3.		8.	
4.		9.	
5.			

ANALYZE

Compare and contrast a homogeneous dispersion and a heterogeneous dispersion.

SYNTHESIZE

Describe the effects of washing hair regularly with hard water.

EVALUATE

Justify why all cosmetic products include a list of ingredients.

Multiple choice. Circle the correct answer.

1. What is the scientific study of matter and the physical and chemical changes affecting matter?
   a. biology
   b. chemistry
   c. chemical analysais
   d. cosmetic regulations

2. Which type of chemistry deals with all matter that is not alive or never will be?
   a. solid chemistry
   b. organic chemistry
   c. physical chemistry
   d. inorganic chemistry

3. This form of matter has a definite weight, volume, and shape:
   a. solid
   b. gas
   c. liquid
   d. carbon

4. Skin care lotions are an example of what distinct form of matter?
   a. gas
   b. solid
   c. liquid
   d. organic

5. Joining of hydrogen and oxygen to form water is an example of:
   a. oxidation
   b. reduction
   c. physical change
   d. chemical change

6. A change in the physical form of a substance without creating a new substance possessing a distinct material composition is an example of a(n):
   a. solid change
   b. organic change
   c. physical change
   d. chemical change

7. All matter – whether living or non-living, solid, liquid or gas – is made up of:
   a. acids
   b. bases
   c. gases
   d. elements

8. Which of the following terms identifies how many protons are in a single atom of an element?
   a. atomic number
   b. electron number
   c. hydrogen number
   d. chemical number

9. Which of the following are the smallest complete units of an element?
   a. atoms
   b. protons
   c. neutrons
   d. electrons

10. The part of the atom that has no electrical charge is the:
    a. protons
    b. neutrons
    c. electrons
    d. electron orbiting shell

11. What is the chemical symbol for sulfur?
    a. S
    b. O
    c. Su
    d. Sr

12. What types of atoms have evenly paired electrons in their outermost orbit shell?
    a. molecules
    b. stable atoms
    c. unstable atoms
    d. compound atoms

13. The process of a substance losing an electron is called:
    a. reduction
    b. oxidation
    c. ionic bonding
    d. covalent bonding

14. When no "trading" is taking place and the atoms are sharing the electrons, they are held together by a(n):
    a. oxidation
    b. reduction
    c. ionic bond
    d. covalent bond

15. Which of the following is NOT one of the major biochemical compound groups?
    a. lipids
    b. proteins
    c. acid mantle
    d. carbohydrates

16. What is the measurement that indicates whether a substance is acidic, neutral or alkaline?
    a. pH
    b. acidity
    c. oxidation
    d. saturation point

17. What is the normal pH of the skin?
    a. 2.3 - 3.3
    b. 3.4 - 4.4
    c. 4.5 - 5.5
    d. 5.6 - 6.6

18. Which of the following terms is defined as a mixture of two or more compounds in which each component is evenly dispersed in the mixture?
    a. gels
    b. powders
    c. solution
    d. suspension

19. What is a substance consisting of two non-mixable substances?
    a. aerosols
    b. powders
    c. ointments
    d. emulsions

20. Which of the following is the first ingredient found in the majority of cosmetic skin care products?
    a. water
    b. Dimethicone
    c. Methylparaben
    d. Cyclomethicone

21. What are the oils and oil-soluble substances named that are used to condition and soften the skin?
    a. emulsions
    b. emollients
    c. fatty acids
    d. humectants

22. Which of the following common ingredient groups has benefits that include being anti-inflammatory, antibacterial, anti-irritant and antioxidant?
    a. vitamins
    b. botanicals
    c. lighteners
    d. hydroxyl acids

23. What active ingredient is used to prevent skin inflammation and damage due to free radicals?
    a. vitamins
    b. lighteners
    c. antibacterials
    d. antioxidants

24. What current government agency is responsible for regulation of cosmetics?
    a. FBI
    b. FDA
    c. CIA
    d. NEA

25. Which of the following is a group of products intended to treat symptoms or cure a medical condition?
    a. drugs
    b. cosmetics
    c. emulsions
    d. humectants

Write Your Own Ticket! For numbers 26, 27 and 28, write your own questions and answer them. Your questions can be true/false, multiple choice or fill-in-the-blank. The only parameter is that your questions cannot already be found on this test. Earn one point each for writing your way to success.

26. Q: _____

    A: _____

27. Q: _____

    A: _____

28. Q: _____

A: _____

BONUS QUESTION!

Question 29 is the ultimate question. To earn two points, design a question for your class. If you stump the class and no one can answer the question within an agreed upon time (between you and the teacher), you earn a **BONUS OF FIVE ADDITIONAL POINTS!**

29. Q: _____

ESSAY QUESTION:

A maximum of five additional points is possible if you answer one of the following essay questions.

30a. Choose one of the six main sections in this chapter, which include classifications of matter, biochemical components of the body and skin, understanding pH, cosmetic products, cosmetic ingredients and cosmetic regulations. Highlight important areas and differences in that section. Explain that section's importance in the field of skin care.

_____
_____
_____
_____
_____
_____
_____
_____
_____
_____
_____
_____
_____
_____
_____
_____
_____
_____
_____
_____
_____

30b. List three ingredients of a common skin care product. List the benefits for each ingredient.
      Explain the use of each ingredient in the given product.

_____

_____

_____

_____

30c. Choose three of the following eight physical product types of cosmetic products: Solution, Suspension,
      Gel, Powder, Ointment, Stick, Aerosol, or Emulsion. Define and explain the importance of each one.
      Also give an example of a product that displays that physical type.

Product	Definition	Importance	Example
1.			
2.			
3.			

FINAL REVIEW

Check your answers as you did before. Place a check mark next to the page number for any incorrect answer. On the lines to the right, jot down topics that you still need to review.

1. page 217
2. page 218
3. page 218
4. page 218
5. page 219
6. page 219
7. page 220
8. page 220
9. page 221
10. page 221
11. page 221
12. page 222

13. page 224
14. page 224
15. page 225
16. page 228
17. page 229
18. page 232
19. page 233
20. page 236
21. page 237
22. page 239
23. page 243
24. page 247
25. page 248

NOTES TO MYSELF — *My Reflections About Chemistry*

Experts agree that it is important to summarize your feelings and reactions about what you are learning. Note especially things that surprised you, things you found difficult to learn and suggestions and ideas you received from friends that helped make learning this chapter easier and more enjoyable.

SKIN PHYSIOLOGY

VALUE

A working understanding of skin physiology, especially the structure and functions of the skin, is a prerequisite to success as an esthetician.

MAIN IDEA

The skin is amazing! It is the largest and perhaps most sensitive organ of the human body. It directs our bodily responses to everything with which we come into contact. It breathes, regulating body temperature. It protects, shielding the body from invasion of dangerous microorganisms. Because its surface is thin enough to be stimulated by a touch, it can be a source of great pleasure when treated with care and expert attention.

Knowledge of the structure, functions and conditions of the skin is the tool you need to recognize and work with different skin types and conditions.

PLAN

| The Integumentary System | ■ Functions of the Skin
■ Layers of the Skin |
| Skin Care | ■ Skin Cell Formation
■ Skin Behavior
■ Skin Conditions |

OBJECTIVES

■ Explain the six primary functions of the skin.

■ Describe the basic physiology of the skin and its appendages.

■ State the process of skin cell formation.

■ Identify the factors that influence ingredient penetration to affect skin behavior.

■ List the common conditions of the skin under the categories of rashes, lesions, infections, acne, sebaceous and sudoriferous gland disorders, rosacea, pigmentation, growths and aging.

Chapter	Section	Page
Chapter 8 Skin Physiology	**The Integumentary System**	**Pages 259-260**

■ Functions of the Skin

⭐ **1** Explain the six primary functions of the skin

Skin Physiology

Skin Histology

Integumentary System

Dermatology

Dermatologist

■ 6 Functions of the Skin

Protection

Absorption

Secretion

Excretion

Regulation

Sensation

Chapter	Section	Page
Chapter 8 Skin Physiology	**The Integumentary System**	**Pages 261-263**

2 Describe the basic physiology of the skin and its appendages

■ **Layers of the Skin**

Keratin

1. Hard keratin

2. Soft keratin

Three Main Layers
of the Skin

1

2

3

Epidermis

5 Layers of the Epidermis
1-Stratum Corneum

1. **Stratum Corneum**

■

■

■

■

■

■

■

■

smartNOTES

Chapter	Section	Page
Chapter 8 Skin Physiology	**The Integumentary System**	**Pages 263-264**

2-Stratum Lucidum

2. Stratum Lucidum

-
-
-

3-Stratum Granulosum

3. Stratum Granulosum

-
-
-
-
-

4-Stratum Spinosum

4. Stratum Spinosum

-
-
-
-

5-Stratum
Germinativum

5. Stratum Germinativum

- ■
- ■

- ■
- ■

- ■
- ■

- ■
- ■

Dermis

Components of
the Dermis

1 Fibroblast Cells

- ■

- ■

2 Elastin

- ■

- ■

3 Collagen

- ■   ■

- ■

                       ■

Chapter	Section	Page
Chapter 8 Skin Physiology	**The Integumentary System**	**Pages 266-267**

Mast Cells

Papillary Dermis

Primary Papillary Receptors

Pain Receptors

Thermoreceptors

Mechanoreceptors

Tactile Receptors

Sensation Receptors   Four main receptors for sensation

    1.

    2.

    3.

    4.

Reticular Dermis

Primary Reticular
Components

Sudoriferous Glands

Duct and Ductless Glands   Endocrine Glands

    ■

    ■

    Exocrine Glands

    ■

    ■

Chapter	Section	Page
Chapter 8 Skin Physiology	The Integumentary System	Pages 267-269

Two Types of Duct Sweat Glands

Apocrine Glands
- ■
- ■
- ■
- ■
- ■

Eccrine Glands
- ■
- ■
- ■
- ■
- ■
- ■

Sebaceous Glands

Sebaceous Glands
- ■
- ■
- ■
- ■
- ■
- ■
- ■
- ■

Acid Mantle

Arrector Pili
- ➤
- ➤
- ➤
- ➤

Subcutaneous Layer

Called the subcutis or subdermis,
- ■
- ■
- ■
- ■

Chapter	Section	Page
Chapter 8 Skin Physiology	**The Integumentary System**	**Page 269**

Five Types of Tissue	**Types of Tissue**	**Location**
	1.	
	2.	
	3.	
	4.	
	5.	

Four examples of
Connective Tissue

➤ Collagen and elastin –

➤ Ligaments –

➤ Tendons –

➤ Cartilage –

In what ways do the functions of the skin affect the condition of the entire body?

LEARNING — **CONNECTION** — **Skin Structure**

The layers of the skin are shown on the left. Beside each layer is a series of numbers.
Fill in the numbered oval that matches the description on the right.

Epidermis	1	2	3	4	5	6
Dermis	1	2	3	4	5	6
Subcutaneous Layer	1	2	3	4	5	6

1. **Body's cushioning**

2. **Insulates and acts as a shock absorber**

3. **Outermost layer of the skin**

4. **True skin**

5. **Skin's main support system**

6. **Provides a protective barrier**

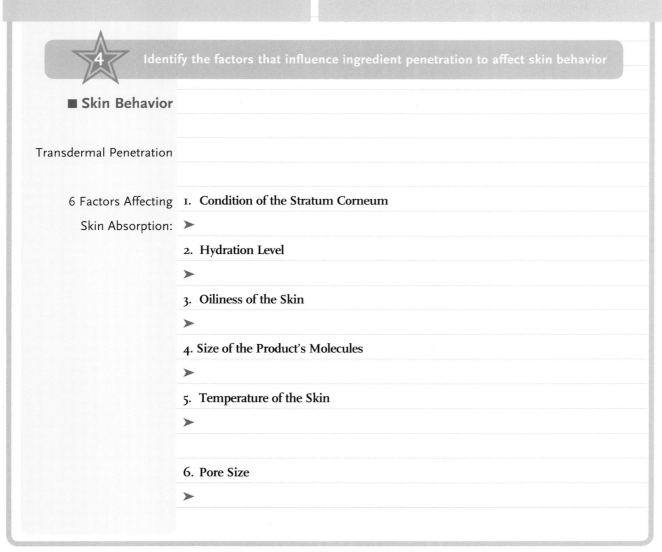

3 State the process of skin cell formation

■ **Skin Cell Formation**

Exfoliation

Mechanical (Manual) Exfoliation   Chemical Exfoliation

4 Identify the factors that influence ingredient penetration to affect skin behavior

■ **Skin Behavior**

Transdermal Penetration

6 Factors Affecting Skin Absorption:

1. **Condition of the Stratum Corneum**
➤

2. **Hydration Level**
➤

3. **Oiliness of the Skin**
➤

4. **Size of the Product's Molecules**
➤

5. **Temperature of the Skin**
➤

6. **Pore Size**
➤

Chapter	Section	Page
Chapter 8 Skin Physiology	Skin Care	**Pages 273-274, 277-278**

Absorption Process | Four primary ways products are absorbed into the skin

1.   3.

2.   4.

⭐ 5 — List the common conditions of the skin under the categories of lesions, rashes, infections, sebaceous and sudoriferous gland disorders, pigmentation, growths and aging

■ **Conditions of the Skin**
Rashes

Atopic Dermatitis

Contact Dermatitis

Dermatitis

Psoriasis

Eczema

Chapter	Section	Page
Chapter 8 Skin Physiology	**Skin Care**	**Pages 275-276, 278**

Hives

Skin Lesions

Primary Skin Lesions

Macule

Wheal

Papule

Pustule

Vesicle

Nodule

Cyst

Secondary Skin Lesions

Crust

Excoriation

Scale

Scar

Fissure

Ulcer

Skin Infections

Herpes Simplex

Herpes Zoster

Impetigo

Tinea

Tinea Corporis

Tinea Versicolor

Warts

Candida Albicans

Pink Eye

Chapter	Section	Page
Chapter 8 Skin Physiology	**Skin Care**	**Page 281**

Sebaceous Gland Disorders

Asteatosis

Seborrhea

Steatoma

Furuncle

Carbuncle

Rosacea

Dilated capillaries at the surface of the skin are called telangiectasia

Rosacea Treatment

Rhinophyma

Chapter	Section	Page
Chapter 8 Skin Physiology	Skin Care	Pages 282-283

Acne

- ▪
- ▪

Hormonal and genetic factors are the two major influences for the cause of acne

Causes of Acne

> **Other Causes**
> - ▪
> - ▪
> - ▪
> - ▪
> - ▪
> - ▪

Advice on Acne

Do not touch lesions	**Do not squeeze lesions**
▪	▪
▪	▪
▪	
▪	
▪	

Recommend a home care treatment program

Involve a client in a series of facial treatments for acne

Chapter	Section	Page
Chapter 8 Skin Physiology	**Skin Care**	**Pages 283-285**

Types of Acne

Blackhead

Whitehead

Papule

Pustule

Milia

Nodular Cystic Acne

Acne Myths

"Acne is caused by a poor diet"

"You just have to let acne run its course"

Grades of Acne

Grade 1 Acne

Description

Treatments include

Grade 2 Acne

Description

Treatments include

Grade 3 Acne

Description

Treatments include

Grade 4 Acne

Description

Treatments include

Chapter	Section	Page
Chapter 8 Skin Physiology	**Skin Care**	**Pages 286-287**

Acne Treatments

Topical Therapies

1. Benzoyl Peroxide

2. Topical Antibiotics

3. Retin-A®

4. Azaleic Acid

5. Salicylic Acid

6. Glycolic Acid

Oral therapies—

Accutane®

Sudoriferous Gland Disorders

Bromidosis

Anhidrosis

Hyperhidrosis

Miliaria Rubra

Skin Growths

Benign Growths or Moles

Pre-malignant Growths

Actinic keratosis =

Malignant Growths

Basal Cell Carcinomas

Squamous Cell Carcinoma

Melanoma

Untreated Growths

If client has lesions that look suspicious, send him or her to a physician immediately

Chapter	Section	Page
Chapter 8 Skin Physiology	**Skin Care**	**Pages 288-290**

Guidelines for Skin Growths

A Asymmetry

B Border

C Color

D Diameter

Pigmentation Disorders

Albinism (oculocutaneous)

Leukoderma

Vitiligo

Nevus

Lentigo

Post Inflammatory Hyperpigmentation

Chloasma or Melasma

Aging Factors

Intrinsic Aging

Extrinsic Aging

Sun Exposure

Smoking and ■

Alcohol ■

■

■

Important Terms

Acute

Allergen

Allergy

Chronic

Contagious

Dermatitis

Dermatitis Venenata

Diagnosis

Edema

Erythema

Etiology

Hyperkeratosis

Inflammation

Chapter	Section	Page
Chapter 8 Skin Physiology	**Skin Care**	**Pages 291-294**

Dr. Thomas B. Fitzpatrick

More important terms

Keratosis

Objective Symptoms

Occupational Disorder

Parasitic Disease

Pathology

Prognosis

Pruritus

Seasonal Disease

Subjective Symptoms

Systemic Disease

Why is it important to be familiar with characteristics and causes of common skin disorders?

LEARNING CONNECTION ——— Skin Growths

Using the A, B, C, D below, list the four guidelines for determining
whether you should refer a client to a physician for further examination.

A = Asymmetry _____

B = Border _____

C = Color _____

D = Diameter _____

1	2	3	4	5	6	7

Your next challenge is to be ready to talk about some of the important ideas in this chapter. Follow the directions listed next to each box and practice talking about your ideas.

1. Describing and Discussing the Main Skin Layers

1.
- ■
- ■
- ■

2.
- ■
- ■

3.
- ■
- ■
- ■

List the three main layers of the skin. Then, with a partner, describe and discuss the importance of each layer.

2. Explaining the Functions of Skin

1.

2.

3.

4.

5.

6.

List and explain the six primary functions of the skin. Discuss the importance of each one with your partner and give a real life example of a function you may have experienced in the past.

3. Aging and Skin Care

Describe extrinsic aging and the role it plays in skin care.

Now it's time to see how well you know your new material. First answer these questions. Then use the Memory Box that follows to check yourself. Look up each answer on the corresponding page in the *Salon Fundamentals™ Esthetics* textbook. Check "got it" for all correct answers and "not yet" for all incorrect responses. Using the "Know Chart," record all of your correct responses in the "I Know" column. After correcting incorrect answers, record all of your corrected responses in the "I Need to Study" column. That way you know exactly what to review before continuing in this Guide.

Directions: Identify whether questions 1 and 2 are True or False by circling TRUE or FALSE. You can earn an extra point for each false statement you appropriately correct. Question 3 requires you to write in an answer in the blank provided. Answers to the questions found in 4 through 10 may be selected by circling a, b, c or d below each statement to indicate your choice.

1. TRUE   FALSE   Skin physiology is the study of the skin's functions.

_____

2. TRUE   FALSE   The dermis is the outermost layer of the skin and provides the body with protection from the environment.

_____

_____

3. _____ is defined as the chemical conversion of living cells into dead protein cells?

4. What is often referred to as the true skin?
   a. dermis
   b. epidermis
   c. melanocytes
   d. subcutaneous layer

5. Where are the apocrine glands located on the body?
   a. on the hands
   b. on the feet
   c. under the arms
   d. beneath the hair follicles

6. Sebum mixes with the secretions of the sweat glands, creating a layer of oil and moisture called the:
   a. dermis
   b. acid mantle
   c. stratum corneum
   d. subcutaneous layer

7. Which layer of the skin provides the body with cushion that insulates and acts as a shock absorber?
   a. dermis
   b. epidermis
   c. stratum corneum
   d. subcutaneous layer

8. What refers to the change in the structure of the skin tissue?
   a. bulla
   b. edema
   c. lesions
   d. dermatitis

9. This type of acne is mild and consists of open and closed comedones scattered over less than half of the area of the face or back?
   a. Grade 1
   b. Grade 2
   c. Grade 3
   d. Grade 4

10. What is a substance that causes an allergy?
   a. acute
   b. allergen
   c. edema
   d. parasitic disease

| 1 | 2 | 3 | 4 | 5 | 6 | 7 |

1. page 259	☐ got it ☐ not yet
2. page 261	☐ got it ☐ not yet
3. page 262	☐ got it ☐ not yet
4. page 265	☐ got it ☐ not yet
5. page 267	☐ got it ☐ not yet
6. page 268	☐ got it ☐ not yet
7. page 269	☐ got it ☐ not yet
8. page 275	☐ got it ☐ not yet
9. page 284	☐ got it ☐ not yet
10. page 291	☐ got it ☐ not yet

I know...

I need to study...

SHOW YOU KNOW...

Describe a skin condition with which you are familiar. Name the specific disease and give the characteristics of the disease and also describe a treatment that would be appropriate for the given condition.

| 1 | 2 | 3 | 4 | 5 | 6 | 7 |

VALUE

Skin care professionals who develop strong interpersonal and consultation skills can expect more repeat business and word-of-mouth referrals.

MAIN IDEA

From the moment your clients walk through the door until the moment they leave, they are forming opinions about you and your work. Skillfully completing each phase in the service process will help you build lasting relationships with your clients. Designed specifically to guarantee client comfort and security with skin care services, this process will help you build trust with your clients.

PLAN

Before the Service	■ Greeting
	■ Ask, Analyze and Assess
	■ Agreement

| During and After the Service | ■ Delivery |
| | ■ Completion |

OBJECTIVES

- ■ Describe the personal impressions that play a key role during the Greeting phase of service.
- ■ Identify the purpose of obtaining a medical history on the Client Consultation Form.
- ■ Explain the Agreement phase of service.

- ■ Describe the elements of client education used in the Delivery phase of service.
- ■ Identify the importance of soliciting feedback, retail sales, rebooking and follow-up care used in the Completion phase of service.
- ■ Identify the various types of follow-up care.

Chapter	Section	Page
Chapter 9 Client Care	Before the Service	Page 299

Goal of Client Care

_____
_____
_____
_____

The 5 Phases of
Client Service

PHASE: 1 Greeting

Objectives:
■ _____
■ _____
■ _____

PHASE: 2 Ask, Analyze, Assess

Objective:
■ _____

PHASE: 3 Agreement

Objectives:
■ _____
■ _____

PHASE: 4 Delivery

Objectives:
■ _____
■ _____

PHASE: 5 Completion

Objectives:
■ _____
■ _____
■ _____
■ _____

Chapter	Section	Page
Chapter 9 Client Care	**Before the Service**	**Pages 300-302**

1 Describe the personal impressions that play a key role during the Greeting phase of service

■ Greeting
Phase 1 of Client Service

Respectful Greeting Techniques

- ■ _____
- ■ _____
- ■ _____
- ■ _____

Eye Contact

Touch

Tone of Voice

Professional Atmosphere

The tone you use when speaking often communicates more than the words you actually say. Experiment with tone of voice to see if the statement is true by trying this easy exercise with a partner.

Find a partner and experiment with the importance of tone when speaking. Using the sentence found in column 'A' below, 'She passed the exam,' repeat the sentence four different times. Each time you repeat the sentence change the level, pitch or enunciation of a different word. Ask your partner to listen to determine if tone makes a difference. Have your partner do the same exercise just described using the sentence found in column 'B' below. Or, you can have fun making up one of your own statements to share with other partners. Shown below is a progression of both practice statements with the words appearing in bold type and capital letters indicating where to change the tone.

Partner A:
1. **SHE** passed the exam.
2. She **PASSED** the exam.
3. She passed **THE** exam.
4. She passed the **EXAM.**

Partner B:
1. **SHE** wore the new dress
2. She **WORE** the new dress.
3. She wore **THE** new dress.
4. She wore the **NEW** dress.
5. She wore the new **DRESS.**

smartNOTES

Chapter	Section	Page
Chapter 9 Client Care	**Before the Service**	**Pages 302-304**

■ **Ask, Analyze and Assess**

Phase 2 of
Client Service
2

5 Components of Client Consultation Forms

1.

2.

3.

4.

5.

Client Consultation Form

Personal Information

Component 1

1 2 3 4 5 6 7

⭐ **2** Identify the purpose of obtaining a medical history on the Client Consultation Form

Medical History

Component 2

Questions Found
in the Medical History

Allergens
Common Allergens
Cosmetic Ingredient Allergens
Hydroxy Acid Allergens

Environmental Allergens

Sunscreen Allergens

Medications
Oral Contraceptives
Hormone Replacement Therapy (HRT)

Oral Antibiotics
Topical Antibiotics
Steroids
Accutane

Retin-A

Chapter	Section	Page
Chapter 9 Client Care	**Before the Service**	**Pages 306-307**

Health Conditions

Common Health Conditions Encountered during Ask, Analyze and Assess Phase

■ _____

■ _____

■ _____

■ _____

■ _____

■ _____

■ _____

■ _____

■ _____

■ _____

■ _____

■ _____

Personal Skin Evaluation
Component 3

Typical Lifestyle
Considerations That
May Affect the Skin:

Client Release Statement

Chapter	Section	Page
Chapter 9 Client Care	**Before the Service**	**Pages 308-309**

Professional Skin Evaluation
Component 4

Skin Evaluation Process

Professional Skin Evaluation Process

1. _____
2. _____
3. _____
4. _____
5. _____
6. _____

7. _____
   _____

Common Differences in Areas of the Face

Eye
■
■

Cheek
■
■

Chin
■

Forehead
■

Treatment Record
Component 5

Chapter	Section	Page
Chapter 9 Client Care	Before the Service	**Pages 310-311**

⭐ **3** Explain the Agreement phase of service

■ **Agreement**

Phase 3 of Client Service

During the Agreement phase:

■

■

■

■

....

Which component of the Client Consultation Form do you think will require the greatest amount of your time?

....

LEARNING **CONNECTION** — Consultation Communication

For each of the four statements below, compare the statements in columns A and B. Decide which statement you feel is the most appropriate communication to use during the consultation and place a check mark in the box to the left of the statement.

	A	B
1.	☐ How did you feel about the results from the enzyme treatment you had last time?	☐ Did you like what Jill did for you last time?
2.	☐ Are you interested in the recommendations I just presented to you?	☐ What do you think you want to do?
3.	☐ I'm happy to tell you that not only are facials on special this week but you will also receive this beautiful candle when you schedule an appointment.	☐ I'm not sure how much this particular facial is. I don't think it's very much. I know you get a candle with it.
4.	☐ What type of cleanser do you currently use? You may want to consider a deep pore cleanser for your skin type.	☐ I've never seen skin like this before! You must not use a deep pore cleanser at all.

Hopefully you will have indicated all four statements in Column A to be the most appropriate communication to use during the consultation. What can you do to improve your communication skills? On the lines provided to the right, list three strategies you might use to improve your overall communication skills.

_____

_____

_____

_____

1	2	3	4	5	6	7

smartNOTES

Chapter	Section	Page
Chapter 9 Client Care	**During and After the Service**	**Pages 312-317**

4 Describe the elements of client education used in the Delivery phase of service

■ Delivery

Phase 4 of Client Service

4

2 Key Guidelines of Client Education

1. Tell

Feature	Benefit	Product Statement

2. Recommend

■ Completion

Phase 5 of Client Service

5

Rebooking

Soliciting

Feedback

5 Identify the importance of soliciting feedback, retail sales, rebooking and follow-up care used in the Completion phase of service.

Home Care Regimen and Retail Sales

Product Statement

Chapter	Section	Page
Chapter 9 Client Care	**During and After the Service**	**Pages 317-321**

Rebooking the Next Appointment

Referrals

★ **6** Identify the various types of follow-up calls

Follow Up | Two primary reasons to follow up with clients:

1.

2.

Care Calls | One of most personal ways to follow up; purpose is to find out:

■

■

■

■

■

Thank-You Notes

Last Two Phases of Service	**How**	**Why**	**What**
Delivery			
Completion			

Which phase of service do you feel the client
will mention when talking with others?

| 1 | 2 | 3 | 4 | 5 | 6 | 7 |

Your next challenge is to be ready to talk about some of the important ideas in this chapter. Follow the directions listed next to each box and practice talking about your ideas.

1. Home Maintenance Dialogue

You have learned that home maintenance is very important to client success. Home maintenance accounts for 80 percent of the condition of the client's skin. In box 1, write a brief dialogue that you can use with your clients to emphasize this point.

2. Client Home Maintenance

Bar soap for cleansing
Alcohol for toning
Available hand & body lotion for moisturizing
Liquid foundation
Face powder
Pencil eyeliner
Eye shadow
Mascara
Lipstick

It is important to never discredit products that a client is currently using. Write a brief dialogue that you can use with a customer that informs you of the products he/she uses at home, which are listed to the left. Practice your professional skills as you present your response.

Share your dialogue with a partner.

3. Similar Ingredients

The ingredients in a skin care product are the key indicators of benefits that the product will provide. Knowledge of the primary ingredients in a product will inform you of its benefits. Look at some of the skin care products you currently use and list on the lines to the left ingredients that are consistently found on the labels.

Share your research with a partner.

Now it's time to see how well you know your new material. First answer these questions. Then use the Memory Box that follows to check yourself. Look up each answer on the corresponding page in the *Salon Fundamentals™ Esthetics* textbook. Check "got it" for all correct answers and "not yet" for all incorrect responses. Using the "Know Chart," record all of your correct responses in the "I Know" column. After correcting incorrect answers, record all of your corrected responses in the "I Need to Study" column. That way you know exactly what to review before continuing in this Guide.

Directions: Identify whether questions 1 and 2 are True or False by circling TRUE or FALSE. You can earn an extra point for each false statement you appropriately correct. Question 3 requires you to write in an answer in the blank provided. Answers to the questions found in 4 through 10 may be selected by circling a, b, c or d below each statement to indicate your choice.

1. TRUE   FALSE   You can win your clients' respect by greeting them professionally and respectfully.

2. TRUE   FALSE   Touch is the least personal of the five senses.

3. Colors and _____ are common ingredients that can cause an allergic reac

4. What effect will the use of topical steroid medications have on the skin?
   a. decreased dryness
   b. increased sensitivity
   c. decreased sensitivity
   d. increased pigmentation

5. Which of the following descriptions identifies Herpes Simplex?
   a. a lack of sebum and dryness
   b. increased sensitivity and irritation
   c. non contagious infection with dry scales
   d. contagious viral infection that causes blister-like outbreaks

6. During which phase of service is the cost of the treatment being performed usua discussed?
   a. Delivery
   b. Greeting
   c. Agreement
   d. Ask, Analyze, Assess

7. The key ingredient a product contains that makes it effective is called the:
   a. core
   b. factor
   c. benefit
   d. feature

8. During what phase would you explain the steps and actions that you are taking during the service?
   a. Delivery
   b. Agreement
   c. Completion
   d. Ask, Analyze, Assess

9. Asking the client to book another appointment in advance is referred to as:
   a. residual
   b. redirecting
   c. completing
   d. rebooking

10. During which of the service phases would you suggest the purchase of product?
   a. Deliver
   b. Agreement
   c. Completion
   d. Ask, Analyze, Assess

1. page 300	☐ got it ☐ not yet	
2. page 301	☐ got it ☐ not yet	
3. page 305	☐ got it ☐ not yet	
4. page 305	☐ got it ☐ not yet	
5. page 306	☐ got it ☐ not yet	
6. page 310	☐ got it ☐ not yet	
7. page 313	☐ got it ☐ not yet	
8. page 313	☐ got it ☐ not yet	
9. page 314	☐ got it ☐ not yet	
10. page 314	☐ got it ☐ not yet	

I know...

I need to study...

SHOW YOU KNOW...

Show you know the five phases of service by relating each phase to a popular song, book, movie or current advertisement or news headline. Allow your creativity to flow as you relate what you know about each phase.

Phase of Service	Popular Song, Book Title, Movie or Current Advertisement or News Headline
Greeting	
Ask, Analyze, Assess	
Agreement	
Delivery	
Completion	

1	2	3	4	5	6	7

KNOWLEDGE GRID

Start at the top of the Knowledge Grid and work your way down, answering each question to check your understanding of Chapter 9, Client Care. The questions found here will help you deepen your understanding, build self-confidence and increase your awareness of different ways of thinking about a subject.

KNOW

List 4 things you can do to make a good impression when meeting a new client.

1.

2.

3.

4.

COMPREHEND

Describe the elements of client education in the Delivery phase of service.

APPLY

Give examples of products that might cause allergic reactions for your clients.

ANALYZE

Specify the difference between verbal and non-verbal communication and offer examples of each.

SYNTHESIZE

Suggest ways to gain feedback from clients on customer satisfaction.

EVALUATE

Justify the need for a client to complete the Client Consultation Form.

Multiple choice. Circle the correct answer.

1. Which of the following statements reflects the purpose of the Greeting phase?
   a. clarify objectives
   b. gain agreement
   c. recommend home care
   d. establish rapport and build trust

2. Which element listed below is usually the first contact a client has with the skin care center?
   a. radio ad
   b. brochure
   c. telephone
   d. newspaper

3. During an introductory handshake, you should:
   a. ask for referrals right away
   b. announce available services
   c. always inform the client of the treatment cost
   d. shake hands firmly and make direct eye contact

4. Looking around the room during a client consultation sends a clear signal that you are:
   a. distracted
   b. interested
   c. intrigued by the color of his/her eyes
   d. giving your undivided attention

5. A professional tone of voice is confident, firm, respectful and:
   a. loud
   b. very soft
   c. high-pitched
   d. non-judgmental

6. A substance or ingredient likely to cause an allergic reaction is referred to as a(n):
   a. HRT
   b. PABA
   c. allergen
   d. accutane

7. All of the following are examples of possible contraindications EXCEPT:
   a. exercise
   b. heart condition
   c. Herpes Simplex
   d. high blood pressure

8. Which of the items listed below may protect the skin care center from claims related to damage that may occur to the client's skin as a result of services provided?
   a. skin evaluation
   b. client medical history
   c. client treatment record
   d. client release statement

9. Which of the following items describes a typical lifestyle consideration?
   a. epilepsy
   b. smoking
   c. telangiectasia
   d. high blood pressure

10. A health condition that will not affect the outcome of the treatment but will affect the comfort level of the patient during treatment is:
    a. epilepsy
    b. accutane
    c. antibiotics
    d. low pain threshold

11. What lifestyle habit can influence hydration levels as well as hormonal imbalances?
    a. dieting
    b. smoking
    c. drinking
    d. exercising

12. Which lifestyle habit can rob nutrients and oxygen from the skin?
    a. dieting
    b. drinking
    c. smoking
    d. exercise

13. Which of the following occurs during the Ask, Analyze and Assess phase?
    a. observe the skin
    b. schedule next appointment
    c. discuss home care regimen
    d. share results of client skin evaluation

14. How often should a professional skin analysis be performed?
    a. annually
    b. only on the first visit
    c. every six months at a minimum
    d. before and after each cleansing step

15. Which of the following is NOT an indicator of an effective skin care treatment?
    a. decreased wrinkles
    b. improved hydration
    c. increased pore size
    d. improved pigmentation

16. Which of the following elements is NOT the purpose of the Agreement phase?
    a. mail thank-you notes
    b. state the cost of the service
    c. summarize recommended treatments
    d. ensure you and the client have the same understanding

17. Which phase of client care satisfies client needs?
    a. Greeting Phase
    b. Delivery Phase
    c. Agreement Phase
    d. Completion Phase

18. What percent of new clients should you strive to acquire each week?
    a. 15 to 20%
    b. 25 to 30%
    c. 35 to 40%
    d. 45 to 50%

19. What is the best form of advertising in any customer service business?
    a. business cards
    b. word-of-mouth
    c. radio advertisements
    d. newspaper advertisements

20. What is the recommended timeline for follow-up calls and notes?
    a. within one week
    b. within 8 hours
    c. within 72 hours
    d. prior to end of business the day after the service

Write Your Own Ticket! For numbers 21, 22, and 23, write your own questions and answer them. Your questions can be true/false, multiple choice or fill-in-the-blank. The only parameter is that your questions cannot already be found on this test. Earn one point each for writing your way to success.

21. Q: _____ A: _____

22. Q: _____ A: _____

23. Q: _____ A: _____

BONUS QUESTION!
Question 24 is the ultimate question. To earn two points, design a question for your class. If you stump the class and no one can answer the question within an agreed upon time (between you and the teacher), you earn a BONUS OF FIVE ADDITIONAL POINTS!

24. Q: _____

ESSAY QUESTION:
A maximum of five additional points is possible if you answer one of the following essay questions.

25a. List three key questions that are asked during a consultation and explain why these questions are important to the consultation.

1. _____
   _____
   _____

2. _____
   _____
   _____

3. _____
   _____

25b.   Describe at least two follow-up techniques and explain why they are important.

_____

_____

_____

_____

_____

_____

_____

_____

_____

_____

25c.   In your opinion, how can referrals and effective recommendations that turn into sales contribute to the growth of a business?

_____

_____

_____

_____

_____

_____

_____

_____

_____

_____

_____

Check your answers as you did before. Place a check mark next to the page number for any incorrect answer. On the lines to the right, jot down topics that you still need to review.

1.   page 299
2.   page 300
3.   page 300
4.   page 301
5.   page 301
6.   page 305
7.   page 306
8.   page 307
9.   page 307
10.   page 307

11.   page 307
12.   page 307
13.   page 308
14.   page 308
15   page 309
16.   page 310
17.   page 313
18.   page 317
19.   page 317
20.   page 319

NOTES TO MYSELF — *My Reflections About Client Care*

Experts agree that it is important to summarize your feelings and reactions about what you are learning. Note especially things that surprised you, things you found difficult to learn and suggestions and ideas you received from friends that helped make learning this chapter easier and more enjoyable.

FACIALS

10

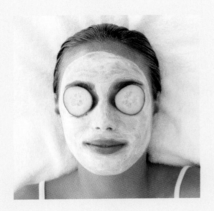

VALUE

The most requested esthetics service is the facial. Estheticians who master basic facial techniques and learn to help their clients maintain a sound home care regimen can expect more referrals and success.

MAIN IDEA

This chapter focuses on the basic facial procedure. Considered by many as the core services of the skin care industry, facials, massage therapy and recommendations for home care regimens are among the most-requested services provided by skin care centers. They are also the services most closely linked to client satisfaction, repeat business and financial success. To perform these services at a professional level, estheticians are expected to master basic facial procedures, general massage techniques and understand the functions of each product. The ability to give clients a refreshing and pleasant facial is the most important entry-level skill for estheticians.

PLAN

Facial Care
- Skin Care
- Massage
- Skin Analysis
- Skin Care Essentials
- Infection Control and Safety
- Client Consultation

Facial Services
- Basic Facial
- Facials with Machines

OBJECTIVES

- Describe the four basic steps of a regular daily skin care regimen to maintain healthy skin.

- Demonstrate the five basic movements of massage and explain when it is inadvisable to perform massage manipulations.

- Explain the process of a skin analysis and identify the basic skin types and the main skin conditions.

- Identify and describe the function for skin care essentials, infection control and safety and the client consultation.

- Demonstrate procedures for the basic facial and facials with machines.

1 2 3 4 5 6 7

smartNOTES

⭐ **1** Describe the four basic steps of a regular daily skin care regimen to maintain healthy skin.

■ **Skin Care**

Proper Skin Care

Daily Care   Follow this regimen twice daily: (morning and evening)

4 Steps in Keeping   1.

Skin in Good Condition 2.

3.

4.

1. Cleansing

2. Toning

3. Moisturizing

SPF

Oily Skin

4. Protecting

90% of wrinkles caused by excess sun exposure   **10%** of wrinkles caused by natural aging process

Sunscreen   **SPF 15**   **SPF 30**

UVA /UVB

Chapter	Section	Page
Chapter 10 Facials	**Facial Care**	**Pages 327-328**

Vitamin C ▪
▪

Additional Care

Mechanical Exfoliant
▪ _____
▪ _____

Chemical Exfoliant
▪ _____
▪ _____
▪ _____

Chemical and mechanical exfoliants are effective for deep-pore cleansing

Masks

Clay/Mud Masks
▪ _____
▪ _____
▪ _____
▪ _____

▪ _____
▪ _____
▪ _____
▪ _____

Crème Masks
▪ _____
▪ _____

Paraffin Masks
▪ _____

▪ _____

Gel Masks
▪ _____

▪ _____

▪ _____

Modeling Masks
▪ _____
▪ _____

▪ _____

Cleansing, toning, moisturizing and protecting are the four steps that create the daily regimen for skin care. What other daily health or wellness regimens that you use can you name?

| 1 | 2 | 3 | 4 | 5 | 6 | 7 |

In the future you may have clients as young as 10 years old. Teaching these youngsters the basics of daily skin care is very important. Creating a rhyme designed to help them remember the importance of daily skin care might be one way you would choose to introduce the topic. In the space to the right, create a rhyme to introduce daily skin care.

Daily Skin Care Rhyme

smartNOTES

Chapter	Section	Page
Chapter 10 Facials	Facial Care	Pages 329-330

■ Massage

Benefits of Massage ■

■

■

■

■

■

Massage Requirements

Massage Therapist

★ 2 — Demonstrate the five basic movements of massage and explain when it is inadvisable to perform massage maniplations

5 Basic Massage Movements

Effleurage ■

Purpose ■

Method ■

Petrissage ■

Purpose ■

Method ■

Tapotement (Percussion) ■

Purpose ■

Method ■

■

Friction ■

Purpose ■

Method ■

Vibration ■

Purpose ■

Method ■

Contraindications → → → → → →

for Massage → → →

Jacquet Movements ■

■

■

■

■

■

■

Important

Massage Points

Can you identify an adjective that could describe the feeling the client would have following each of the different massage movements? **For example, a client would feel pacified following an effleurage session**.

Petrissage _____

Tapotement _____

Friction _____

Vibration _____

| 1 | 2 | 3 | 4 | 5 | 6 | 7 |

Music is similar to massage in the sense that both involve a rhythm. Review the five massage movements and identify a popular, recognizable song that associates with the rhythm of the massage movement. If the massage movement is light and airy, then a light and airy song would be associated. Let your creativity feel the rhythm!

Massage Movement	Associated Song
1. Effleurage	
2. Petrissage	
3. Tapotement	
4. Friction	
5. Vibration	

smartNOTES

Chapter	Section	Page
Chapter 10 Facials	**Facial Care**	**Page 333**

3 Explain the process of a skin analysis and identify the basic skin types and the main skin conditions

■ **Skin Analysis**
  Skin Types
  Normal Skin

  Dry Skin

  Oily Skin

  Combination Skin

  Mature/Aging Skin

Chapter	Section	Page
Chapter 10 Facials	**Facial Care**	**Pages 333-334**

Skin Conditions/ Disorders

Dehydration

Couperose

Rosacea

Acne

Performing Skin Analysis   **Check for:**

Chin

Eyes

Cheeks

Chapter	Section	Page
Chapter 10 Facials	Facial Care	Pages 333-334

Performing Skin Analysis

Check for:

Forehead

Nose

Mouth

Entire Face

What is your skin type and condition? With a partner perform a skin analysis of each other and document the results.

LEARNING — CONNECTION — Reading the Signs

The skin analysis is the process of investigating and looking for signs to indicate particular conditions. In what other areas of your life do you look at signs to indicate conditions? Can you name at least three instances when signs give you important clues about what to do?

Sign	Condition
1.	
2.	
3.	

Chapter	Section	Page
Chapter 10 Facials	**Facial Care**	**Page 335**

⭐ **4** Identify and describe the function for skin care essentials, infection control and safety and the client consultation

■ **Skin Care Essentials**

Skin Care Products   Functions:

Antiseptic   Assists in _____ the growth of bacteria on the skin

Cleansing Crème   _____ impurities from the skin

Astringent   Cleanses skin and returns oily skin to a normal _____

Toner   Assists in _____ skin and returns normal to dry skin to a normal pH

Chemical Exfoliant   Removes dead skin cells by using _____ or _____ hydroxy acids

Manual Exfoliant   Removes _____ skin cells by using a granular product manipulated on the skin; also called facial scrub

Massage Crème/Oil   Reduces _____ and provides "slip" to the skin

Clay/mud Mask   Absorbs excess _____; prevents clogging; tightens and refines pores

Crème Mask   _____ and _____

Gel Mask   _____ and _____ skin

Modeling Mask   Delivers _____ ingredients

Paraffin Mask   Increases _____; promotes product penetration

Moisturizer   _____ and _____ the skin

Eye Product   Protects and _____ delicate eye area

Sunscreen   Protects skin from _____ and _____ rays

Skin Care Implements/Supplies

Use:

Spatula	
Gloves	
Fan Brush	
Distilled Water	
Comedone Extractor	
Clean Sheets/Blankets	
Client Robe/Gown	
Towel	
Cotton Pads	
Disposable Facial Sponge	
Facial Tissue	
Head Band/Covering	
Rubber Mixing Bowls	

Skin Care Equipment

	Multifunction Machine	Magnifying Lamp	Facial Steamer
Description			
Benefit			

	Infrared Lamp	Wood's Lamp	Vacuum
Description			
Benefit			

Skin Care Equipment

	High Frequency Service	Galvanic Current Service	Rotating Brush
Description			
Benefit			

■ **Infection Control and Safety**

1.

2.

3.

4.

5.

6.

7.

8.

9.

10.

11.

12.

13.

14.

■ **Client Consultation**
Important Steps in Client Consultation

Greeting –

Ask, Analyze and Assess –

Agreement –

Delivery –

Completion –

About which piece of electrical equipment do you feel clients will have the most questions? Why?

Column 1 identifies a piece of electrical equipment. Column 2 identifies the function of a piece of equipment. Match the correct function with the appropriate piece of equipment by placing the matching letter from Column 1 on the line in front of Column 2.

Column 1 Equipment

A. Multifunction Machine

B. Wood's Lamp

C. Facial Steamer

D. Infrared Lamp

Column 2 Function

_____ Uses warm, humid mist to open follicles

_____ Provides a soothing heat that penetrates into the tissues of the body

_____ Allows analysis of skin surface and deeper layers to aid in determining treatment

_____ Offers four or more treatment options

smartNOTES

Chapter	Section	Page
Chapter 10 Facials	Facial Services	Pages 341-366

5 Demonstrate procedures for the basic facial and basic facial with machines

Listed below are facial services offered in the chapter. Rubrics for these services can be found on the pages following the matching exercise in this study guide.

1. Basic Facial Procedure
2. Facial with Multifunction Machine
3. Facial with Galvanic/Desincrustation
4. Facial with Galvanic/Iontophoresis
5. Facial with Indirect High Frequency
6. Facial with Direct High Frequency

Dry/Dehydrated Skin

☐ _____

☐ _____

☐ _____

Mature Skin

☐ _____

Combination Skin

☐ _____

☐ _____

Oily Skin

☐ _____

☐ _____

Chapter	Section	Page
Chapter 10 Facials	Facial Services	**Pages 341-366**

Acneic Skin

- _____
- _____
- _____
- _____
- _____

Acneic Skin

Desincrustation Solution

- _____
- _____
- _____
- _____
- _____

Make solution

1 tsp. sodium bicarbonate + 1 cup distilled

Towel Steaming

- _____
- _____
- _____
- _____
- _____
- _____
- _____

Men's Skin Care

Goal

Tips for Men's Skin Care

Which of the procedures do you think will take the most time when offered to a client for the first time? Why?

1 2 3 4 5 6 7

Column A		Column B
A. Vibration		A light, relaxing, smoothing, gentle stroking or circular movement
B. Dehydration		A light tapping or slapping movement applied with the fingertips or partly flexed fingers
C. Moisturizing		Light or heavy kneading, pinching and rolling of the muscles
D. Combination skin		A shaking movement achieved when the esthetician quickly shakes his/her arms while fingertips or palms are touching the client
E. Effleurage		Product that aids in preventing the growth of bacteria
F. Oily skin		A lack of moisture (water) in the skin
G. Acne		Skin type that contains sufficient moisture and sebum production
H. Tapotement		Skin type that displays areas that are both dry and oily
I. Excessive sun exposure		Compensates for the unavoidable losses skin sustains from aging and exposure to the environment
J. Friction		Type of skin that lacks adequate sebum production
K. Rosacea		Skin condition caused by overactivity of sebaceous glands
L. Antiseptic		Cause of 90% of wrinkles
M. Petrissage		A circular or wringing movement with no gliding, usually performed with fingertips or palms of hands
N. Dry skin		Type of skin that has excess sebum production and appears thick and shiny
O. Normal		Skin condition characterized by flushed redness, dilated capillaries and small red bumps

Basic Facial Procedure

This rubric is designed to compare your skill to industry expectations. Indicate your present level of performance by checking the appropriate box. Your teacher will direct you in the completion of this rubric.

Rubric Assessment

The Basic Facial is one of the most requested services in the skin care center. By following and practicing the steps in this rubric, you will be prepared to offer a basic facial service for your clients. Note that the numbers for each step correspond with the step-by-step technical images found in the textbook.

	Level 1	Level 2	Level 3	To Improve, I Need To:	Teacher Assessment
PREPARATION					
■ Disinfect facial service area; set up facial bed; arrange products; check equipment; perform a proper draping	☐	☐	☐		☐
PROCEDURE					
1. Wash and sanitize hands (wear protective gloves if required)	☐	☐	☐		☐
2. Drape client	☐	☐	☐		☐
CLEANSE FACE					
3. Obtain cleansing crème	☐	☐	☐		☐
4. Apply cleansing crème	☐	☐	☐		☐
5. Remove cleansing crème	☐	☐	☐		☐
REPEAT CLEANSING PROCEDURE					
6. Apply toner	☐	☐	☐		☐
ANALYZE					
7. Place eye pads over client's eyes	☐	☐	☐		☐
8. Analyze client's skin	☐	☐	☐		☐
EXFOLIATE AND STEAM					
9. a) Apply exfoliant	☐	☐	☐		☐
b) Steam	☐	☐	☐		☐
10. Remove exfoliant	☐	☐	☐		☐
EXTRACTION					
11. Apply desincrustation solution, if necessary, and steam	☐	☐	☐		☐
12. Perform any necessary extractions	☐	☐	☐		☐
13. Apply toner	☐	☐	☐		☐
MASSAGE					
14. Obtain massage crème	☐	☐	☐		☐
15. Apply massage crème	☐	☐	☐		☐
16. Perform massage movements	☐	☐	☐		☐
17. Remove massage crème	☐	☐	☐		☐

Rubric Assessment Continued

	Level 1	Level 2	Level 3	To Improve, I Need To:	Teacher Assessment
FACIAL MASK					
18. Apply facial mask	☐	☐	☐		☐
19. Cover the mask	☐	☐	☐		☐
20. Allow mask to set	☐	☐	☐		☐
21. Remove mask	☐	☐	☐		☐
22. Apply toner	☐	☐	☐		☐
PROTECT					
23. Apply eye product	☐	☐	☐		☐
24. Apply moisturizing crème and sun protection if necessary	☐	☐	☐		☐
COMPLETION					
■ Have client dress; lead client to front counter; offer to rebook client's next visit; recommend retail; throw away non-reusable materials; replace used linens; disinfect implements and facial bed; arrange items for next service; wash hands with liquid antibacterial soap; place unused cotton pads and sponges in covered container	☐	☐	☐		☐

Total = Addition of all Teacher Assessment Boxes ☐

Percentage = Student Score Divided by 81 (Highest Possible Score)　　Percentage 　＿＿＿ %

Basic Facial With Multifunction Machine

This rubric is designed to compare your skill to industry expectations. Indicate your present level of performance by checking the appropriate box. Your teacher will direct you in the completion of this rubric.

Rubric Assessment

The basic facial in this rubric is performed utilizing the Multifunction Machine and its attachments, including the rotating brush for exfoliating, the vacuum and toner spray. By following and practicing the steps in this rubric, you will be prepared to offer a basic facial with multifunction machine service for your clients. Note that the numbers for each step correspond with the step-by-step technical images found in the textbook.

	Level 1	Level 2	Level 3	To Improve, I Need To:	Teacher Assessment
PREPARATION					
■ Disinfect facial service area; set up facial bed; arrange products; check equipment; perform a proper draping	☐	☐	☐		☐
PROCEDURE					
1. Wash and sanitize hands (wear protective gloves if required)	☐	☐	☐		☐
2. Drape client	☐	☐	☐		☐
CLEANSE FACE					
3. Obtain cleansing crème	☐	☐	☐		☐
4. Apply cleansing crème	☐	☐	☐		☐
5. Remove cleansing crème	☐	☐	☐		☐
REPEAT CLEANSING PROCEDURE					
6. Apply toner	☐	☐	☐		☐
ANALYZE					
7. Place eye pads over client's eyes	☐	☐	☐		☐
8. Analyze client's skin	☐	☐	☐		☐
EXFOLIATE AND STEAM					
9. a) Apply exfoliant and exfoliate with rotating brush	☐	☐	☐		☐
b) Apply manual exfoliant product	☐	☐	☐		☐
c) Dampen brush attachment and insert it into handpiece	☐	☐	☐		☐
d) Increase rotation slowly from jawline contact point	☐	☐	☐		☐
e) Work around the entire face two to three times	☐	☐	☐		☐
f) Steam	☐	☐	☐		☐
10. Remove exfoliant	☐	☐	☐		☐
EXTRACTION					
11. Apply desincrustation solution, if necessary, and steam	☐	☐	☐		☐
12. a) Perform any necessary extractions	☐	☐	☐		☐
b) Cover hole in side of ventouse; hold skin taut; gently glide across forehead	☐	☐	☐		☐
c) Repeat on the sides of nose and chin	☐	☐	☐		☐
13. Apply toner	☐	☐	☐		☐

Rubric Assessment Continued

	Level 1	Level 2	Level 3	To Improve, I Need To:	Teacher Assessment
MASSAGE					
14. Obtain massage crème	☐	☐	☐		☐
15. Apply massage crème	☐	☐	☐		☐
16. Perform massage movements	☐	☐	☐		☐
17. Remove massage crème	☐	☐	☐		☐
FACIAL MASK					
18. Apply facial mask	☐	☐	☐		☐
19. Cover the mask	☐	☐	☐		☐
20. Allow mask to set	☐	☐	☐		☐
21. Remove mask	☐	☐	☐		☐
22. Apply toner	☐	☐	☐		☐
PROTECT					
23. Apply eye protection	☐	☐	☐		☐
24. Apply moisturizing crème and sun protection if necessary	☐	☐	☐		☐

COMPLETION

- Have client dress; lead client to front counter; offer to rebook client's next visit; recommend retail; throw away non-reusable materials; replace used linens; disinfect implements and facial bed; arrange items for next service; wash hands with liquid antibacterial soap; place unused cotton pads and sponges in covered container ☐ ☐ ☐ ☐

Total = Addition of all Teacher Assessment Boxes ☐

Percentage = Student Score Divided by 99 (Highest Possible Score)   **Percentage**   %

Basic Facial With Galvanic/Desincrustation Procedure

This rubric is designed to compare your skill to industry expectations. Indicate your present level of performance by checking the appropriate box. Your teacher will direct you in the completion of this rubric.

Basic Facial with Galvanic/Desincrustation Procedure

The basic facial with Galvanic/Desincrustation treatment utilizes Galvanic Current in conjunction with an alkaline solution to force the solution deep into the skin. This process liquifies (saponifies) sebum trapped within the pores and greatly eases the extraction process. By following and practicing the steps in this rubric, you will be prepared to offer a basic facial with Galvanic/Desincrustation service for your clients. Note that the numbers for each step correspond with the step-by-step technical images found in the textbook.

	Level 1	Level 2	Level 3	To Improve, I Need To:	Teacher Assessment
PREPARATION					
■ Disinfect facial service area; set up facial bed; arrange products; check equipment; perform a proper draping	☐	☐	☐		☐
PROCEDURE					
1. Wash and sanitize hands (wear protective gloves if required)	☐	☐	☐		☐
2. Drape client	☐	☐	☐		☐
CLEANSE FACE					
3. Obtain cleansing crème	☐	☐	☐		☐
4. Apply cleansing crème	☐	☐	☐		☐
5. Remove cleansing crème	☐	☐	☐		☐
REPEAT CLEANSING PROCEDURE					
6. Apply toner	☐	☐	☐		☐
ANALYZE					
7. Place eye pads over client's eyes	☐	☐	☐		☐
8. Analyze client's skin	☐	☐	☐		☐
EXFOLIATE AND STEAM					
9. a) Apply exfoliant	☐	☐	☐		☐
b) Steam	☐	☐	☐		☐
10. a) Remove exfoliant	☐	☐	☐		☐
b) Prepare inactive electrode; cover with damp sponge; place in client's hand or under shoulder blade	☐	☐	☐		☐
c) Prepare the active electrode by covering with damp cotton	☐	☐	☐		☐
d) Apply the desincrustation solution to the skin with cotton pad and to cotton on the active electrode	☐	☐	☐		☐
e) Place the active electrode at the client's jawline; turn on the power and negative current	☐	☐	☐		☐
f) Increase the milliamperemeter slowly until client feels a slight prickle on the skin or has a metallic taste in his or her mouth	☐	☐	☐		☐

Rubric Assessment Continued

	Level 1	Level 2	Level 3	To Improve, I Need To:	Teacher Assessment
g) Move the electrode in small circular motions across the face; work up one side of the face, across the forehead and down other side to the chin; repeat twice; finish at jawline	☐	☐	☐		☐
h) Perform any necessary extractions	☐	☐	☐		☐
i) Turn on the positive polarity and move the electrode in small circular motions across the face again; finish at the jawline	☐	☐	☐		☐
j) Turn the milliamperemeter down to zero	☐	☐	☐		☐
k) Turn off the current and the power	☐	☐	☐		☐
l) Remove the electrode from the client's face and the client's hand or back	☐	☐	☐		☐
EXTRACTION					
13. Apply toner	☐	☐	☐		☐
MASSAGE					
14. Obtain massage crème	☐	☐	☐		☐
15. Apply massage crème	☐	☐	☐		☐
16. Perform massage movements	☐	☐	☐		☐
17. Remove massage crème	☐	☐	☐		☐
FACIAL MASK					
18. Apply facial mask	☐	☐	☐		☐
19. Cover the mask	☐	☐	☐		☐
20. Allow mask to set	☐	☐	☐		☐
21. Remove mask	☐	☐	☐		☐
22. Apply toner	☐	☐	☐		☐
PROTECT					
23. Apply eye product	☐	☐	☐		☐
24. Apply moisturizing crème and/or sun protection if necessary	☐	☐	☐		☐
COMPLETION					
■ Have client dress; lead client to front counter; offer to rebook client's next visit; recommend retail; throw away non-reusable materials; replace used linens; disinfect implements and facial bed; arrange items for next service; wash hands with liquid antibacterial soap; place unused cotton pads and sponges in covered container	☐	☐	☐		☐

Total = Addition of all Teacher Assessment Boxes ☐

Percentage = Student Score Divided by 81 (Highest Possible Score)   **Percentage** _____ %

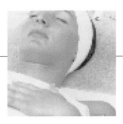

Basic Facial With Galvanic/Iontophoresis Procedure

This rubric is designed to compare your skill to industry expectations. Indicate your present level of performance by checking the appropriate box. Your teacher will direct you in the completion of this rubric.

Rubric Assessment

The basic facial with Galvanic/Iontophoresis treatment utilizes Galvanic Current to penetrate nourishing, hydrating and firming ingredients deep into the skin. By following and practicing the steps in this rubric, you will be prepared to offer a basic facial with Galvanic/Iontophoresis service for your clients. Note that the numbers for each step correspond with the step-by-step technical images found in the textbook.

	Level 1	Level 2	Level 3	To Improve, I Need To:	Teacher Assessment
PREPARATION					
■ Disinfect facial service area; set up facial bed; arrange products; check equipment; perform a proper draping	☐	☐	☐		☐
PROCEDURE					
1. Wash and sanitize hands (wear protective gloves if required)	☐	☐	☐		☐
2. Drape client	☐	☐	☐		☐
CLEANSE FACE					
3. Obtain cleansing crème	☐	☐	☐		☐
4. Apply cleansing crème	☐	☐	☐		☐
5. Remove cleansing crème	☐	☐	☐		☐
REPEAT CLEANSING PROCEDURE					
6. Apply toner	☐	☐	☐		☐
ANALYZE					
7. Place eye pads over client's eyes	☐	☐	☐		☐
8. Analyze client's skin	☐	☐	☐		☐
EXFOLIATE AND STEAM					
9. a) Apply exfoliant	☐	☐	☐		☐
b) Steam	☐	☐	☐		☐
10. Remove exfoliant	☐	☐	☐		☐
EXTRACTION					
11. Apply desincrustation solution, if necessary, and steam	☐	☐	☐		☐
12. Perform any necessary extractions	☐	☐	☐		☐
13. Apply toner	☐	☐	☐		☐
MASSAGE					
14. Obtain massage crème	☐	☐	☐		☐
15. Apply massage crème	☐	☐	☐		☐
16. Perform massage movements	☐	☐	☐		☐
17. a) Remove massage crème	☐	☐	☐		☐

Rubric Assessment Continued

	Level 1	Level 2	Level 3	To Improve, I Need To:	Teacher Assessment
17. b) Prepare inactive electrode; cover with damp sponge; place in client's hand or under his or her shoulder blade	☐	☐	☐		☐
c) Prepare an active electrode by covering with damp cotton	☐	☐	☐		☐
d) Apply the nourishing serum or concentrate generously to skin with cotton pad	☐	☐	☐		☐
e) Apply the nourishing serum or concentrate to active electrode with sponge	☐	☐	☐		☐
f) Place the active electrode at the client's jawline	☐	☐	☐		☐
g) Turn on the power	☐	☐	☐		☐
h) Turn on the positive current	☐	☐	☐		☐
i) Increase the milliamperemeter slowly until the client feels a slight prickle or has a metallic taste in his or her mouth	☐	☐	☐		☐
j) Move the electrode in small circular motions acrosS the face; work up one side of the face, across the forehead and down other side to the chin; repeat twice	☐	☐	☐		☐
k) Finish at the jawline	☐	☐	☐		☐
l) Turn the milliamperemeter down to zero	☐	☐	☐		☐
m) Turn off the current and the power	☐	☐	☐		☐
n) Remove the electrode from the client's face and hand or back	☐	☐	☐		☐
FACIAL MASK					
18. Apply facial mask	☐	☐	☐		☐
19. Cover the mask	☐	☐	☐		☐
20. Allow mask to set	☐	☐	☐		☐
21. Remove mask	☐	☐	☐		☐
22. Apply toner	☐	☐	☐		☐
PROTECT					
23. Apply eye product	☐	☐	☐		☐
24. Apply moisturizing crème and/or sun protection if necessary	☐	☐	☐		☐
COMPLETION					
■ Have client dress; lead client to front counter; offer to rebook client's next visit; recommend retail; throw away non-reusable materials; replace used linens; disinfect implements and facial bed; arrange items for next service; wash hands with liquid antibacterial soap; place unused cotton pads and sponges in covered container	☐	☐	☐		☐

Total = Addition of all Teacher Assessment Boxes ☐

Percentage = Student Score Divided by 81 (Highest Possible Score)   **Percentage** _____ %

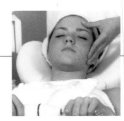

Basic Facial With Indirect High Frequency

This rubric is designed to compare your skill to industry expectations. Indicate your present level of performance by checking the appropriate box. Your teacher will direct you in the completion of this rubric.

Rubric Assessment

The basic facial utilizes Indirect High Frequency Current during the massage to amplify the effects of the massage movements for relaxation or stimulation. By following and practicing the steps in this rubric, you will be prepared to offer a basic facial with Indirect High Frequency service for your clients. Note that the numbers for each step correspond with the step-by-step technical images found in the textbook.

	Level 1	Level 2	Level 3	To Improve, I Need To:	Teacher Assessment
PREPARATION					
■ Disinfect facial service area; set up facial bed; arrange products; check equipment; perform a proper draping	☐	☐	☐		☐
PROCEDURE					
1. Wash and sanitize hands (wear protective gloves if required)	☐	☐	☐		☐
2. Drape client	☐	☐	☐		☐
CLEANSE FACE					
3. Obtain cleansing crème	☐	☐	☐		☐
4. Apply cleansing crème	☐	☐	☐		☐
5. Remove cleansing crème	☐	☐	☐		☐
REPEAT CLEANSING PROCEDURE					
6. Apply toner	☐	☐	☐		☐
ANALYZE					
7. Place eye pads over client's eyes	☐	☐	☐		☐
8. Analyze client's skin	☐	☐	☐		☐
EXFOLIATE AND STEAM					
9. a) Apply exfoliant	☐	☐	☐		☐
b) Steam	☐	☐	☐		☐
10. Remove exfoliant	☐	☐	☐		☐
EXTRACTION					
11. Apply desincrustation solution, if necessary, and steam	☐	☐	☐		☐
12. Perform any necessary extractions	☐	☐	☐		☐
13. Apply toner	☐	☐	☐		☐

Basic Facial With Indirect High Frequency

Rubric Assessment Continued

	Level 1	Level 2	Level 3	To Improve, I Need To:	Teacher Assessment
MASSAGE					
14. Obtain massage crème	☐	☐	☐		☐
15. a) Apply massage crème	☐	☐	☐		☐
b) Have the client hold the glass rod electrode	☐	☐	☐		☐
c) Place one hand on client's face before turning on the High Frequency Current; turn on the current, slowly increasing the strength	☐	☐	☐		☐
16. a) Perform massage movements, being careful to not lift fingers away from client's skin to avoid shock	☐	☐	☐		☐
b) Massage for no more than 7 minutes per Indirect High Frequency treatment	☐	☐	☐		☐
c) Turn off current before removing fingers from client's face to avoid shock	☐	☐	☐		☐
d) Remove the inactive electrode from the client's hand	☐	☐	☐		☐
17. Remove massage crème	☐	☐	☐		☐
FACIAL MASK					
18. Apply facial mask	☐	☐	☐		☐
19. Cover the mask	☐	☐	☐		☐
20. Allow mask to set	☐	☐	☐		☐
21. Remove mask	☐	☐	☐		☐
22. Apply toner	☐	☐	☐		☐
PROTECT	☐	☐	☐		☐
23. Apply eye product					
24. Apply moisturizing crème and/or sun protection if necessary	☐	☐	☐		☐

COMPLETION

- Have client dress; lead client to front counter; offer to rebook client's next visit; recommend retail; throw away non-reusable materials; replace used linens; disinfect implements and facial bed; arrange items for next service; wash hands with liquid antibacterial soap; place unused cotton pads and sponges in covered container ☐ ☐ ☐ ☐

Total = Addition of all Teacher Assessment Boxes ☐

Percentage = Student Score Divided by 81 (Highest Possible Score) **Percentage** _____ %

Basic Facial With Direct High Frequency Procedure

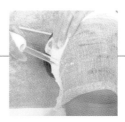

This rubric is designed to compare your skill to industry expectations. Indicate your present level of performance by checking the appropriate box. Your teacher will direct you in the completion of this rubric.

Rubric Assessment

The basic facial with Direct High Frequency treatment delivers antibacterial and drying benefits to the skin. It is best suited for skin that is oily or acneic and is performed immediately following any extractions to prevent further breakouts. By following and practicing the steps in this rubric, you will be prepared to offer a basic facial with Direct High Frequency service for your clients. Note that the numbers for each step correspond with the step-by-step technical images found in the textbook.

	Level 1	Level 2	Level 3	To Improve, I Need To:	Teacher Assessment
PREPARATION					
■ Disinfect facial service area; set up facial bed; arrange products; check equipment; perform a proper draping	☐	☐	☐		▭
PROCEDURE					
1. Wash and sanitize hands (wear protective gloves if required)	☐	☐	☐		▭
2. Drape client	☐	☐	☐		▭
CLEANSE FACE					
3. Obtain cleansing crème	☐	☐	☐		▭
4. Apply cleansing crème	☐	☐	☐		▭
5. Remove cleansing crème	☐	☐	☐		▭
REPEAT CLEANSING PROCEDURE					
6. Apply toner	☐	☐	☐		▭
ANALYZE					
7. Place eye pads over client's eyes	☐	☐	☐		▭
8. Analyze client's skin	☐	☐	☐		▭
EXFOLIATE AND STEAM					
9. a) Apply exfoliant	☐	☐	☐		▭
b) Steam	☐	☐	☐		▭
10. Remove exfoliant	☐	☐	☐		▭
EXTRACTION					
11. Apply desincrustation solution, if necessary, and steam	☐	☐	☐		▭
12. Perform any necessary extractions	☐	☐	☐		▭
13. a) Apply toner (non-alcoholic type)	☐	☐	☐		▭
b) Turn on High Frequency Current; place finger on glass electrode and make contact with client's face; lift finger	☐	☐	☐		▭
c) Glide electrode across face, concentrating on areas that were extracted	☐	☐	☐		▭

Rubric Assessment Continued

	Level 1	Level 2	Level 3	To Improve, I Need To:	Teacher Assessment
d) Repeat until the entire face has been covered at least once; do not exceed 5 minutes for the entire treatment	☐	☐	☐		☐
e) Turn down the current slowly until it is completely off	☐	☐	☐		☐
f) Remove the active electrode from your client's skin	☐	☐	☐		☐
MASSAGE					
14. Obtain massage crème	☐	☐	☐		☐
15. Apply massage crème	☐	☐	☐		☐
16. Perform massage movements	☐	☐	☐		☐
17. Remove massage crème	☐	☐	☐		☐
FACIAL MASK					
18. Apply facial mask	☐	☐	☐		☐
19. Cover the mask	☐	☐	☐		☐
20. Allow mask to set	☐	☐	☐		☐
21. Remove mask	☐	☐	☐		☐
22. Apply toner	☐	☐	☐		☐
PROTECT					
23. Apply eye product	☐	☐	☐		☐
24. Apply moisturizing crème and/or sun protection if necessary	☐	☐	☐		☐

COMPLETION

■ Have client dress; lead client to front counter; offer to rebook client's next visit; recommend retail; throw away non-reusable materials; replace used linens; disinfect implements and facial bed; arrange items for next service; wash hands with liquid antibacterial soap; place unused cotton pads and sponges in covered container ☐ ☐ ☐ ☐

Total = Addition of all Teacher Assessment Boxes ☐

Percentage = Student Score Divided by 81 (Highest Possible Score)   Percentage _____ %

Your next challenge is to be ready to talk about some of the important ideas in this chapter. Follow the directions listed next to each box and practice talking about your ideas.

1. Full-Time Facials

If a facial takes from 60 to 90 minutes to perform, discuss with a partner how many facials you could perform during one week, working full time. You can use the box to the left to store your calculations.

2. Facial Fees

Using the number you calculated above as the number of facials possible to perform in one week, calculate the total dollars generated if each client purchased $15 in retail products and each facial was priced at $40.

3. My Dream Machine

If you could design a machine to be used for skin care services, what would it look like and what specific function would it perform?

Write notes about your new machine on the lines provided to the left.

Discuss your idea with a partner.

Now it's time to see how well you know your new material. First answer these questions. Then use the Memory Box that follows to check yourself. Look up each answer on the corresponding page in the *Salon Fundamentals™ Esthetics* textbook. Check "got it" for all correct answers and "not yet" for all incorrect responses. Using the "Know Chart," record all of your correct responses in the "I Know" column. After correcting incorrect answers, record all of your corrected responses in the "I Need to Study" column. That way you know exactly what to review before continuing in this Guide.

Directions: Identify whether questions 1 and 2 are True or False by circling TRUE or FALSE. You can earn an extra point for each false statement you appropriately correct. Question 3 requires you to write in an answer in the blank provided. Answers to the questions found in 4 through 10 may be selected by circling a, b, c or d below each statement to indicate your choice.

1. TRUE   FALSE   90% of wrinkles are caused by excessive sun exposure.

_____

2. TRUE   FALSE   The basic regimen of skin care is recommended to be followed three times each day.

_____

3. _____ is the systematic, therapeutic method of manipulating the body by rubbing, pinching, tapping, kneading or stroking with hands, fingers or an instrument.

4. A product with an SPF of 15 indicates:
   a. the number of hours of protection from sun exposure
   b. sun exposure can be 15% longer than without protection
   c. the time in minutes between reapplications of the sunscreen
   d. the number of times sunscreen should be applied for a full day of protection

5. Which of the following terms describes an exfoliant that contains a granular substance with a slightly grainy or rough texture?
   a. toning
   b. chemical
   c. moisturizing
   d. mechanical

6. Masks with the primary purpose of absorbing excess oil, tightening and refining the pores and aiding in preventing clogging are:
   a. gel masks
   b. clay masks
   c. paraffin masks
   d. modeling masks

7. The actual action or movement performed during the massage treatment is referred to as:
   a. massage
   b. ventouse
   c. saponificatio
   d. manipulation

8. A light or heavy kneading, pinching and rolling of a muscle is called:
   a. chucking
   b. petrissage
   c. effleurag
   d. tapotement

9. Which of the following is NOT a characteristic of rosacea?
   a. a vascular disorder
   b. small red bumps
   c. occurs between the ages of 30 – 40
   d. overactivity of the sebaceous glands

10. An overactivity of the sebaceous glands causes:
   a. acne
   b. rosacea
   c. couperose
   d. dehydration

| 1 | 2 | 3 | 4 | 5 | 6 | 7 |

1. page 326	☐ got it ☐ not yet	
2. page 325	☐ got it ☐ not yet	
3. page 329	☐ got it ☐ not yet	
4. page 327	☐ got it ☐ not yet	
5. page 327	☐ got it ☐ not yet	
6. page 328	☐ got it ☐ not yet	
7. page 329	☐ got it ☐ not yet	
8. page 330	☐ got it ☐ not yet	
9. page 333	☐ got it ☐ not yet	
10. page 333	☐ got it ☐ not yet	

I know...

I need to study...

SHOW YOU KNOW...

Imagine that you are a representative of the regulating agency that oversees your profession. You have just been asked to represent this prestigious group at a meeting to discuss the safety and infection control procedures for facials with and without machines. In the space provided below, write an opening statement you would use to gain interest and an effective closing statement to present yourself as a knowledgeable representative of the regulating agency.

OPENING STATEMENT: _____
_____
_____
_____

CLOSING STATEMENT: _____
_____
_____
_____

1	2	3	④	⑤	6	7

The Line Up

Put the following 24 steps for the basic facial procedure in the correct order with 1 being the first step, 2 being the second step and so forth.

NUMBER	STEP
	Apply facial mask
	Remove cleansing crème
	Obtain massage crème from the container with a spatula
	Remove massage crème
	Apply cleansing crème
	Apply moisturizing crème and sun protection, if needed
	Cover the mask
	Perform any necessary extractions
	Allow mask to set
	Apply desincrustation solution, if necessary, and steam
	Obtain cleansing crème with a spatula
	Apply eye product
	Analyze client's skin
	Apply toner following necessary extractions
	Wash and sanitize hands
	Apply exfoliant and steam
	Place eye pads over client's eyes
	Remove mask
	Apply massage crème
	Perform massage movements
	Remove exfoliant
	Apply toner following cleanser
	Drape client
	Apply toner following removal of mask

KNOWLEDGE GRID

Start at the top of the Knowledge Grid and work your way down, answering each question to check your understanding of Chapter 10, Facials. The questions found here will help you deepen your understanding, build self-confidence and increase your awareness of different ways of thinking about a subject.

KNOW

What is the meaning of the word saponification?

COMPREHEND

Why are butterfly eye pads preferred to ordinary eye pads?

APPLY

Demonstrate your knowledge of the five basic massage manipulations by drawing a quick sketch next to each term that would represent the effects of that manipulation.

Effleurage   Petrissage   Tapotement   Friction   Vibration

ANALYZE

Compare the effects of a massage using primarily effleurage manipulations to a massage using vibration manipulations.

SYNTHESIZE

Create a promotional phrase for a facial using lavender aromatherapy and effleurage massage movements.

EVALUATE

What is your opinion of performing facials without machines?

Multiple choice. Circle the correct answer.

1. The first step in the skin care regimen that is designed to remove dirt, oil, makeup and environmental pollutants is:
   a. toning
   b. protecting
   c. cleansing
   d. moisturizing

2. Skin care products used for cleansing the skin while properly balancing the pH are:
   a. toners
   b. cleansers
   c. sunscreens
   d. moisturizers

3. Moisturizers are responsible for:
   a. balancing the pH
   b. removing dirt, oil and makeup
   c. protecting the skin from UVA and UVB rays
   d. replenishing and balancing moisture and oil

4. What percentage of wrinkles is caused by the natural aging process?
   a. 10%
   b. 40%
   c. 70%
   d. 90%

5. If you are selecting a sunscreen, it is recommended that you choose one that has protection from:
   a. UVA rays only
   b. UVB rays only
   c. UVA and UVB rays
   d. neither UVA nor UVB rays

6. Which term below identifies a type of exfoliant that contains a granular substance with a rough texture that works as an abrasive to remove dead skin cells?
   a. enzyme
   b. chemical
   c. mechanical
   d. alpha hydroxy acid

7. Which type of mask can be pulled from the face in one piece?
   a. gel
   b. paraffin
   c. clay/mud
   d. modeling

8. All of the following are benefits of massage EXCEPT:
    a. relaxation
    b. pain relief
    c. strengthening muscles
    d. decreasing blood supply to the skin

9. The method of massage used to soothe muscles and relax the sensory nerve endings at the surface of the skin is called:
    a. friction
    b. petrissage
    c. effleurage
    d. tapotement

10. Effleurage is used on all of the following parts of the body EXCEPT:
    a. face
    b. legs
    c. neck
    d. arms

11. Fulling is a form of which type of massage movement?
    a. vibration
    b. effleurage
    c. petrissage
    d. tapotement

12. Which of the following methods of massage is a light tapping or slapping movement applied with the fingertips or partly flexed fingers?
    a. friction
    b. vibration
    c. effleurage
    d. tapotement

13. Which type of massage should NEVER be used on a client with sensitive skin or on certain skin conditions such as acne or rosacea?
    a. friction
    b. vibration
    c. petrissage
    d. tapotement

14. A motion that resembles a chopping movement using the edge of the hands is referred to as:
    a. fulling
    b. hacking
    c. wringing
    d. chucking

| 1 | 2 | 3 | 4 | 5 | 6 | 7 |

15. Which of the following movements of massage is a circular or wringing movement with no gliding?
    a. friction
    b. vibration
    c. petrissage
    d. tapotement

16. A shaking movement achieved when the esthetician quickly shakes his or her arms while the fingertips or palms are touching the client is called:
    a. vibration
    b. effleurage
    c. petrissage
    d. tapotement

17. Which of the following is NOT a contraindication for massage?
    a. headache
    b. heart condition
    c. previous stroke
    d. high blood pressure

18. Which skin type demonstrates sufficient moisture and sebum production?
    a. oily
    b. normal
    c. dehydration
    d. combination

19. The type of skin that lacks adequate sebum production and exhibits heightened sensitivity is referred to as:
    a. dry
    b. oily
    c. normal
    d. combination

20. Which of the following is a characteristic of oily skin?
    a. small pore size
    b. fine broken capillaries
    c. excess sebum production
    d. heightened sensitivity

21. The most common skin type is referred to as:
    a. dry
    b. normal
    c. combination
    d. mature/aging

22. Which of the following is a characteristic of a couperose skin condition?
    a. superficial dryness
    b. lacks elasticity and firmness
    c. displays excess sebum production
    d. frequently found on the cheeks and corners of the nose

23. Which skin condition is characterized by flushed redness, dilated capillaries and small red bumps?
    a. oily
    b. rosacea
    c. combination
    d. dehydration

24. All of the following are considered skin types EXCEPT:
    a. dry
    b. oily
    c. acne
    d. combination

25. If you suspect a client has a medical condition, you should always:
    a. perform a facial
    b. diagnose the condition yourself
    c. treat the condition with medication
    d. refer your client to a dermatologist or specialist

26. Which of the products listed below assists in preventing the growth of bacteria?
    a. toner
    b. antiseptic
    c. astringent
    d. moisturizer

27. All of the following are types of masks EXCEPT:
    a. dry skin
    b. calming
    c. oily skin
    d. ventouse

28. Which of the following is NOT a skin care product?
    a. toner
    b. sunscreen
    c. moisturizer
    d. infrared lamp

29. Which of the following is NOT a contraindication for facials with and without machines?
    a. diabetes
    b. epilepsy
    c. prosthesis
    d. common cold

30. All of the following take place in the Greeting phase EXCEPT:
    a. handshake
    b. eye contact
    c. facial services
    d. professional demeanor

31. During the Completion phase one of the goals is to:
    a. ensure client comfort
    b. ask questions to discover the client's needs
    c. request satisfaction feedback from your client
    d. communicate to build rapport and develop a relationship with the client

32. Which of the following procedures is one of the most requested services in the skin care center?
    a. basic facial
    b. facial with Galvanic/iontophoresis
    c. facial with Galvanic/desincrustation
    d. facial wih Indirect High Frequency

33. Which of the following is NOT a massage tip?
    a. apply firm pressure
    b. use caution around the eyes and eyelids to avoid stretching sensitive skin
    c. maintain physical contact with your client as you massage with a constant rhythm
    d. never use up-and-out motions to help protect the underlying muscle tissue

34. After the basic facial is complete, the esthetician should do all of the
    following EXCEPT:
    a. wash your hands with liquid antibacterial soap
    b. replace used towels and sheets with fresh ones
    c. keep non-reusable materials used during the service
    d. place unused cotton pads and sponges in a covered container

35. A desincrustation facial treatment utilizes what current in conjunction with an
    alkaline solution?
    a. Galvanic
    b. Penetrating
    c. Direct High Frequency
    d. Indirect High Frequency

36. Indirect High Frequency Current is used to amplify the effects of the massage movements for relaxation or:
    a. hydration
    b. cleansing
    c. penetration
    d. stimulation

37. Which of the following procedures CANNOT be performed with gloves?
    a. basic facials
    b. iontophoresis
    c. Direct High Frequency
    d. Indirect High Frequency

38. A Direct High Frequency treatment is best suited for skin that is:
    a. dry
    b. normal
    c. combination
    d. oily or acneic

39. To avoid discomfort and irritation when performing a facial on a male client, all movements should be made in a(an):
    a. circular motion
    b. upward motion
    c. downward motion
    d. side-to-side motion

40. Which of the following would be recommended to use for a soothing, hydrating treatment for a bearded male client?
    a. gel
    b. clay mask
    c. crème mask
    d. modeling mask

Write Your Own Ticket! For numbers 41, 42, and 43, write your own questions and answer them. Your questions can be true/false, multiple choice or fill-in-the-blank. The only parameter is that your questions cannot already be found on this test. Earn one point each for writing your way to success.

41. Q: _____

    A: _____

42. Q: _____

    A: _____

43. Q: _____

    A: _____

BONUS QUESTION!

Question 44 is the ultimate question. To earn two points, design a question for your class. If you stump the class, and no one can answer the question within an agreed upon time (between you and the teacher), you earn a BONUS OF FIVE ADDITIONAL POINTS.

44. _____

ESSAY QUESTION:

45.   A maximum of five additional points is possible by selecting one of the following essay questions to answer.

45a.   List the five basic movements of massage and the benefit of those movements.

Movement	Benefit

45b. Choose two of the five important points to remember when performing massage that were highlighted in this chapter and list them below.

_____

_____

_____

_____

_____

_____

_____

_____

_____

_____

_____

45c. In your opinion, how can referrals and effective recommendations that turn into sales contribute to the growth of a business?

_____

_____

_____

_____

_____

_____

_____

_____

Check your answers as you did before. Place a check mark next to the page number for any incorrect answer. On the lines to the right, jot down topics that you still need to review.

1.	page 326	21.	page 333
2.	page 326	22.	page 333
3.	page 326	23.	page 333
4.	page 326	24.	page 333
5.	page 327	25	page 334
6.	page 327	26.	page 335
7.	page 328	27.	page 335
8.	page 329	28.	page 335
9.	page 330	29.	page 338
10.	page 330	30.	page 339
11.	page 330	31.	page 340
12.	page 330	32.	page 341
13.	page 331	33.	page 350
14.	page 331	34.	page 352
15.	page 331	35.	page 356
16.	page 331	36.	page 360
17.	page 332	37.	page 361
18.	page 333	38.	page 362
19.	page 333	39.	page 365
20.	page 333	40.	page 365

NOTES TO MYSELF — *My Reflections About Facials*

Experts agree that it is important to summarize your feelings and reactions about what you are learning. Note especially things that surprised you, things you found difficult to learn, and suggestions and ideas you received from friends that helped make learning this chapter easier and more enjoyable.

VALUE

By learning modern temporary and permanent hair removal procedures, you can offer specialized services to your clients and add value to your business.

MAIN IDEA

Societal norms, and occasionally certain medical or genetic conditions, compel clients to remove unwanted body hair. This chapter will help you develop a thorough knowledge of hair growth, as well as the various types of hair removal options, including temporary and permanent methods. In addition, you will learn to perform, step-by-step, the waxing method of hair removal for the face and body.

PLAN

Hair Growth and Removal Methods
- Hair Growth Cycle
- Temporary Removal Methods
- Permanent Removal Methods
- Waxing Essentials
- Infection Control and Safety
- Client Consultation

Waxing Services
- Eyebrow Wax
- Upper Lip Wax
- Underarm Wax
- Bikini Wax
- Lower Leg Wax

OBJECTIVES

- Explain the hair growth cycle.
- Differentiate between temporary and permanent hair removal services.
- Explain techniques for each type of hair removal and how procedures differ for face and body.
- Identify the considerations for waxing.
- Describe the waxing essentials including products, implements and supplies, equipment and types of waxes.
- Demonstrate infection control, safety measures and the client consultation for each waxing service.

- Demonstrate the basic preparation, procedures and completion steps for:
  - Eyebrow waxing
  - Upper lip waxing
  - Underarm waxing
  - Bikini waxing
  - Lower leg waxing

Chapter	Section	Page
Chapter 11 Hair Removal	Hair Growth and Removal Methods	**Pages 371-372**

⭐ **1** Explain the hair growth cycle

Hair Growth

Hirsutism

Hypertrichosis

Technical Hair Terms
- Capilli:
- Barba:
- Cilia:
- Supercilia:
- Lanugo:
- Vellus:
- Terminal:

■ **Hair Growth Cycle** — Consists of 3 phases; all hair is in one of the 3 phases at any given time

ANAGEN >>>>>>>	CATAGEN >>>>>>>>>>	TELOGEN >>>>>>>>>>>>>>>
■	■	■
■	■	■

Waxing

Chapter	Section	Page
Chapter 11 Hair Removal	Hair Growth and Removal Methods	Pages 372-373

2 Differentiate between temporary and permanent hair removal services

3 Explain techniques for each type of hair removal and how procedures differ for face and body

■ **Temporary Removal Methods**

Procedure of shaving, chemical depilatories, tweezing, waxing, threading and sugaring

Considerations:

Shaving

- ■
- ■
- ■
- ■
- ■

Chemical Depilatories

- ■
- ■
- ■
- ■
- ■
- ■
- ■
- ■

Chapter	Section	Page
Chapter 11 Hair Removal	Hair Growth and Removal Methods	Pages 372-374

■ **Temporary Removal Methods continued**

Hair Lighteners (Bleach)

Considerations:

Tweezing

■

■

■

Eyebrow Tweezing Guidelines

1. Assemble materials; prepare workspace
2. Wash and sanitize hands
3. Cleanse the area to be tweezed
4. _____ eyebrows; thick? thin?
5. _____ the hairs up to see the base
6. Hold skin _____ tweeze above and below eyebrow
7. Tweeze in an _____ direction from inside beginning of eyebrow to top arch
8. Tweeze downward toward the outer edge of the eyebrow
9. Complete one eyebrow, then the other
10. Apply _____ then soothing crème
11. Rebook the client within ____ weeks to keep eyebrows in shape
12. Perform _____ procedures

Chapter	Section	Page
Chapter 11 Hair Removal	Hair Growth and Removal Methods	Pages 373-375

4 Identify the considerations for waxing

Waxing

Considerations:

- ■
- ■
- ■
- ■

- ■

Considerations Prior to Waxing

Factors to consider prior to hair removal include:

Soft Wax

Hard Wax

SOFT WAX

- ■
- ■
- ■

- ■

HARD WAX

- ■
- ■

- ■

smartNOTES

Chapter	Section	Page
Chapter 11 Hair Removal	Hair Growth and Removal Methods	Pages 375-376

Threading

Considerations:

■

■

■

Sugaring

Considerations:

■

■

■

■

■

■ **Permanent Removal Methods**

Electrolysis

Considerations:

■

■

■

Chapter	Section	Page
Chapter 11 Hair Removal	Hair Growth and Removal Methods	Pages 376-377

Electrologist

Three Methods of Electrolysis

GALVANIC	THERMOLYSIS	BLEND
▪	▪	▪
▪	▪	▪
▪	▪	
	▪	
▪		

Considerations:

Laser Hair Removal
- ▪
- ▪

- ▪
- ▪

Considerations:

Photo Epilation or Pulsed Light
- ▪

- ▪

- ▪

- ▪

Which of the permanent hair removal methods would you prefer if you were going be a client?

5 Describe the waxing essentials including products, implements and supplies, equipment and types of waxes

6 Demonstrate infection control, safety measures and the client consultation for each waxing service.

LEARNING ── CONNECTION ── Fill in the Blanks

Use the following section to help you organize essential information such as general waxing considerations, eyebrow shaping guidelines, waxing implements, supplies and equipment and contraindications.

General Waxing Considerations (page 378)

Before	
the Waxing Service	■ Cease shaving or tweezing area to be waxed at least _____ to _____ weeks prior to service
	■ Avoid exfoliating at least 48 hours _____ to the waxing service to avoid skin sensitivity
	■ Avoid excessive _____ at least 48 hours prior to the waxing service
	■ Advise clients to wear loose clothing in case the skin is sensitive after the appointment
	■ Book waxing appointments at least _____ to special occasions in case of an adverse reaction

During	
the Waxing Service	■ ____, _____ and _____ all affect the temperature of wax
	■ Keep the temperature of your room between 70° and 75° Fahrenheit (21°-24° Celsius) at all times
	■ Do not wax under _____ or _____ vents or in excessively drafty areas
	■ Keep client _____ ; if necessary, use blankets and heated table pads
	■ Wear protective gloves to protect you and your client from _____, viruses or bacteria

After	
the Waxing Service	Avoid:
	■ Applying _____, other than loose powder, for two hours after facial waxing
	■ Applying highly _____ or lotions over the waxed areas
	■ Using excessively _____, saunas or steam rooms for several hours after waxing
	■ Using harsh or _____ over waxed areas immediately following the service
	■ Exposing the waxed areas to sun or tanning beds for _____ hours, use of physical or chemical exfoliants, and/or swimming in lakes or oceans the same day of waxing services

1	2	3	4	5	6	7

Salon Fundamentals™ Esthetics

Eyebrow Shaping Guidelines (page 379)

1. Space between the eyebrows should be equal to the _____ .

2. Inner edge of the eyebrow should start above the _____ . To establish that point, hold a pencil to the side of the nose straight up to the eyebrow.

3. Establish the length of the eyebrow, hold the pencil _____ from the _____ and extend it to the outer corner of the eye. The eyebrow should not exceed this point.

4. Determine highest part of the _____ by using a pencil to connect the nostril to the outside edge of the _____ . The eyebrow should not exceed this point. If extremely thick, may also decide to remove the hair above the eyebrow.

Waxing Products, Implements and Supplies (page 380-382)

Product	Function
Antiseptic preparation	_____ skin; removes _____ on body
Cornstarch or powder	Buffers the skin from wax and prevents skin from _____ ; absorbs _____ remaining on skin
Soothing lotion	_____ the skin after waxing
Wax	Removes _____ hair
Wax remover	Removes wax _____ from skin
Hair growth retardant	Slows growth of hair _____ waxing
Eyebrow brush and comb	Shape and groom _____
Gloves	Protect _____ and skin
Headband and hairnet	Holds _____ out of the way
Long-handled cotton swabs	Apply _____
Muslin or Pellon® (fiber)	Removes wax and _____
Plastic bags	_____ discarded materials
Small scissors	_____ longer hair
Sheets	Protect _____ bed; cover client
Tissues	Aid application of _____
Tweezers	Remove _____ hairs and shapes brows
Wooden application sticks/spatulas	Applies wax to skin
Hand-held mirror	Allows client to view results
Equipment cleaner	Removes wax, dirt and _____ from the cart and other surfaces
Professional cart	Holds all supplies and implements; can be moved to any location in the skin care center
Facial chair or bed	Holds client for comfort
Wax warmer (pot)	Melts and holds _____

Create a Thinking Map to help yourself make sense of how your SmartNotes fit together. Use all of the words in the Jump-Start Box as well as pictures to make a visual that will help you connect the important ideas in this section to each other. Be creative!

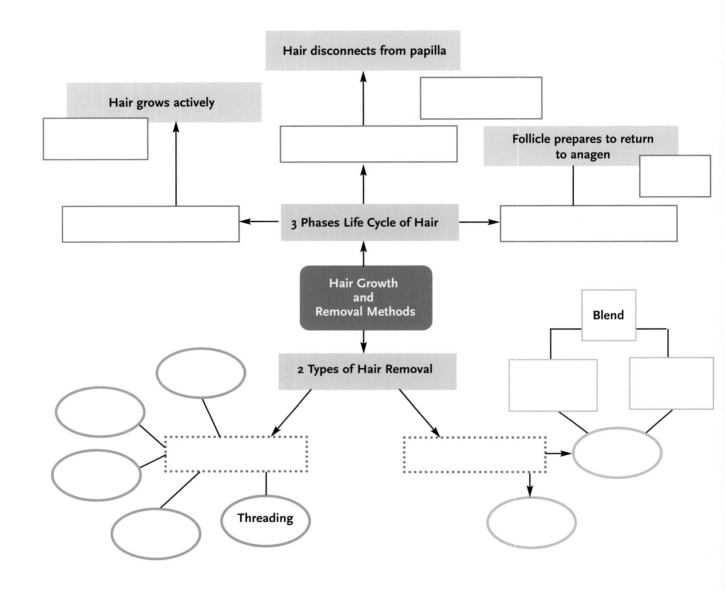

JUMP START BOX	Anagen	Catagen	Telogen	Temporary
	Shaving	Tweezing	Waxing	Laser
	Electrolysis	Hair sheds	Permanent	Transitional phase
	Thermolysis	Longest phase	Chemical Depilatories	Galvanic

Try to find the words that are listed in the Jump Start Box below in the chart shown here. Highlight each word you can locate.

```
l c l i e n t d f a n t i s e p t i c m c b x e e r t w e e z e r s w q o p n p o r e a s i m n a l a f h g y
a o l s o f t w a x s o t h s o o t h i n g l o t i o n o n l h e a t e d w a x p o t b i d d g b u d g e t a
u n d e r a r m r m a s a i o u s f a c i a l h a i r t r t o u q m x s e n s i t i v e s k i n s d a l o p e t
i a t r s t b a k t e r i a i c z v a i m p l e m e n t s a o p g h c o r n s t a r c h d u n w o n t e d l e i
b u f f e r u n m a t m o i s t u r e f k j i i s d f p h a n d h e l d m i r r o r t r a c b i k i n i p o f i f
p r o f e s s i o n a l c a r t i y t q l k s a f g h h a r d w a x s k n n s t r a y h a i r s s p o o t a a t k
d y h n m c s k a l a p p l i c a t i o n s t i c k s d o p a b a c t e r i a a c z s l s m a l l s c i s s o r s
t e s s i u t i s s u e w e d s e y e b r o w b r u s h s a t s a l s a n i t i z e s q w a m n d s z o p o t
d k k l a s l d k s p a t u l a s e r e h e a d b a n d b v c x g u i t e u n w a n t e d h a i r s t w a x i
```

JUMP START BOX

antiseptic	client	headband	sensitive skin	tissue
application sticks	cornstarch	heated wax pot	small scissors	tweezers
bacteria	eyebrow brush	implements	soft wax	underarm
bikini	facial hair	moisture	soothing lotion	unwanted hair
budget	hand-held mirror	professional cart	spatulas	wax
buffer	hard wax	sanitize	stray hairs	

1	2	3	4	5	6	7

Chapter	Section	Page
Chapter 11 Hair Removal	Hair Growth and Removal Methods	Pages 382-383

■ Infection Control and Safety

Guidelines for safety and sanitation:

1.

2.

3.

4.

5.

6.

7.

8. Before every client: >

>

>

>

Contraindications

Avoid waxing over areas with contraindications that may cause excessive irritation

CAUTION !!!

Skin Conditions	Health Conditions
■	■
■	■
■	■
■	■
■	■
■	■
■	
■	
■	

Oral and Topical Medications
■
■
■
■
■
■

Chapter	Section	Page
Chapter 11 Hair Removal	**Hair Growth and Removal Methods**	**Pages 384-385**

■ **Client Consultation**

Client consultations conducted prior to hair removal service should cover:

■

■

■

■

■

Five Phases of Service

Phase: GREETING

How?

Why?

Phase: ASK, ANALYZE, ASSESS

How?

Why?

Phase: AGREEMENT

How?

Why?

Phase: DELIVERY

How?

Why?

Phase: COMPLETION

How?

Why?

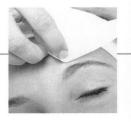

Eyebrow Waxing Procedure

This rubric is designed to compare your skill to industry expectations. Indicate your present level of performance by checking the appropriate box. Your teacher will direct you in the completion of this rubric.

Rubric Assessment

The eyebrow waxing procedure is requested by clients wishing to improve and shape the look of the entire face. A client's eyes can appear brighter and wider after an eyebrow wax. Since this procedure is quick and easy to perform, it is also a great income generator. By following and practicing the steps in this rubric, you will be prepared to offer an eyebrow waxing service to your clients. Note that the numbers for each step correspond with the step-by-step technical images found in the textbook.

	Level 1	Level 2	Level 3	To Improve, I Need To:	Teacher Assessment
PREPARATION					
Disinfect facial service area; place protective cover on facial bed; cut removal strips to be used in advance; arrange antiseptic preparation, powder, wax, remover, soothing gel or medicated lotion, spatulas, tweezers, gloves; wax warmed at least 30 minutes prior to client arrival	☐	☐	☐		☐
PROCEDURE					
1. Wash and sanitize hands (wear protective gloves if required)	☐	☐	☐		☐
2. Drape client	☐	☐	☐		☐
PREPARE SKIN					
3. Assess direction of the hair growth	☐	☐	☐		☐
4. Apply antiseptic preparation or pre-wax solution; lightly dust area with powder	☐	☐	☐		☐
APPLY WAX					
5. Obtain wax	☐	☐	☐		☐
6. Apply wax (test temperature prior to application)	☐	☐	☐		☐
7. Discard the spatula	☐	☐	☐		☐
REMOVE WAX and HAIR					
8. Apply removal strip; press and rub strip	☐	☐	☐		☐
9. Pull skin taut and remove strip	☐	☐	☐		☐
10. Apply pressure	☐	☐	☐		☐
REPEAT					
11. Repeat procedure on new area	☐	☐	☐		☐

Rubric Assessment Continued

	Level 1	Level 2	Level 3	To Improve, I Need To:	Teacher Assessment
CLEAN and PROTECT SKIN					
12. Remove any excess wax; remove stray hairs with tweezers	☐	☐	☐		☐
13. Apply soothing gel	☐	☐	☐		☐
COMPLETION					
Offer to rebook next appointment; recommend retail products for home care; dispose of non-reusable materials used during the waxing treatment; replace used linens with fresh linens and arrange all products and implements in proper order; disinfect waxing service implements, work area and facial bed; wash hands with liquid antibacterial soap	☐	☐	☐		☐

Total = Addition of all Teacher Assessment Boxes ☐

Percentage = Student Score Divided by 45 (Highest Possible Score)   **Percentage** _____ %

Upper Lip Waxing Procedure

This rubric is designed to compare your skill to industry expectations. Indicate your present level of performance by checking the appropriate box. Your teacher will direct you in the completion of this rubric.

Rubric Assessment

The upper lip waxing procedure is requested by clients wishing to remove excess hair on the upper lip, sides of the face or chin and/or along the hairline. By following and practicing the steps in this rubric, you will be prepared to offer this waxing service to your clients. Note that the numbers for each step correspond with the step-by-step technical images found in the textbook.

	Level 1	Level 2	Level 3	To Improve, I Need To:	Teacher Assess
PREPARATION					
■ Disinfect facial service area; place protective cover on facial bed; cut removal strips to be used in advance; arrange antiseptic preparation, powder, wax, remover, soothing gel or medicated lotion, spatulas, tweezers, gloves; wax warmed at least 30 minutes prior to client arrival	☐	☐	☐		☐
PROCEDURE					
1. Wash and sanitize hands (wear protective gloves if required)	☐	☐	☐		☐
2. Drape client	☐	☐	☐		☐
PREPARE SKIN					
3. Assess direction of the hair growth	☐	☐	☐		☐
4. Apply antiseptic preparation or pre-wax solution; lightly dust area with powder	☐	☐	☐		☐
APPLY WAX					
5. Obtain wax	☐	☐	☐		☐
6. Apply wax (test temperature prior to application)	☐	☐	☐		☐
7. Discard the spatula	☐	☐	☐		☐
REMOVE WAX and HAIR					
8. Apply removal strip; press and rub strip	☐	☐	☐		☐
9. Pull skin taut and remove strip	☐	☐	☐		☐
10. Apply pressure	☐	☐	☐		☐
REPEAT					
11. Repeat procedure on new area	☐	☐	☐		☐

Rubric Assessment Continued

	Level 1	Level 2	Level 3	To Improve, I Need To:	Teacher Assessment
CLEAN and PROTECT SKIN					
12. Remove any excess wax; remove stray hairs with tweezers	☐	☐	☐		☐
13. Apply soothing gel	☐	☐	☐		☐
COMPLETION					
■ Offer to rebook next appointment; recommend retail products for home care; dispose of non-reusable materials used during the waxing treatment; replace used linens with fresh linens and arrange all products and implements in proper order; disinfect waxing service implements, work area and facial bed; wash hands with liquid antibacterial soap	☐	☐	☐		☐

Total = Addition of all Teacher Assessment Boxes ☐

Percentage = Student Score Divided by 45 (Highest Possible Score)   **Percentage** _____ %

Underarm Waxing Procedure

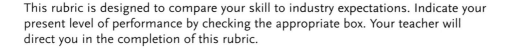

This rubric is designed to compare your skill to industry expectations. Indicate your present level of performance by checking the appropriate box. Your teacher will direct you in the completion of this rubric.

Rubric Assessment

The underarm waxing procedure is designed for clients choosing to remove the hair from underneath their arms. By following and practicing the steps in this rubric, you will be prepared to offer this waxing service to your clients. Note that the numbers for each step correspond with the step-by-step technical images found in the textbook.

	Level 1	Level 2	Level 3	To Improve, I Need To:	Teacher Assessment
PREPARATION					
■ Disinfect facial service area; place protective cover on facial bed; cut removal strips to be used in advance; arrange antiseptic preparation, powder, wax, remover, soothing gel or medicated lotion, spatulas, tweezers, gloves; wax warmed at least 30 minutes prior to client arrival	☐	☐	☐		▭
PROCEDURE					
1. Wash and sanitize hands (wear protective gloves if required)	☐	☐	☐		▭
2. Drape client	☐	☐	☐		▭
PREPARE SKIN					
3. Assess direction of the hair growth	☐	☐	☐		▭
4. Apply antiseptic preparation or pre-wax solution; lightly dust area with powder	☐	☐	☐		▭
APPLY WAX					
5. Obtain wax	☐	☐	☐		▭
6. Apply wax (test temperature prior to application)	☐	☐	☐		▭
7. Discard the spatula	☐	☐	☐		▭
REMOVE WAX and HAIR					
8. Apply removal strip; press and rub strip	☐	☐	☐		▭
9. Pull skin taut and remove strip	☐	☐	☐		▭
10. Apply pressure	☐	☐	☐		▭
REPEAT					
11. Repeat procedure on new area	☐	☐	☐		▭

Salon Fundamentals™ Esthetics

Rubric Assessment Continued

	Level 1	Level 2	Level 3	To Improve, I Need To:	Teacher Assessment
CLEAN and PROTECT SKIN					
12. Remove any excess wax; remove stray hairs with tweezers	☐	☐	☐		☐
13. Apply soothing gel	☐	☐	☐		☐
COMPLETION					
■ Offer to rebook next appointment; recommend retail products for home care; dispose of non-reusable materials used during the waxing treatment; replace used linens with fresh linens and arrange all products and implements in proper order; disinfect waxing service implements, work area and facial bed; wash hands with liquid antibacterial soap	☐	☐	☐		☐

Total = Addition of all Teacher Assessment Boxes ☐

Percentage = Student Score Divided by 45 (Highest Possible Score)   **Percentage** _____ %

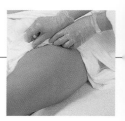

Bikini Waxing Procedure

This rubric is designed to compare your skill to industry expectations. Indicate your present level of performance by checking the appropriate box. Your teacher will direct you in the completion of this rubric.

Rubric Assessment

The classic bikini waxing procedure removes unwanted hair that appears along the panty line. By following and practicing the steps in this rubric, you will be prepared to offer this waxing service to your clients. Note that the numbers for each step correspond with the step-by-step technical images found in the textbook.

	Level 1	Level 2	Level 3	To Improve, I Need To:	Teacher Assessment
PREPARATION					
■ Disinfect facial service area; place protective cover on facial bed; cut removal strips to be used in advance; arrange antiseptic preparation, powder, wax, remover, soothing gel or medicated lotion, spatulas, tweezers, gloves; wax warmed at least 30 minutes prior to client arrival	☐	☐	☐		▭
PROCEDURE					
1. Wash and sanitize hands (wear protective gloves if required)	☐	☐	☐		▭
2. Drape client	☐	☐	☐		▭
PREPARE SKIN					
3. Assess direction of the hair growth	☐	☐	☐		▭
4. Apply antiseptic preparation or pre-wax solution; lightly dust area with powder	☐	☐	☐		▭
APPLY WAX					
5. Obtain wax	☐	☐	☐		▭
6. Apply wax (test temperature prior to application)	☐	☐	☐		▭
7. Discard the spatula	☐	☐	☐		▭
REMOVE WAX and HAIR					
8. Apply removal strip; press and rub strip	☐	☐	☐		▭
9. Pull skin taut and remove strip	☐	☐	☐		▭
10. Apply pressure	☐	☐	☐		▭
REPEAT					
11. Repeat procedure on new area	☐	☐	☐		▭

Bikini Waxing Procedure

Rubric Assessment Continued

	Level 1	Level 2	Level 3	To Improve, I Need To:	Teacher Assessment
CLEAN and PROTECT SKIN					
12. Remove any excess wax; remove stray hairs with tweezers	☐	☐	☐		☐
13. Apply soothing gel	☐	☐	☐		☐
COMPLETION					
■ Offer to rebook next appointment; recommend retail products for home care; dispose of non-reusable materials used during the waxing treatment; replace used linens with fresh linens and arrange all products and implements in proper order; disinfect waxing service implements, work area and facial bed; wash hands with liquid antibacterial soap	☐	☐	☐		☐

Total = Addition of all Teacher Assessment Boxes ☐

Percentage = Student Score Divided by 45 (Highest Possible Score) **Percentage** _____ %

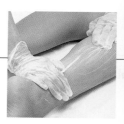

This rubric is designed to compare your skill to industry expectations. Indicate your present level of performance by checking the appropriate box. Your teacher will direct you in the completion of this rubric.

Rubric Assessment

The lower leg waxing procedure is offered for clients desiring to remove hair from the top of the knee to ankles. By following and practicing the steps in this rubric, you will be prepared to offer this waxing service to your clients. Note that the numbers for each step correspond with the step-by-step technical images found in the textbook.

	Level 1	Level 2	Level 3	To Improve, I Need To:	Teacher Assessment
PREPARATION					
◼ Disinfect facial service area; place protective cover on facial bed; cut removal strips to be used in advance; arrange antiseptic preparation, powder, wax, remover, soothing gel or medicated lotion, spatulas, tweezers, gloves; wax warmed at least 30 minutes prior to client arrival	☐	☐	☐		☐
PROCEDURE					
1. Wash and sanitize hands (wear protective gloves if required)	☐	☐	☐		☐
2. Drape client	☐	☐	☐		☐
PREPARE SKIN					
3. Assess direction of the hair growth	☐	☐	☐		☐
4. Apply antiseptic preparation or pre-wax solution; lightly dust area with powder	☐	☐	☐		☐
APPLY WAX					
5. Obtain wax	☐	☐	☐		☐
6. Apply wax (test temperature prior to application)	☐	☐	☐		☐
7. Discard the spatula	☐	☐	☐		☐
REMOVE WAX and HAIR					
8. Apply removal strip; press and rub strip	☐	☐	☐		☐
9. Pull skin taut and remove strip	☐	☐	☐		☐
10. Apply pressure	☐	☐	☐		☐
REPEAT					
11. Repeat procedure on new area	☐	☐	☐		☐

Lower Leg Waxing Procedure

	Level 1	Level 2	Level 3	To Improve, I Need To:	Teacher Assessment
CLEAN and PROTECT SKIN					
12. Remove any excess wax; remove stray hairs with tweezers	☐	☐	☐		⬜
13. Apply soothing gel	☐	☐	☐		⬜
COMPLETION					
▪ Offer to rebook next appointment; recommend retail products for home care; dispose of non-reusable materials used during the waxing treatment; replace used linens with fresh linens and arrange all products and implements in proper order; disinfect waxing service implements, work area and facial bed; wash hands with liquid antibacterial soap	☐	☐	☐		⬜

Total = Addition of all Teacher Assessment Boxes ⬜

Percentage = Student Score Divided by 45 (Highest Possible Score)   **Percentage** _____ %

Column A		Column B
A. Waxing		Technique that removes hair at the surface of the skin, with hair usually growing back within 24 - 48 hours
B. Temporary hair removal		Method that offers best results to clients with excessive or resistant hair growth
C. Hypertrichosis		Technique that uses wavelengths of light to diminish and destroy hair follicles
D. Shaving		Technique that employs a paste applied to the skin in a rolling motion
E. Chemical depilatories		Temporary hair removal technique that removes unwanted hair from smaller areas
F. Tweezing		Permanent method of hair removal in which a needle is inserted into each hair follicle and conducts an electric current that destroys the papilla
G. Threading		Often the most requested service for estheticians
H. Sugaring		Method that sends a current to the papilla for less than one second, reducing client discomfort
I. Electrolysis		Excessive growth of hair
J. Galvanic method		Technique that utilizes an intense pulsed light to destroy hair bulbs with minimal scarring
K. Thermolysis method		Includes shaving, the use of chemical depilatories, tweezing and waxing
L. Blend method		Technique that utilizes 100 percent cotton thread that is twisted and rolled along the surface of the skin
M. Laser hair removal		Method sometimes called the "multiple-needle process"
N. Photo-epilation		A painless method of hair removal that dissolves the hair at skin level

TALKING POINTS

> Your next challenge is to be ready to talk about some of the important ideas in this chapter. Follow the directions listed next to each box and practice talking about your ideas.

1. Practice Conversation

Esthetician: _____

Client: _____

Esthetician: _____

_____

Client: _____

_____

Esthetician: _____

_____

Think about the waxing procedures that are presented in this chapter and write a script to represent a conversation that might occur between a potential waxing client and yourself.

2. Referral Campaign

A sample referral campaign might look something like this:

_____
_____
_____
_____
_____
_____
_____
_____
_____
_____
_____
_____
_____
_____
_____
_____
_____
_____
_____

Waxing services depend largely on word-of-mouth information that is passed on by satisfied clients. On the lines to the left, create a referral campaign that would reward clients for referring other clients to you for waxing services.

Now it's time to see how well you know your new material. First answer these questions. Then use the Memory Box that follows to check yourself. Look up each answer on the corresponding page in the *Salon Fundamentals™ Esthetics* textbook. Check "got it" for all correct answers and "not yet" for all incorrect responses. Using the "Know Chart," record all of your correct responses in the "I Know" column. After correcting incorrect answers, record all of your corrected responses in the "I Need to Study" column. That way you know exactly what to review before continuing in this Guide.

Directions: Identify whether questions 1 and 2 are True or False by circling TRUE or FALSE. You can earn an extra point for each false statement you appropriately correct. Question 3 requires you to write in an answer in the blank provided. Answers to the questions found in 4 through 10 may be selected by circling a, b, c or d below each statement to indicate your choice.

1. TRUE   FALSE   Because the materials are so expensive, waxing is often a very unprofitable service.

_____

2. TRUE   FALSE   Tweezing can be very beneficial in finishing eyebrow design.

_____

3. A _____ is a painless method of hair removal that dissolves hair at skin level.

4. How long are chemical depilatories generally left on the skin?
    a. 5 minutes
    b. 10 minutes
    c. 15 minutes
    d. 20 minutes

5. Galvanic electrolysis is also known as:
    a. short-wave method
    b. pulsed light method
    c. high frequency method
    d. the "multiple-needle" process

6. Performing patch tests, testing the temperature of the wax and disinfecting the workspace are all guidelines for:
    a. the follow up
    b. client consultation
    c. the Agreement phase
    d. safety and sanitation

7. All of the following are examples of contraindications, factors that could cause irrita during a waxing service, EXCEPT:
    a. ingrown hair
    b. skin conditions
    c. health conditions
    d. topical medications

8. Which of the following must be completed in order to assess all health and medical conditions and ensure that it is safe to perform the service?
    a. follow up
    b. consultation
    c. Delivery phase
    d. Agreement phase

9. Which phase of client consultation encourages referrals for other clients?
    a. Delivery
    b. Agreement
    c. Completion
    d. Ask, Analyze, Assess

10. Which of the following should be the first step taken in a basic waxing procedure?
    a. obtain wax
    b. prepare client
    c. wash and sanitize hands
    d. apply antiseptic or pre-wax

| 1 | 2 | 3 | 4 | 5 | 6 | 7 |

1. page 373	☐ got it ☐ not yet	6. page 382	☐ got it ☐ not yet	
2. page 373	☐ got it ☐ not yet	7. page 383	☐ got it ☐ not yet	
3. page 373	☐ got it ☐ not yet	8. page 384	☐ got it ☐ not yet	
4. page 373	☐ got it ☐ not yet	9. page 385	☐ got it ☐ not yet	
5. page 376	☐ got it ☐ not yet	10. page 387	☐ got it ☐ not yet	

I know...

I need to study...

SHOW YOU KNOW...

A mystery shopper is a client that is asked by a teacher or manager to offer an evaluation of the quality of the service offered following a visit to the skin care center. The teacher offers the mystery shopper a range of time, usually over two to three weeks, for the visit to occur. It is a mystery to the teacher and to the student when the shopper will schedule the appointment. The mystery shopper is given an evaluation form that allows input on the quality of the service offered to the mystery shopper.

Show you know by creating at least 10 mystery shopper questions that could be placed on the evaluation form.

KNOWLEDGE GRID

Start at the top of the Knowledge Grid and work your way down, answering each question to check your understanding of Chapter 11, Hair Removal. The questions found here will help you deepen your understanding, build self-confidence and increase your awareness of different ways of thinking about a subject.

KNOW

List the six temporary hair removal techniques mentioned in this chapter.

COMPREHEND

Explain the life cycle of hair in your own words.

APPLY

Offer an example of a client that would not be a good candidate for a laser hair removal treatment.

ANALYZE

Classify the temporary methods of hair removal based on popularity in your area.

SYNTHESIZE

Suggest several ways to ensure client satisfaction following a waxing service.

EVALUATE

In your opinion, what considerations limit the number of waxing services a client should have within a 24-hour period?

Multiple choice. Circle the correct answer.

1. All of the following are examples of temporary hair removal procedures EXCEPT:
   a. shaving
   b. waxing
   c. tweezing
   d. electrolysis

2. During what phase of the life cycle does the hair actively grow?
   a. anagen phase
   b. catagen phase
   c. telogen phase
   d. agreement phase

3. During which phase of the life cycle of hair does the hair disconnect from the papilla?
   a. anagen phase
   b. catagen phase
   c. telogen phase
   d. delivery phase

4. During which phase of the life cycle of hair does the follicle rest?
   a. anagen phase
   b. catagen phase
   c. telogen phase
   d. completion phase

5. In which of the following types of temporary hair removal techniques does the hair usually grow back within 24 – 48 hours?
   a. waxing
   b. shaving
   c. tweezing
   d. chemical depilatory

6. Which of the following types of temporary hair removal techniques is a painless method?
   a. waxing
   b. sugaring
   c. tweezing
   d. chemical depilatory

7. Which of the following temporary hair removal techniques utilizes a 100 percent cotton thread that is twisted and rolled along the surface of the skin?
   a. waxing
   b. shaving
   c. threading
   d. sugaring

1	2	3	4	5	6	7

8. How long does the sugaring method of hair removal generally last?
   a. one to 2 weeks
   b. 2 to 4 weeks
   c. 4 to 6 weeks
   d. 6 to 8 weeks

9. A necessity for preventing irreparable damage while performing any type of electrolysis is:
   a. client relaxation
   b. proper training
   c. several years of experience
   d. the newest and most expensive equipment

10. Which method of electrolysis utilizes multiple-wire needles or probes?
    a. blend method
    b. Galvanic method
    c. laser hair removal
    d. thermolysis method

11. In which method of electrolysis does the client only feel a tiny "flash" of heat?
    a. blend method
    b. Galvanic method
    c. laser hair removal
    d. thermolysis method

12. Which method of electrolysis offers the best results to clients with excessive or resistant hair growth?
    a. blend method
    b. Galvanic method
    c. laser hair removal
    d. thermolysis method

13. Which method of permanent hair removal uses wavelengths of light to diminish or destroy hundreds of hair bulbs?
    a. electrolysis
    b. thermolysis
    c. photo-epilation
    d. laser hair removal

14. Which type of permanent hair removal uses an intense pulsed light to destroy hair bulbs with minimal scarring?
    a. electrolysis
    b. thermolysis
    c. photo-epilation
    d. laser hair removal

15. During a waxing service you should do all of the following EXCEPT:
    a. keep the client warm
    b. keep the client relaxed
    c. wear protective gloves
    d. apply fragrant oils to the client

16. The function of a hair growth retardant is:
    a. removes unwanted hair
    b. slows the growth of hair after waxing
    c. sanitizes skin prior to service
    d. calms the skin after waxing

17. Which phase of service consultation educates the esthetician about client skin condition, concerns and contraindications?
    a. Greeting
    b. Ask, Analyze, Assess
    c. Agreement
    d. Delivery

18. Which phase of service consultation educates the client in regards to skin needs, as well as products and services that can help?
    a. Greeting
    b. Ask, Analyze, Assess
    c. Agreement
    d. Delivery

19. Which phase of service consultation ensures client satisfaction and understanding?
    a. Ask, Analyze, Assess
    b. Agreement
    c. Delivery
    d. Completion

20. Which basic waxing procedure would include applying a soothing gel:
    a. washing and sanitizing hands
    b. assessing direction of hair growth
    c. cleaning and protecting skin
    d. removing wax and hair

ESSAY QUESTION:

A maximum of five additional points is possible by selecting one of the following essay questions to answer.

21a. Select three products used during the delivery of a professional waxing service and list their function.

Product   Function

21b. Name at least three health conditions that could cause a client to bruise, swell or experience excessive pain during a waxing service.

■   ■
■   ■
■   ■

21c. Compare soft and hard wax using the various benefits of each.

_____
_____
_____
_____
_____
_____
_____

Check your answers as you did before. Place a check mark next to the page number for any incorrect answer. On the lines to the right, jot down topics that you still need to review.

1. page 371
2. page 372
3. page 372
4. page 372
5. page 373
6. page 373
7. page 375
8. page 376
9. page 376
10. page 376
11. page 377
12. page 377
13. page 377
14. page 377
15. page 378
16. page 380
17. page 384
18. page 385
19. page 385
20. page 387

1 2 3 4 5 6 7

Experts agree that it is important to summarize your feelings and reactions about what you are learning. Note especially things that surprised you, things you found difficult to learn, suggestions and ideas you received from friends that helped make learning this chapter easier and more enjoyable.

VALUE

Makeup design offers you an opportunity to enhance your client's best features, minimize flaws and accent natural beauty while cross-promoting your services and earning commissions on retail sales

MAIN IDEA

This chapter will help you understand color theory, face shapes and features as they relate to makeup design and application. Techniques for evening, brides and mature clients as well as camouflage and corrective techniques will also be addressed.

Courtesy of *Design Forum*.

PLAN

Makeup Design	■ The Law of Color
	■ Facial Shapes and Features
	■ Makeup Products and Techniques
	■ Makeup Essentials
	■ Infection Control and Safety
	■ Client Consultation
Makeup Services	■ Preparing the Skin
	■ Basic Makeup Procedure
	■ Specialty Makeup

OBJECTIVES

■ Describe the law of color as it applies to makeup.

■ Identify the seven face shapes and the corrective steps to create the illusion of the classic oval shape.

■ Explain the guidelines for makeup design including products, techniques and considerations.

■ Identify and demonstrate the appropriate use of the essentials of makeup, infection control and safety guidelines and the client consultation.

■ Demonstrate the ability to perform basic makeup procedures and recognize the considerations for specialty makeup.

1 Describe the law of color as it applies to makeup

■ The Law of Color

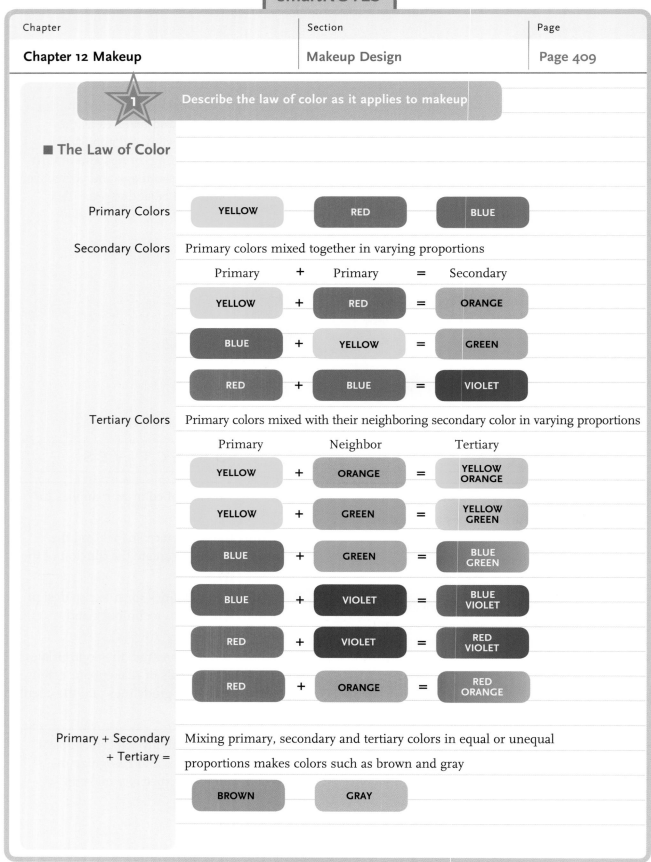

Primary Colors

| YELLOW | RED | BLUE |

Secondary Colors — Primary colors mixed together in varying proportions

Primary	+	Primary	=	Secondary
YELLOW	+	RED	=	ORANGE
BLUE	+	YELLOW	=	GREEN
RED	+	BLUE	=	VIOLET

Tertiary Colors — Primary colors mixed with their neighboring secondary color in varying proportions

Primary		Neighbor		Tertiary
YELLOW	+	ORANGE	=	YELLOW ORANGE
YELLOW	+	GREEN	=	YELLOW GREEN
BLUE	+	GREEN	=	BLUE GREEN
BLUE	+	VIOLET	=	BLUE VIOLET
RED	+	VIOLET	=	RED VIOLET
RED	+	ORANGE	=	RED ORANGE

Primary + Secondary + Tertiary = — Mixing primary, secondary and tertiary colors in equal or unequal proportions makes colors such as brown and gray

| BROWN | GRAY |

Chapter	Section	Page
Chapter 12 Makeup	**Makeup Design**	**Pages 409-410**

The Color Wheel

Complementary Color Schemes
■

■

Color Vocabulary
Hue

Tint

Shade

Value

Intensity

Tone

Warm and Cool
■

■

■

■

■

■

Monochromatic   **Color schemes that use**

Analogous   **Color schemes that use**

Triadic   **Color schemes that use**

★ 2   Identify the seven face shapes and the corrective steps to create the illusion of the classic oval shape

■ **Facial Shapes and Features**

—   —   —

—   —   —

Contour

Cosmetic Products

Chiaroscuro

Face Shapes

Esthetic
Considerations

Notes:

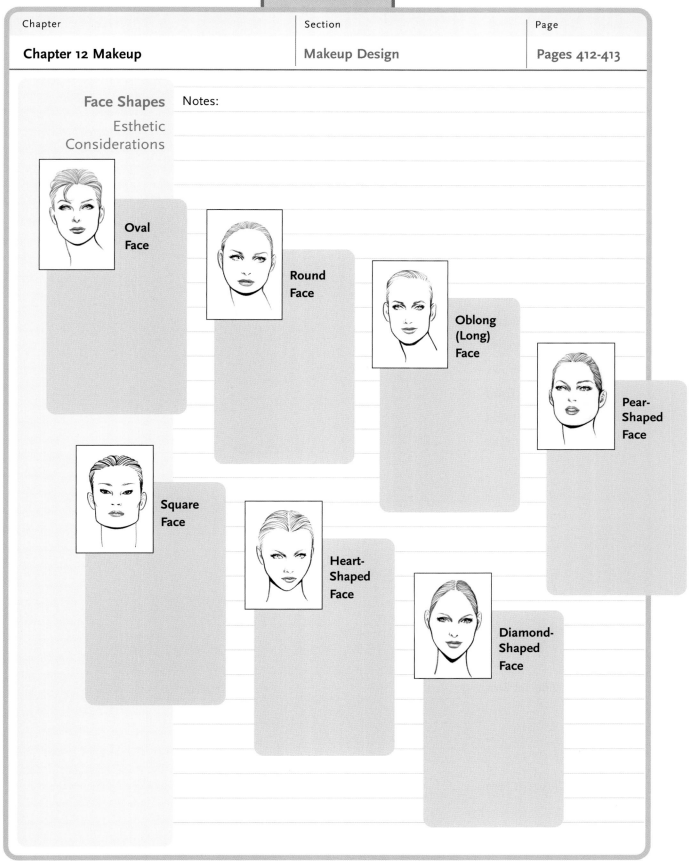

Oval
Face

Round
Face

Oblong
(Long)
Face

Pear-
Shaped
Face

Square
Face

Heart-
Shaped
Face

Diamond-
Shaped
Face

Chapter	Section	Page
Chapter 12 Makeup	**Makeup Design**	**Pages 414-415**

Eyebrow Design ■

■

Esthetic Considerations

No Eyebrows

Thin, Sculpted Arches

Classic Arches

Horizontal Arches

Thin, High Eyebrows

Full Arches

Missing Arches

Natural Brows

Eyes

Esthetic Considerations

Deep-Set Eyes

Drooping Eyes

Almond Eyes

Wide-Set Eyes

Close-Set Eyes

Chapter	Section	Page
Chapter 12 Makeup	Makeup Design	Pages 416-417

Small Eyes

Bulging Eyes

Asian Eyes

Hooded Eyes

Lips

Esthetic Considerations

Full Top Lips

Uneven Lips

Downturned Lips

Small Lips

Thin Lips

Full Lips

Full Bottom Lips

3 Explain the guidelines for makeup design including products, techniques and considerations

■ **Makeup Products and Techniques**

Appropriate lighting is an important aspect of professional makeup

Combine Fluorescent and Incandescent Lighting

Principles of Light and Dark

Brushes

Makeup Guidelines

Position of Client

Artificial Eyelash Considerations
➤
➤

Measuring Eyelashes for Eye Length
➤

➤

Blush Considerations
➤

➤

Types of Blush
➤
➤
➤

Selecting a Blush
➤
➤
➤
➤

Lip Color Considerations
➤
➤

Lip Liner

Chapter	Section	Page
Chapter 12 Makeup	**Makeup Design**	**Page 431**

Lip Color ➤

➤

➤

Types of
Lip Color ➤

➤

➤

➤

LEARNING   CONNECTION — Lips: Front and Side Views

The guidelines found on page 431 of your textbook outline the ideal mouth and lips. In the space provided below, draw a frontal view and a side view of the lip to represent these guidelines.

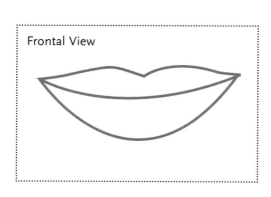

Frontal View

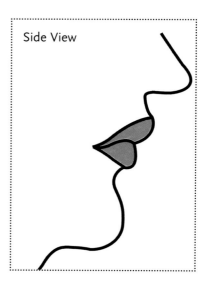

Side View

Makeup Considerations
Makeup for Teenagers

➤

➤

Makeup for Men

➤

➤

➤

➤

4 Identify and demonstrate the appropriate use of the essentials of makeup, infection control and safety guidelines and the client consultation

■ **Makeup Essentials**

➤

➤

➤

Makeup Products

➤

➤

➤

➤

➤

➤

➤

➤

➤

➤

➤

➤

Chapter	Section	Page
Chapter 12 Makeup	**Makeup Design**	**Pages 438-440**

Makeup Products
continued

➤

➤

➤

➤

■ Infection Control and Safety Guidelines

■ Client Consultation

5 Phases of Service

1.   2.   3.

4.   5.

Think of people you have seen wearing makeup and then later not wearing makeup. What are the differences you notice when makeup is not worn?

LEARNING CONNECTION — Know Your Brushes

Being able to reach for the right brush will be important as you offer makeup services in the future. Identify the brush pictured below by placing the name of the brush on the line to the right of the corresponding letter shown above the brush.

A. _____   H. _____

B. _____   I. _____

C. _____   J. _____

D. _____   K. _____

E. _____   L. _____

F. _____   M. _____

G. _____   N. _____

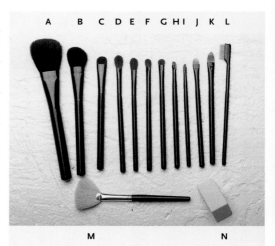

| 1 | 2 | 3 | 4 | 5 | 6 | 7 |

Chapter	Section	Page
Chapter 12 Makeup	Makeup Services	**Pages 441-453**

5 Demonstrate the ability to perform basic makeup procedures and recognize the considerations for specialty makeup

Preparing the Skin

Basic Makeup Procedures

Makeup Considerations for Darker Skin

Makeup Considerations for Asian Skin

Makeup Considerations for Mature Skin
- ■
- ■
- ■
- ■
- ■

Makeup Considerations for Bridal Makeup
- ■
- ■
- ■
- ■

■ Specialty Makeup

Camouflage Makeup Considerations
- ■
- ■
- ■ Camouflage experts work with the following types of client needs:

-	-
-	-
-	-
-	-

- ■

Chapter	Section	Page
Chapter 12 Makeup	**Makeup Design**	**Pages 457-461**

Product Knowledge

Recommended to have 3 types of products on hand

1.

2.

3.

Cystic acne –

Port wine stain –

Additional Training Required

Corrective Makeup Considerations

Eyelash/Eyebrow Tinting

Product Knowledge

Airbrushing

Permanent Makeup

Makeup trends and colors quite often change with the fashion seasons. How can you stay abreast of current makeup trends and colors?

1 2 3 4 5 6 7

Match the term from Column A with the corresponding description in Column B by placing the letter of the term in the box provided in front of the description.

Column A		Column B
A. Secondary colors		Three pure colors
B. Tint		Represented as a wider forehead with a narrow jaw and chinline
C. Monochromatic color schemes		Refers to the vibrancy of a color
D. Primary colors		To create an outline, especially of a curving or irregular figure or shape
E. Value		Orange, green and violet
F. Triadic color schemes		Represented as predominant width through the cheekbones that is contrasted by a narrow forehead, chin and jaw area
G. Tertiary colors		Refers to the warmth or coolness of a color
H. Chiaroscuro		Use three colors that are adjacent to each other on the color wheel
I. Intensity		A hue with black added
J. Contour		A hue with white added
K. Tone		Use the same color with variations in value and intensity throughout the entire makeup design
L. Diamond-shaped face		Result of mixing primary colors with their neighboring secondary color in varying proportions
M. Analog color schemes		Use three colors located in a triangular position on the color wheel
N. Heart-shaped face		The lightness or darkness of a color
O. Shade		The art of arranging light and dark so as to produce three dimensional shapes

Basic Daytime Makeup Procedure

This rubric is designed to compare your skill to industry expectations. Indicate your present level of performance by checking the appropriate box. Your teacher will direct you in the completion of this rubric.

Rubric Assessment

The basic daytime makeup procedure is a service designed to enhance the visual appearance of your client. By following and practicing the steps in this rubric, you will be prepared to offer a basic daytime makeup procedure for your clients. Note that the numbers for each step correspond with the step-by-step technical images found in the textbook.

	Level 1	Level 2	Level 3	To Improve, I Need To:	Teacher Assessment
PREPARATION					
■ Set up makeup station and arrange products, implements, supplies and equipment in a neat, organized manner; sanitize service area; check lighting	☐	☐	☐		☐
PROCEDURE					
1. Wash and sanitize hands (wear protective gloves if required)	☐	☐	☐		☐
2. Drape client	☐	☐	☐		☐
PREPARE SKIN					
3. Apply lightweight cleanser	☐	☐	☐		☐
4. Apply toner	☐	☐	☐		☐
5. Apply moisturizer	☐	☐	☐		☐
6. Apply eye crème	☐	☐	☐		☐
7. Assess face shape and skin tone	☐	☐	☐		☐
GROOM EYEBROWS					
8. Determine natural growth direction	☐	☐	☐		☐
9. Tweeze stray hairs	☐	☐	☐		☐
FOUNDATION and CONCEALER					
10. Select appropriate foundation color	☐	☐	☐		☐
11. Apply and blend foundation	☐	☐	☐		☐
12. Apply concealer as needed	☐	☐	☐		☐
POWDER					
13. Apply loose powder	☐	☐	☐		☐
14. Blend away excess powder	☐	☐	☐		☐
EYEBROW COLOR					
15. Select and apply eyebrow color	☐	☐	☐		☐
16. Blend eyebrow color	☐	☐	☐		☐

Rubric Assessment Continued

	Level 1	Level 2	Level 3	To Improve, I Need To:	Teacher Assessment
EYE SHADOW					
17. Apply highlighter	☐	☐	☐		☐
18. Apply contour color	☐	☐	☐		☐
EYELINER and MASCARA					
19. Curl eyelashes	☐	☐	☐		☐
20. Apply eyeliner	☐	☐	☐		☐
21. Blend eyeliner	☐	☐	☐		☐
22. Apply mascara	☐	☐	☐		☐
LIP COLOR					
23. Apply lip liner	☐	☐	☐		☐
24. Fill lips with lip liner	☐	☐	☐		☐
25. Apply and blend lip color	☐	☐	☐		☐
BLUSH					
26. Apply blush	☐	☐	☐		☐
27. Blend powder over edges of blush	☐	☐	☐		☐

COMPLETION

■ Lead client to front counter; offer to rebook client's next visit; recommend retail; throw away non-reusable materials; replace used linens; disinfect implements and facial bed; arrange items for next service; wash hands with liquid antibacterial soap; place unused cotton pads and sponges in covered container ☐ ☐ ☐ ☐

Total = Addition of all Teacher Assessment Boxes ☐

Percentage = Student Score Divided by 87 (Highest Possible Score) **Percentage** _____ %

Basic Evening Makeup Procedure

This rubric is designed to compare your skill to industry expectations. Indicate your present level of performance by checking the appropriate box. Your teacher will direct you in the completion of this rubric.

Rubric Assessment

The basic evening makeup procedure is service designed to enhance the visual appearance of your client. By following and practicing the steps in this rubric, you will be prepared to offer a basic evening makeup procedure for your clients. Note that the numbers for each step correspond with the step-by-step technical images found in the textbook.

	Level 1	Level 2	Level 3	To Improve, I Need To:	Teacher Assessment
PREPARATION					
■ Set up makeup station and arrange products, implements, supplies and equipment in a neat, organized manner; sanitize service area; check lighting	☐	☐	☐		☐
PROCEDURE					
1. Wash and sanitize hands (wear protective gloves if required)	☐	☐	☐		☐
2. Drape client	☐	☐	☐		☐
PREPARE SKIN					
3. Apply lightweight cleanser	☐	☐	☐		☐
4. Apply toner	☐	☐	☐		☐
5. Apply moisturizer	☐	☐	☐		☐
6. Apply eye crème	☐	☐	☐		☐
7. Assess face shape and skin tone	☐	☐	☐		☐
GROOM EYEBROWS					
8. Determine natural growth direction	☐	☐	☐		☐
9. Tweeze stray hairs	☐	☐	☐		☐
FOUNDATION and CONCEALER					
10. Select appropriate foundation color	☐	☐	☐		☐
11. Apply and blend foundation	☐	☐	☐		☐
12. Apply concealer as needed	☐	☐	☐		☐
POWDER					
13. Apply loose powder	☐	☐	☐		☐
14. Blend away excess powder	☐	☐	☐		☐
EYEBROW COLOR					
15. Select and apply eyebrow color	☐	☐	☐		☐
16. Blend eyebrow color	☐	☐	☐		☐

Rubric Assessment Continued

	Level 1	Level 2	Level 3	To Improve, I Need To:	Teacher Assessment
EYE SHADOW					
17. Apply highlighter using a bright, slightly luminized eye shadow	☐	☐	☐		☐
18. Apply contour color; use darker crease color across contour of the eye socket	☐	☐	☐		☐
EYELINER and MASCARA					
19. Curl eyelashes	☐	☐	☐		☐
20. Apply black pencil eyeliner	☐	☐	☐		☐
21. Blend eyeliner; add black liquid eyeliner to increase intensity	☐	☐	☐		☐
22. Apply mascara; consider applying artificial strip or individual lashes	☐	☐	☐		☐
LIP COLOR					
23. Apply lip liner using a deeper shade than daytime makeup	☐	☐	☐		☐
24. Fill lips with lip liner	☐	☐	☐		☐
25. Apply and blend lip color; use a high shine, metallic gloss	☐	☐	☐		☐
BLUSH					
26. Apply blush; blend a highlighter crème to the cheekbone	☐	☐	☐		☐
27. Blend powder over edges of blush	☐	☐	☐		☐
COMPLETION					
■ Lead client to front counter; offer to rebook client's next visit; recommend retail; throw away non-reusable materials; replace used linens; disinfect implements and facial bed; arrange items for next service; wash hands with liquid antibacterial soap; place unused cotton pads and sponges in covered container	☐	☐	☐		☐

Total = Addition of all Teacher Assessment Boxes ☐

Percentage = Student Score Divided by 87 (Highest Possible Score)   **Percentage** _____ %

TALKING POINTS

Your next challenge is to be ready to talk about some of the important ideas in this chapter. Follow the directions listed next to each box and practice talking about your ideas.

1. Enhancing the Pear-Shaped Face

BEFORE

AFTER

In the 'before' box to the left, a pear-shaped face has been placed. Using colored pencils, apply your skill in the box marked 'after' to show how you would enhance the pear-shaped face when doing a daytime makeup application.

Discuss your final sketch with a partner or other classmates.

2. Enhancing the Square-Shaped Face

BEFORE

AFTER

In the 'before' box to the left a square-shaped face has been placed. Using colored pencils, apply your skill in the box marked 'after' to show how you would enhance the square-shaped face when doing a daytime makeup application.

Discuss your final sketch with a partner or other classmates.

3. Enhancing Your Own Makeup

On the lines provided to the left, jot down some notes that describe what you feel you could do differently to update or freshen your makeup application.

Discuss your conclusions with a partner.

Now it's time to see how well you know your new material. First answer these questions. Then use the Memory Box that follows to check yourself. Look up each answer on the corresponding page in the *Salon Fundamentals™ Esthetics* textbook. Check "got it" for all correct answers and "not yet" for all incorrect responses. Using the "Know Chart," record all of your correct responses in the "I Know" column. After correcting incorrect answers, record all of your corrected responses in the "I Need to Study" column. That way you know exactly what to review before continuing in this Guide.

Directions: Identify whether questions 1 and 2 are True or False by circling TRUE or FALSE. You can earn an extra point for each false statement you appropriately correct. Question 3 requires you to write in an answer in the blank provided. Answers to the questions found in 4 through 10 may be selected by circling a, b, c or d below each statement to indicate your choice.

1. TRUE   FALSE   The law of color states that, out of all the colors in the universe, only five are pure.

_____

2. TRUE   FALSE   The three secondary colors are orange, green and violet.

_____

3. _____ colors contain red or yellow undertones while_____ colors contain blue undertones.

4. Which of the following statements describes the term shade?
   a. another term for color
   b. hue with black added
   c. a hue with white added
   d. the vibrancy of a color

5. Monochromatic color schemes use:
   a. three colors located in a triangular position on the color wheel
   b. three colors that are adjacent to each other on the color wheel
   c. three colors that are across from each other on the color wheel
   d. the same color with variations in value and intensity throughout

6. Tone refers to the:
   a. hue of a color
   b. warmth or coolness of a color
   c. amount of black and white in a color
   d. amount of lightness or darkness of a color

7. Which of the following facial shapes has been considered the ideal or classical shape
   a. oval
   b. heart
   c. square
   d. diamond

8. Which of the following techniques would be used to create a longer look on a round face?
   a. blend highlighting down from the cheekbone
   b. blend contouring down from the cheekbone
   c. highlight the lower portion of the face to diminish fullness
   d. highlight the lower portion of the face to emphasize fullness

9. All of the following are characteristics of the diamond-shaped face EXCEPT:
   a. narrow forehead
   b. broad, square jawline
   c. narrow chin and jaw area
   d. predominant width through the cheekbones

10. Which of the following is NOT a characteristic of the pear-shaped face?
    a. wide jawline
    b. narrow forehead
    c. the width is 3/4 its length
    d. forehead is smaller than the jaw area

1. page 409	☐ got it ☐ not yet	
2. page 409	☐ got it ☐ not yet	
3. page 410	☐ got it ☐ not yet	
4. page 410	☐ got it ☐ not yet	
5. page 410	☐ got it ☐ not yet	
6. page 410	☐ got it ☐ not yet	
7. page 411	☐ got it ☐ not yet	
8. page 412	☐ got it ☐ not yet	
9. page 413	☐ got it ☐ not yet	
10. page 413	☐ got it ☐ not yet	

I know...

I need to study...

SHOW YOU KNOW...

It is important to identify both the facial shape and the undertone color of the skin in order to determine the appropriate techniques and/or colors or shades to use during a daytime makeup application. In the chart below, the facial shape and undertone have been identified. Write in the primary technique you would use during a makeup application for this client, along with the description of the shade or color you would apply.

Facial Shape	Undertone	Primary Technique	Appropriate Color
Diamond	Blue/violet		
Heart	Red		
Square	Brown/gray		

1	2	3	4	5	6	7

KNOWLEDGE GRID

Start at the top of the Knowledge Grid and work your way down, answering each question to check your understanding of Chapter 12, Makeup. The questions found here will help you deepen your understanding, build self-confidence and increase your awareness of different ways of thinking about a subject.

KNOW
Define the triadic color scheme.

COMPREHEND
Explain why it is important for you to have an understanding of secondary and tertiary colors.

APPLY
Demonstrate your knowledge of the color wheel by identifying the primary, secondary and tertiary colors. You can place the color name on the corresponding numbered lines to the left of the color wheel. Number 1 has been completed as an example.

1. _____
2. _____
3. _____
4. _____

5. _____
6. _____
7. _____
8. _____

9. _____
10. _____
11. _____
12. _____

ANALYZE
Compare the characteristics of a heart-shaped face with that of a diamond-shaped face.

SYNTHESIZE
Create an advertising slogan or promotional statement for a makeup trend that features a bright red lip color.

EVALUATE
Defend the importance of infection control regulations when performing permanent makeup techniques.

Multiple choice. Circle the correct answer.

1. The law of color states that, out of all the colors in the universe, only:
    a. one color is pure
    b. two colors are pure
    c. three colors are pure
    d. secondary colors are pure

2. Which of the following is NOT a primary color?
    a. red
    b. blue
    c. yellow
    d. green

3. Orange, green and violet are called:
    a. pure colors
    b. primary colors
    c. tertiary colors
    d. secondary colors

4. All of the following are true about primary colors EXCEPT:
    a. they are also called pure colors
    b. they cannot be created by combining other colors
    c. when mixed together in varying proportions, they produce three tertiary colors
    d. when mixed together in varying proportions, primary colors create all other colors

5. Mixing a primary color with a neighboring secondary color in varying proportions will produce a:
    a. pure color
    b. tertiary color
    c. secondary color
    d. monochromatic color

6. What color scheme is used most often to enhance eye color?
    a. triadic
    b. analog
    c. monochromatic
    d. complementary

7. The lightness or darkness of a color is called:
    a. hue
    b. tint
    c. value
    d. shade

| 1 | 2 | 3 | 4 | 5 | 6 | 7 |

8. What do the terms warm and cool describe about a color?
   a. hue
   b. tint
   c. tone
   d. shade

9. All of the following are true about warm colors EXCEPT they:
   a. contain blue undertones
   b. contain red or yellow undertones
   c. are used to describe the tones of colors
   d. are generally categorized in the orange and red half of the color wheel

10. Tones that are a combination of warm and light are considered:
    a. cool colors
    b. warm colors
    c. neutral colors
    d. complementary colors

11. All of the following statements are true about contouring EXCEPT:
    a. it can appear to reshape the face
    b. it can add illusion of increased dimension to the face
    c. dark colors appear to diminish the appearance of features
    d. lighter colors make features or areas appear smaller

12. In order to add dimension to an oblong face, a hint of contour should be added directly:
    a. below the cheekbone
    b. above the jawline and eye area
    c. above the cheekbone and blended down the face
    d. below the forehead and blending toward the eye area

13. What facial shape has a narrow forehead and a wide jawline?
    a. oval
    b. oblong
    c. pear-shaped
    d. heart-shaped

14. Which of the following is NOT a characteristic of the square face shape?
    a. broad, square jawline
    b. most symmetric and balanced
    c. broad, straight forehead and hairline
    d. very angular and somewhat masculine

15. A heart-shaped face is characterized by:
    a. a rounded hairline and chin-line
    b. a narrow forehead and a wide jawline
    c. a wider forehead with a narrow jaw and chinline
    d. predominant width through the cheekbones contrasted by a narrow forehead, chin, and jaw area

16. Which facial shape requires contouring to reduce the high points of the forehead and the extended portion of the chin to create balance?
    a. round
    b. square
    c. oblong
    d. diamond

17. What is the result created by thin, sculpted arches when doing eyebrow design?
    a. expressionless face
    b. over-dramatized look
    c. balance and symmetry
    d. narrow forehead and surprised look

18. Which of the following eyebrow designs provides balance and symmetry?
    a. full arches
    b. missing arches
    c. classic arches
    d. horizontal arches

19. Defining the natural shape with a smudgy eyeliner application over the entire upper and lower lids enhances the:
    a. almond eyes
    b. wide-set eyes
    c. drooping eyes
    d. close-set eyes

20. Full top lips can be corrected by drawing a line:
    a. just past the outer edge of the natural lipline
    b. extending just above the natural fall of the lips
    c. slightly inside the natural shape of the upper lip
    d. slightly outside the natural shape of the upper and lower lip

21. Drawing a line beyond the natural fullness of the lip creates a fuller appearance for:
    a. thin lips
    b. uneven lips
    c. full bottom lips
    d. downturned lips

22. Which of the following is NOT a benefit of using a brush?
    a. blending colors
    b. softening or smudging hard edges
    c. providing better directional control
    d. making hard edges evident on face or neck

23. When applying makeup design, the facial chair should not recline more than:
    a. 15°
    b. 25°
    c. 35°
    d. 45°

24. The most common form of foundation generally preferred because of its sheer, natural coverage and easy application and blending is called:
    a. crème
    b. liquid
    c. powder
    d. pancake

25. Which type of foundation is suitable for most skin types?
    a. liquid
    b. powder
    c. pancake
    d. greasepaint

26. Unless correction is required, the general guideline is to match the foundation to the:
    a. clothing
    b. eye color
    c. skin tone
    d. hair color

27. The skin on the neck is generally lighter than the skin on the face, so the best foundation choice:
    a. matches the skin on the neck
    b. matches the skin on the face
    c. is a balance between these two areas
    d. appears darker than the skin on both the face and neck

28. A golden skin tone has:
    a. yellow cast
    b. yellowish-green color
    c. carmel-colored light to dark brown
    d. light yellow to slightly peach undertone

29. Which of the following is considered a warm undertone?
    a. red
    b. light peach
    c. light brown
    d. yellowish-green

30. A translucent powder may be combined with any foundation shade since it is designed to allow the skin and foundation shade to show through without adding any:
    a. color
    b. powder
    c. concealer
    d. foundation

31. Which of the following is NOT one of the six basic eyebrow shapes?
    a. bowed
    b. tipped
    c. angled
    d. squared

32. Before applying mascara, curl top lashes with an eyelash curler to create the illusion that the eyes are opened and:
    a. lifted up
    b. pulled left
    c. pulled right
    d. pulled down

33. At least how many brushes should you have on hand when applying eye and cheek color?
    a. one
    b. two
    c. three
    d. four

34. The lip color should not overpower the amount of color applied to the:
    a. nose and eyes
    b. eyelids and eyes
    c. cheeks and eyes
    d. eyebrows and eyes

35. Which of the following products purifies and balances the pH level of the skin?
    a. toner
    b. exfoliator
    c. eye crème
    d. moisturizer

36. Which of the following products replenishes moisture or oil to the skin?
    a. exfoliator
    b. concealer
    c. eye crème
    d. moisturizer

37. Which of the following products removes excess surface skin cells?
    a. blush
    b. concealer
    c. exfoliator
    d. foundation

38. Which of the following makeup implements and/or supplies is used for cleaning up and correcting errors?
    a. cotton
    b. headband
    c. cotton swabs
    d. hand sanitizer

39. Which of the following makeup implements and/or supplies cleanses, sanitizes and maintains makeup brushes?
    a. eyelash curler
    b. brush cleaner
    c. mascara wand
    d. lash separator or comb

40. The makeup implement used to curl and enhance the lashes is a(n):
    a. eyelash curler
    b. mascara wand
    c. makeup brush
    d. lash separator

Write Your Own Ticket! For numbers 41, 42 and 43, write your own questions and answer them. Your questions can be true/false, multiple choice or fill-in-the-blank. The only parameter is that your questions cannot already be found on this test. Earn one point each for writing your way to success.

41. Q: _____ A: _____

42. Q: _____ A: _____

43. Q: _____ A: _____

BONUS QUESTION!

Question 44 is the ultimate question. To earn two points, design a question for your class. If you stump the class, and no one can answer the question within an agreed upon time (between you and the teacher), you earn a BONUS OF FIVE ADDITIONAL POINTS.

44. Q: _____

45. A maximum of five additional points is possible by selecting one of the following essay questions to answer.

46. List the 3 primary colors, 3 secondary colors and 6 tertiary colors found on the color wheel.

Primary Colors	Secondary Colors	Tertiary Colors	
■	■	■	■
■	■	■	■
■	■	■	■

47. List the seven facial shapes and draw a shape to represent each one.

ESSAY QUESTION

48. In the space below identify at least two considerations for mature skin and two considerations for Asian skin.

Mature skin considerations

Asian skin considerations

Check your answers as you did before. Place a check mark next to the page number for any incorrect answer. On the lines to the right, jot down topics that you still need to review.

1.	page 409	21.	page 417
2.	page 409	22.	page 418
3.	page 409	23.	page 418
4.	page 409	24.	page 419
5.	page 409	25.	page 419
6.	page 410	26.	page 420
7.	page 410	27.	page 420
8.	page 410	28.	page 421
9.	page 410	29.	page 421
10.	page 410	30.	page 423
11.	page 411	31.	page 424
12.	page 412	32.	page 427
13.	page 413	33.	page 430
14.	page 413	34.	page 431
15.	page 413	35.	page 435
16.	page 413	36.	page 435
17.	page 414	37.	page 435
18.	page 414	38.	page 437
19.	page 415	39.	page 437
20.	page 417	40.	page 437

NOTES TO MYSELF —— *My Reflections About Makeup*

Experts agree that it is important to summarize your feelings and reactions about what you are learning. Note especially things that surprised you, things you found difficult to learn and suggestions and ideas you received from friends that helped make learning this chapter easier and more enjoyable.

VALUE

Not every esthetician knows how to provide advanced treatments. These treatments are in demand, and estheticians who learn how to provide them can offer a broader spectrum of services to their clients, generate more revenue and experience greater success.

MAIN IDEA

Performing advanced face and body services takes skill. Some advanced treatments can be incorporated into basic services, but many others require a specialized knowledge of anatomy and physiology and a thorough understanding of the products and ingredients used to perform the treatment. This chapter serves as an introduction to these advanced face and body treatments and techniques.

PLAN

Advanced Face and Body Treatments	■ Hand or Foot Treatments ■ Body Scrubs ■ Body Wraps ■ Cellulite Wraps ■ Water Therapy Treatments ■ Superficial Chemical Peels ■ Microdermabrasion
Advanced Massage Techniques	■ Reflexology Treatments ■ Manual Lymphatic Drainage Massage ■ Cellulite Massage Treatments
Advanced Therapies	■ Phytotherapy ■ Aromatherapy ■ Algotherapy

OBJECTIVES

■ Differentiate among the various face and body treatments used in the skin care center and their specific contraindications

■ Explain the difference between the various advanced massage techniques and their specific contraindications

■ Describe the function and types of advanced therapies that are available in the esthetics setting

smartNOTES

Chapter	Section	Page
Chapter 13 Advanced Treatments	**Advanced Face and Body Treatments**	**Pages 465-469**

★1 Differentiate among the various face and body treatments used skin care center and their specific contraindications

Prior to Any Treatment

■ **Contraindications for Advanced Treatments**
- ■   ■
- ■   ■
- ■   ■
- ■   ■
- ■

Room Preparation   **When setting up the service space, consider these steps:**

1.

2.

3.

4.

5.

Hand or Foot Treatments

Contraindication for Hand or Foot Treatments
- ■   ■ Arthritis

Body Scrubs

Gomage, Manual Exfoliants and Hand-Held Exfoliators

Gomage
- ■

Manual exfoliants
- ■
- ■

Hand-held exfoliators
- ■
- ■

Contraindications for Body Scrubs
- ■
- ■
- ■

Chapter	Section	Page
Chapter 13 Advanced Treatments	Advanced Face and Body Treatments	Pages 469-476

■ Body Wraps

Absorption and Compaction

Absorption	Compaction
■	■
■	■
■	■

Do not make specific weight or inch loss claims for body wraps

Contraindications for Body Wraps

■

■

■

■

■ Cellulite Wraps

Cellulite

Cellulite Treatments

> **Cellulite treatments**
>
> *Inch loss from treatments is not permanent*

Contraindications for Cellulite Wraps

■

■

■

■

■

Chapter	Section	Page
Chapter 13 Advanced Treatments	Advanced Face and Body Treatments	Pages 476-482

■ **Water Therapy Treatments**

Hydrotherapy Tub Treatments

> Hydrotherapy tub treatments

Affusion Therapy

> Affusion therapy

Saunas and Steam Baths

> **Saunas and steam baths**
> ■
> ■

Contraindications for Water Therapy

■   ■

■ **Superficial Chemical Peels**

Contraindications for Chemical Peels

■   ■

■   ■

■   ■

■ **Microdermabrasion**

Chapter	Section	Page
Chapter 13 Advanced Treatments	Advanced Face and Body Treatments	**Page 485**

Contraindications for Microdermabrasion

- ▪
- ▪
- ▪
- ▪
- ▪

List two ways in which body wraps create temporary tightness and explain each one.

_____

_____

_____

_____

_____

LEARNING **CONNECTION** — The Wrap Up

Using the clues below, name the type of face or body treatment being described and place it in the blank next to the correct clue.

Clue	Face or Body Treatment
1. Means "to peel"	
2. Performed on the roughest and thickest skin	
3. Create temporary tightness	
4. Contain coarse (grainy) ingredients	
5. Reduce appearance of cellulite	
6. Also referred to as balneotherapy	
7. Used for fine wrinkling and areas of dryness	
8. Used to apply cleanser to dry skin	
9. Lightly resurfaces the epidermis	
10. Use warm steam to induce relaxation	

1	2	3	4	5	6	7

Chapter	Section	Page
Chapter 13 Advanced Treatments	Advanced Massage Techniques	Pages 486-490

> ⭐ **2** Explain the difference between the various advanced massage techniques and their specific contraindications

■ **Reflexology Treatment**

Reflexologists

Contraindications for Reflexology Treatment
- ■
- ■
- ■
- ■

■ **Manual Lymphatic Drainage Massage**

Lymph

Contraindications for Manual Lymphatic Drainage Massage
- ■   ■
- ■   ■
- ■   ■

> Acupressure is another massage technique which involves applying pressure to specific points on the body.

■ **Cellulite Massage Treatments**

Contraindications for Cellulite Massage Treatments
- ■
- ■
- ■

What are some factors that cause toxins to build up in your body?

Fill in the blanks to complete the descriptions of the three advanced massage techniques.

1. Reflexology technique uses _____ on specific points of the feet, hands and sometimes the ears to _____ certain body conditions. According to _____, distinct regions of the feet, hands and ears correspond with the body's _____.

2. Manual lymphatic drainage massage works to reduce this bloat, or puffiness. MLD helps ciculate _____, helping the body rid itself of toxins, waste and excess water. This drainage promotes healthy functioning and _____ of the body.

3. Cellulite massage treatments are very popular since they may reduce the appearance of _____. Cellulite massage treatments may also reduce the appearance of cellulite by increasing _____. The increase in circulation helps remove excess _____ _____ as well as firming the muscle tissue so that the skin lies flatter against the muscles.

smartNOTES

Chapter	Section	Page
Chapter 13 Advanced Treatments	Advanced Therapies	Pages 493-496

3 ★ Describe the function and types of advanced therapies that are available in the esthetics settings

■ **Phytotherapy**

Phytocosmetics

History of Phytotherapy

How Phytotherapy Works

How Plant Ingredients are Obtained

Tinctures

Ointment

1 2 3 4 5 6 7

Phytotherapy Uses Within the Skin Care Center

Infusions
■

Decoctions
■

Fomentation
■

Poultice
■

■ Aromatherapy

Carrier Oil

History of Aromatherapy

Ayurveda

About Fragrance

Fixatives

Floral	Fruit blend	Forest or wood blend	Oriental	Modern blend	Floral bouquet	Spice blend

Chapter	Section	Page
Chapter 13 Advanced Treatments	Advanced Therapies	Pages 499-506

How Aromatherapy Works

Antiseptic oils help _____ bacteria and heal skin eruptions

Astringent oils temporarily _____ tissue and _____ secretions

Anti-inflammatory oils _____ inflammation and _____ swollen muscles

Analgesic oils help _____ surface pain

Antioxidant oils help _____ skin-ravaging free radicals

Healing oils promote cells to _____ so the skin can repair itself

Moisturizing oils soften _____ or _____ skin

Soothing oils help reduce _____

Stimulating oils _____ circulation to skin

How Essential Oils are Obtained

Steam Distillation _____

Expression _____

Extraction _____

Enfleurage _____

Maceration _____

Aromatherapy Uses

Chapter	Section	Page
Chapter 13 Advanced Treatments	Advanced Therapies	Pages 502-505

Common Aromatherapy Essential Oils

Tea tree has _____ and _____ benefits

Sandalwood has _____ and _____ properties

Rose is known for its _____ and _____ benefits

Neroli can be used to treat _____ and _____ skin

Lavender has many different properties, _____ , _____ , soothing, _____ and healing

Eucalyptus is beneficial in body treatments aimed at _____ stiff, sore muscles or _____ circulation

Chamomile can be used for _____ skin condition or in any treatment

Ylang-ylang can be incorporated into body therapies aimed at enhancing _____

■ Algotherapy

History of Algotherapy

How Algotherapy Works

Phytohormones

How Algae is Obtained

Algotherapy Uses

Describe the major differences between aromatherapy and algotherapy.

1	2	3	4	5	6	7

Separate each scent into one of the seven categories for fragrances based on its type.

- Vanilla

- Sandalwood

- Citrus

- Chocolate

- Almond

- Pear

- Musk

- Wildflower Blend

- Jasmine

- Ginger

- Eucalyptus

- Rose

Category	Scent
1. FLORAL	
2. FLORAL BOUQUET	
3. ORIENTAL	
4. FRUIT BLEND	
5. SPICE BLEND	
6. FOREST OR WOOD BLEND	
7. MODERN BLEND	

1	2	3	4	5	6	7

Match the term from Column A with the corresponding description in Column B by placing the letter of the term in the box provided in front of the description.

Column A		Column B
A. Emollient		Relieves pain either by relaxing muscles or reducing pain signals to the brain
B. Analgesic		Increases blood flow at the surface of the skin
C. Stimulant		Prevents bacterial growth on skin with external application
D. Antioxidant		The medicinal use of plants
E. Soother		Helps the body fight off harmful bacteria
F. Aromatherapy		Provides a constricting, drying effect; helps contract tissue and reduce secretions
G. Astringent		Softens, soothes, and protects skin; synonym for moisturizer
H. Ointment		Reduces swelling of tissues
I. Anti-inflammatory		Fights harmful oxidation which leads to free radical attack
J. Antiseptic		Involve steeping an herb in boiling water
K. Circulatory stimulant		Require soaking an herb in alcohol to extract the active ingredient from the plant
L. Antibacterial		Quiets the nervous system
M. Phytotherapy		The controlled use of essential oils, which happen to be highly fragranced for specific outcomes
N. Infusions		A thick crème or salve made from the combination of herbs and petroleum
O. Tinctures		Increases the body's energy

TALKING POINTS

Your next challenge is to be ready to talk about some of the important ideas in this chapter. Follow the directions listed next to each box and practice talking about your ideas.

1. Body Image Awareness

Discuss, with a partner, the increased awareness of body image in today's society and how that has affected the esthetics industry. Use the box on the left to write your notes.

2. Reflexology Benefits

Create a list, with a partner, of the benefits derived from reflexology. Use the box to the left to write your list.

3. Create a Fragrance

Create a fragrance by combining aromatherapy scents from the seven categories floral—floral bouquet, oriental, spice blend, forest or wood blend, fruit blend, or modern blend. Name your fragrance and describe the healing, moisturizing or other effects that your fragrance will cause.

Use the box to the left to write your formula.

1 2 3 4 5 6 7

Salon Fundamentals™ Esthetics

413

Now it's time to see how well you know your new material. First answer these questions. Then use the Memory Box that follows to check yourself. Look up each answer on the corresponding page in the *Salon Fundamentals™ Esthetics* textbook. Check "got it" for all correct answers and "not yet" for all incorrect responses. Using the "Know Chart," record all of your correct responses in the "I Know" column. After correcting incorrect answers, record all of your corrected responses in the "I Need to Study" column. That way you know exactly what to review before continuing in this Guide.

Directions: Identify whether questions 1 and 2 are True or False by circling TRUE or FALSE. You can earn an extra point for each false statement you appropriately correct. Question 3 requires you to write in an answer in the blank provided. Answers to the questions found in 4 through 10 may be selected by circling a, b, c or d below each statement to indicate your choice.

1. TRUE   FALSE   Gomage are products that contain coarse (grainy) ingredients that rub against dead skin cells, removing them from the epidermis.

_____

2. TRUE   FALSE   Do not make specific weight or inch loss claims for body wraps.

_____

3. _____ is made of deposits of fat, water and waste materials trapped between skin fibers.

4. What uses a warm steam to induce relaxation, expand pores, and promote sweating, which is said to release toxins from the body?
   a. hydrotherapy
   b. cellulite wraps
   c. affusion therapy
   d. saunas and steam baths

5. Which of the following is performed by estheticians using alpha hydroxy acid, glycolic acid or lactic acid?
   a. hydrotherapy
   b. cellulite wraps
   c. affusion therapy
   d. superficial chemical peels

6. What procedure lightly resurfaces the epidermis, removing 20% to 30% of the epidermis?
   a. hydrotherapy
   b. cellulite wraps
   c. microdermabrasion
   d. reflexology treatments

7. What technique uses pressure on specific points of the feet, hands and sometimes the ears to influence certain body conditions?
   a. reflexology
   b. hydrotherapy
   c. affusion therapy
   d. manual lymphatic drainage massage

8. What organic compounds with medicinal attributes give plants their healing properties?
   a. tinctures and glucosides
   b. infusions and decoctions
   c. alkaloids and glucosides
   d. phytocosmetics and tinctures

9. Which of the following is NOT a classification of fragrances?
   a. floral
   b. oriental
   c. fruit blend
   d. earth blend

10. Which type of oil helps destroy bacteria and heal skin eruptions?
    a. antiseptic
    b. astringent
    c. analgesic
    d. anti-inflammatory

| 1 | 2 | 3 | 4 | 5 | 6 | 7 |

1. page 469	☐ got it ☐ not yet	
2. page 472	☐ got it ☐ not yet	
3. page 474	☐ got it ☐ not yet	
4. page 477	☐ got it ☐ not yet	
5. page 479	☐ got it ☐ not yet	
6. page 482	☐ got it ☐ not yet	
7. page 486	☐ got it ☐ not yet	
8. page 494	☐ got it ☐ not yet	
9. page 499	☐ got it ☐ not yet	
10. page 500	☐ got it ☐ not yet	

I know...

I need to study...

SHOW YOU KNOW...

Imagine you have been asked to give a presentation on the healing powers of plants. Create an opening statement to draw attention to your topic, and also write a closing statement that sums up your presentation.

OPENING STATEMENT:

CLOSING STATEMENT:

1	2	3	4	5	6	7

The Line Up

Put the following 13 guidelines for a microdermabrasion procedure in the correct order with 1 being the first step, 2 being the second step and so forth.

NUMBER	STEP
	Complete one pass over the face, and assess capillary activity before proceeding
	Place a new disposable microdermabrasion tip on the handpiece. Use a new tip for each patient
	Recommend a proper line of products for the client to use for home care between treatments
	Turn on the microdermabrasion machine and set to its lowest level. Use manufacturer recommended crystals
	Dust residual crystals from the face with a warm, wet sponge or cloth
	Discard all disposable implements, cotton, tissue, gloves and tips
	Cleanse the skin with a slightly detergent cleanser to remove all makeup, dirt, and sebum
	Hold the skin at the center of the forehead taut, and use quick strokes across the face from the center of the forehead to the hairline. Strokes should be no longer than 2" (5 cm)
	Follow the hairline, in accordance with directions and techniques outlined on the microdermabrasion machine. Do not perform additional passes if the skin is noticeably pink
	Place eye goggles over client's eyes, and cover client's hair with a hair net or wrap
	Advise clients to avoid saunas and steam for 24 to 48 hours and sun exposure for at least 72 hours
	Dry thoroughly with tissue and a small hand-held dryer
	Wash and sanitize hands, put on protective gloves

KNOWLEDGE GRID

Start at the top of the Knowledge Grid and work your way down, answering each question to check your understanding of Chapter 13, Advanced Treatments. The questions found here will help you deepen your understanding, build self-confidence and increase your awareness of different ways of thinking about a subject.

KNOW

List the contraindications for all advanced body and face treatments.

COMPREHEND

Explain how to set up the service space before a basic facial.

APPLY

Offer a description that explains how aromatherapy works.

ANALYZE

Analyze the importance of asking clients if they have contraindications for a treatment before beginning.

SYNTHESIZE

Suggest a treatment for a client who complains about 'dimply fat' on her belly and hips.

EVALUATE

What is your opinion of performing facials without machines?

| 1 | 2 | 3 | 4 | 5 | 6 | 7 |

Salon Fundamentals™ Esthetics

Multiple choice. Circle the correct answer.

1. Which hand and foot treatment product is used to hydrate, calm and soothe the skin?
   a. mask
   b. exfoliant
   c. sugar scrub
   d. massage lubricant

2. The hand and foot treatment product that reduces friction during massage is called a(n):
   a. salt scrub
   b. essential oil
   c. massage lubricant
   d. aromatherapy soaking formula

3. The exfoliating treatment in which a layer of crème is applied to the skin, allowed to dry and then rubbed away is called:
   a. gomage
   b. manual exfoliants
   c. hand-held exfoliants
   d. synthetic microbeads

4. Products that contain coarse ingredients that rub against dead skin cells, removing them from the epidermis are known as:
   a. gomage
   b. manual exfoliants
   c. skin-purifying wipes
   d. hand-held exfoliants

5. Body wraps offer a quick way to firm all of the following areas EXCEPT:
   a. hips
   b. face
   c. belly
   d. thighs

6. What two principles give wraps the ability to create temporary tightness?
   a. absorption and secretion
   b. circulation and absorption
   c. compaction and circulation
   d. absorption and compaction

7. How long does a typical body wrap procedure last?
   a. 10 to 20 minutes
   b. 20 to 35 minutes
   c. 30 to 60 minutes
   d. 80 to 90 minutes

8. What is used to promote detoxification, constrict blood vessels and tighten skin during a cellulite wrap procedure?
   a. mylar wrap
   b. cellulite crème
   c. cellophane wrap
   d. skin purifying wipes

9. Which of the following refers to the use of fresh water treatments?
   a. steam bath
   b. hose treatment
   c. affusion therapy
   d. hydrotherapy tub treatments

10. The method of water therapy in which the client is sprayed with water, seawater or mineral water infused with herbs or essential oils is called:
    a. steam baths
    b. balneotherapy
    c. affusion therapy.
    d. hydrotherapy tub treatment

11. Which of the following is NOT an alternate name for affusion therapy?
    a. balneotherapy
    b. hose treatment
    c. jet blitz treatment
    d. Vichy shower treatment

12. Which method of water therapy involves the use of warm steam to induce muscle relaxation, expand pores and promote sweating?
    a. steam baths
    b. hose treatment
    c. affusion therapy
    d. hydrotherapy tub treatment

13. What percentage of glycolic acid is used in superficial chemical peels?
    a. 10%
    b. 20%
    c. 30%
    d. 50%

14. What treatment is responsible for lightly resurfacing the epidermis?
    a. reflexology
    b. dermabrasion
    c. microdermabrasion
    d. aluminum oxide crystals

15. Which of the terms listed below requires the patient to be anesthetized?
    a. reflexology
    b. dermabrasion
    c. microdermabrasion
    d. aluminum oxide crystals

16. The degree of exfoliation during microdermabrasion depends on all of the following EXCEPT:
    a. level of crystal spray
    b. time of day performed
    c. number of passes over the skin
    d. number of treatments performed

17. Following a microdermabrasion treatment, the client should avoid sun exposure for at least:
    a. 12 hours
    b. 24 hours
    c. 48 hours
    d. 72 hours

18. A technique that uses finger-point pressure to influence certain body conditions is referred to as:
    a. reflexology
    b. dermabrasion
    c. cellulite treatments
    d. manual lymphatic drainage massage

19. All of the following are contraindications for performing a reflexology treatment EXCEPT:
    a. arthritis
    b. pregnancy
    c. osteoporosis
    d. high blood pressure

20. A fluid that circulates through the blood system via muscular contractions is known as:
    a. MLD
    b. water
    c. lymph
    d. alcohol

21. Which of the special massage techniques helps circulate lymph, helping the body rid itself of toxins, waste and excess water?
    a. reflexology
    b. dermabrasion
    c. cellulite massage treatments
    d. manual lymphatic drainage massage (MLD)

22. The treatment that increases circulation, promoting the removal of excess fluids and waste material as well as firming the muscle tissue is known as:
    a. reflexology
    b. microdermabrasion
    c. cellulite massage treatments
    d. manual lymphatic drainage massage (MLD)

23. Which of the following refers to the medicinal use of plants?
    a. algotherapy
    b. phytotherapy
    c. aromatherapy
    d. phytocosmetics

24. Phytotherapy preparations used for cosmetic purposes are known as:
    a. tinctures
    b. alkaloids
    c. glucosides
    d. phytocosmetics

25. Chemicals such as alkaloids and glucosides that give plants their healing properties are called:
    a. tinctures
    b. antimicrobials
    c. active ingredients
    d. inactive ingredients

26. Commercial extractions that require soaking an herb in alcohol to extract the active ingredient from the plant are known as:
    a. tinctures
    b. ointments
    c. glucosides
    d. active ingredients

27. Soaking a clean towel in the liquid from both infusions and decoctions and applying it to a specific area of the body is known as:
    a. poultice
    b. Ayurveda
    c. fomentation
    d. aromatherapy

28. Which of the following involves mixing crushed herbs and hot liquid to form a paste?
    a. infusion
    b. poultice
    c. decoction
    d. fomentation

1	2	3	4	5	6	7

29. The controlled use of essential oils is referred to as:
    a. algotherapy
    b. fomentation
    c. phytotherapy
    d. aromatherapy

30. The category of fragrance that is one of the easiest to identify is:
    a. floral
    b. oriental
    c. spice blend
    d. floral bouquet

31. The fragrance group that distinct odors like vanilla, cinnamon, ginger and nutmeg belong to is called:
    a. oriental
    b. wood blend
    c. spice blend
    d. modern blend

32. The category of fragrance that encompasses many men's fragrances is called:
    a. oriental
    b. spice blend
    c. wood blend
    d. modern blend

33. The category of oils that helps destroy bacteria and heal skin eruptions is called a(n):
    a. emollient
    b. antiseptic
    c. astringent
    d. rubefacient

34. Which of the following categories fights skin-ravaging free radicals?
    a. antiseptic oils
    b. antioxidant oils
    c. moisturizing oils
    d. anti-inflammatory oils

35. The most common method of removing essential oils from raw plant material is:
    a. extraction
    b. enfleurage
    c. expression
    d. steam distillation

36. Which method of extracting essential oils from raw plant materials uses a chemical solvent, such as petroleum or ether, to leach the aromatic component from an ingredient?
    a. extraction
    b. enfleurage
    c. expression
    d. steam distillation

37. Which type of essential oil is often used in treating acne?
    a. rose
    b. tea tree
    c. lavender
    d. sandalwood

38. This essential oil is used to treat stiff, sore muscles or to boost circulation:
    a. rose
    b. neroli
    c. lavender
    d. eucalyptus

39. What is the therapeutic use of marine plants to cleanse and revitalize the skin and body called?
    a. reflexology
    b. algotherapy
    c. phytotherapy
    d. aromatherapy

40. Mineral salts, essential amino acids, polysaccharides, vitamins, enzymes, helpful bacteria, natural antibiotics and plant hormones are known as:
    a. antioxidants
    b. brown algae
    c. analgesic oils
    d. phytohormones

Write Your Own Ticket! For numbers 41, 42, and 43, write your own questions and answer them. Your questions can be true/false, multiple choice or fill-in-the-blank. The only parameter is that your questions cannot already be found on this test. Earn one point each for writing your way to success.

41. Q: _____ A: _____

42. Q: _____ A: _____

43. Q: _____ A: _____

BONUS QUESTION!
Question 44 is the ultimate question. To earn two points, design a question for your class. If you stump the class, and no one can answer the question within an agreed upon time (between you and the teacher), you earn a **BONUS OF FIVE ADDITIONAL POINTS.**

44. _____

ESSAY QUESTION:
45. A maximum of five additional points is possible by selecting one of the following essay questions to answer.

45a. Compare and contrast two body treatments and their specific contraindications.

45b. Choose one of the three special massage techniques and describe and give the contraindications for that special massage technique.

45c. In the space below, give a brief description of the three special therapies described in this chapter.

FINAL REVIEW

Check your answers as you did before. Place a check mark next to the page number for any incorrect answer. On the lines to the right, jot down topics that you still need to review.

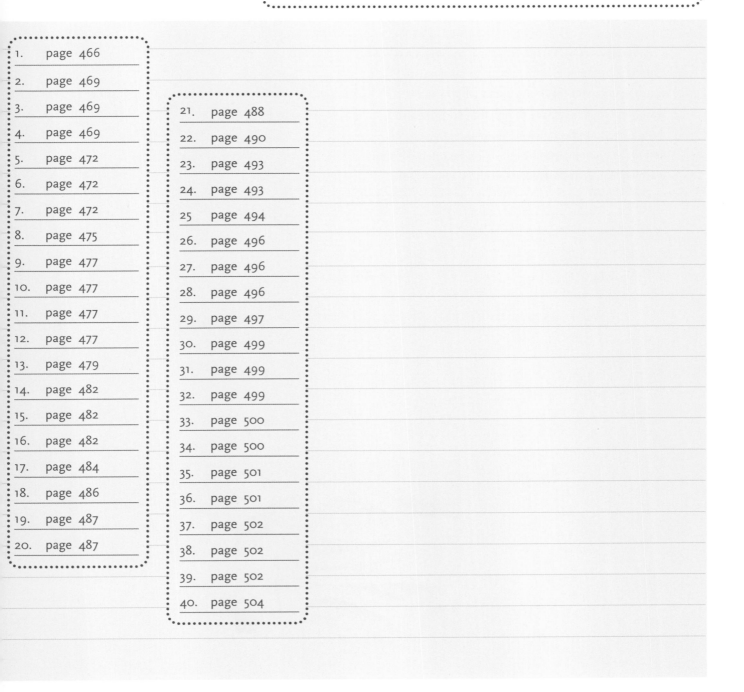

1. page 466
2. page 469
3. page 469
4. page 469
5. page 472
6. page 472
7. page 472
8. page 475
9. page 477
10. page 477
11. page 477
12. page 477
13. page 479
14. page 482
15. page 482
16. page 482
17. page 484
18. page 486
19. page 487
20. page 487

21. page 488
22. page 490
23. page 493
24. page 493
25. page 494
26. page 496
27. page 496
28. page 496
29. page 497
30. page 499
31. page 499
32. page 499
33. page 500
34. page 500
35. page 501
36. page 501
37. page 502
38. page 502
39. page 502
40. page 504

1 2 3 4 5 6 7

Experts agree that it is important to summarize your feelings and reactions about what you are learning. Note especially things that surprised you, things you found difficult to learn and suggestions and ideas you received from friends that helped make learning this chapter easier and more enjoyable.

VALUE

The medical field presents opportunities for estheticians to work cooperatively with medical practitioners in a challenging, highly structured professional environment.

MAIN IDEA

Estheticians who wish to work with medical practitioners need to understand the relationship between esthetics and approved health practices and procedures. The esthetician who chooses this path will work within a team of physicians, nurses and other ancillary staff and will need to stay apprised of continuously changing regulatory controls. This chapter will provide you with guidelines of what may be expected of an esthetician in a medical environment.

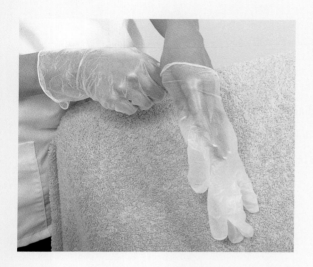

PLAN

The Medical Environment	■ Dermatology and PlasticSurgery ■ Esthetics in a Medical Practice
Advanced Training	■ Continuing Education ■ Scope of Practice

OBJECTIVES

■ Describe the different types of medical procedures performed by physicians that are related to the esthetics profession.

■ Explain the various esthetics procedures applied in a medical practice.

■ Identify various ways of gaining additional and advanced training to become qualified to work in a medical setting.

■ Define the phrase "scope of practice."

Chapter	Section	Page
Chapter 14 Estheticians in the Medical Field	The Medical Environment	Pages 509-511

Goals for Estheticians in the Medical Setting	Your goals in a medical setting are to:
	1.
	2.
	3.
IMPORTANT!	Esthetics license permits estheticians to treat the epidermis only

> ★ **1** Describe the different types of medical procedures performed by physicians that are related to the esthetics profession

■ **Dermatology and Plastic Surgery**	
Cosmetic Procedures	Dermatologists specialize in diagnosing and treating diseases of the skin and nails
	Some of the procedures that dermatologists perform include chemical peels,
	collagen/fat injections, Botox injections, dermabrasion and dermaplaning
Plastic Surgery	
Plastic Surgeon	
Reconstructive Surgery	
Chemical Peels	

Chemical Peels

Results:
- ■
- ■
- ■

Recommended for:
- ■

Side-Effects:
- ■
- ■
- ■
- ■

Phenol treatment may result in:
- ■
- ■

Recovery:
- ■
- ■

Duration of Results:
- ■
- ■

Chapter	Section	Page
Chapter 14 Estheticians in the Medical Field	**The Medical Environment**	**Pages 511-513**

Depth of Penetration

EMDA

IMPORTANT!   Estheticians are only permitted to perform light or superficial peels; medium to deep peels can only be performed by physicians

Medium-Depth Peels   ■

■

■

■

Deep Peels   ■

■

Collagen or Fat Injections

Collagen Injections

Human Collagen

Injectable Collagen

Chapter	Section	Page
Chapter 14 Estheticians in the Medical Field	The Medical Environment	Pages 513-514

Fat Injections

Collagen or Fat Injection

Results: _____

■

■

Recommended for: _____

■

Side-Effects: _____

■

■

■

■

■

Recovery: _____

■

Duration of Results: _____

■

Pre- and Post-Operative Treatments ■

■

■

Botox® Cosmetic Injections

smartNOTES

Chapter	Section	Page
Chapter 14 Estheticians in the Medical Field	The Medical Environment	Pages 514-515

Botox® Cosmetic Injections (continued)

Botox® Injections

Results:
■

Recommended for:
■

Side-Effects:
■

■
■
■
■
■

Recovery:
■

Duration of Results:
■

Dermabrasion and Dermaplaning
■

■

■

■

Dermabrasion vs. Microdermabrasion

Dermabrasion
■
■

■

Microdermabrasion
■

■

■

Chapter	Section	Page
Chapter 14 Estheticians in the Medical Field	The Medical Environment	Pages 514-516

Dermabrasion or
Dermaplaning

Dermabrasion or Dermaplaning

Results:
■
■

Recommended for:
■

Side-Effects:
■
■
■
■
■
■
■

Recovery:
■
■

■

Duration of Results:
■

Blepharoplasty
(Eyelid Surgery)

Blepharoplasty (Eyelid Surgery)

Results:
■
■

Recommended for:
■

Side-Effects:
■
■
■
■

■
■

■

Recovery:
■

■

■

Duration of Results:
■

Rhytidectomy
(Facelift)

Chapter	Section	Page
Chapter 14 Estheticians in the Medical Field	**The Medical Environment**	**Pages 516-517**

Rhytidectomy (Facelift)

Results:
-
-
-

Recommended for:
-

Side-Effects:
-
-
-

Recovery:
-

-

Duration of Results:
-

Ablative and Non-ablative Lasers

Non-ablative Lasers	**Ablative Lasers**

Laser Resurfacing

Laser Resurfacing

Results:
-
-
-

Recommended for:
-

Side-Effects:
-
-
-
-

Recovery:
-

-

Duration of Results:
-

Side-Effects

1 2 3 4 5 6 7

Chapter	Section	Page
Chapter 14 Estheticians in the Medical Field	The Medical Environment	Pages 518-519

Rhinoplasty (Nose Surgery)

Rhinoplasty (Nose Surgery)

Results:
-

Recommended for:
-

Side-Effects:
-
-
-

Recovery:
-

-

Duration of Results:
-

2 Explain the various esthetics procedures applied in a medical practice

■ Esthetics Procedures in a Medical Practice

Proper skin care before and after medical procedures produces superior results

Dermatological Disorders

Post-Operative Complications

➤

➤

➤

➤

➤

➤

➤

➤

➤

Chapter	Section	Page
Chapter 14 Estheticians in the Medical Field	**The Medical Environment**	**Pages 518-520**

Wound Healing

Infections

Bacterial Infections

Conjunctivitis (Pink Eye)

Yeast Infections

Herpetic Infections
(Cold Sores)

Ecchymosis (Bruising)

Erythema
(Redness of the Skin)

Scarring

smartNOTES

Chapter	Section	Page
Chapter 14 Estheticians in the Medical Field	**The Medical Environment**	**Pages 520-521**

Burn Care

1. First-degree burns
   - ■
   - ■
   - ■
   - ■
   - ■

2. Second-degree burns
   - ■
   - ■
   - ■
   - ■

3. Third-degree burns
   - ■
   - ■

   - ■
   - ■

   - ■

Medications for Post-Operative Complications

Topical Medications

Anti-Inflammatory Medications

Keratolytic Medications

Antibacterial Medications

Salon Fundamentals™ Esthetics

Chapter	Section	Page
Chapter 14 Estheticians in the Medical Field	**The Medical Environment**	**Page 521**

Systemic Medications

Antibiotics

Antihistamines

Accutane® (Isotretinoin)

Laser resurfacing is a medical procedure that many believe carries a high risk for patients. Explain why you think this belief could be true.

LEARNING — **CONNECTION** — Professionals and Procedures

Specialized medical professionals perform many different medical procedures. Match the procedure in Column A with the appropriate description in Column B.

Column A	Column B
A. Chemical Peel	Surgical procedures that improve uneven skin textures due to acne, facial scars and fine wrinkles
B. Collagen/Fat Injection	A surgical procedure used to fill in creased, furrowed or sunken facial skin, lines and wrinkles
C. Blepharoplasty	Surgery to reshape the nose
D. Dermabrasion and Dermaplaning	Surgery to remove excess fat, skin or muscle from the upper and lower eyelids
E. Rhinoplasty	Use of chemical solutions to exfoliate the surface of the skin

| 1 | 2 | 3 | 4 | 5 | 6 | 7 |

Chapter	Section	Page
Chapter 14 Estheticians in the Medical Field	Advanced Training	Pages 522-524

3 Identify various ways of gaining additional and advanced training to become qualified to work in a medical setting

Continuing Education
Credits

2 Important Considerations
- ▢
- ▢

■ **Continuing Education**

Medical Facilities

Product Manufacturers

Professional Associations

Medical Esthetics Courses

Chapter	Section	Page
Chapter 14 Estheticians in the Medical Field	Advanced Training	Pages 523-524

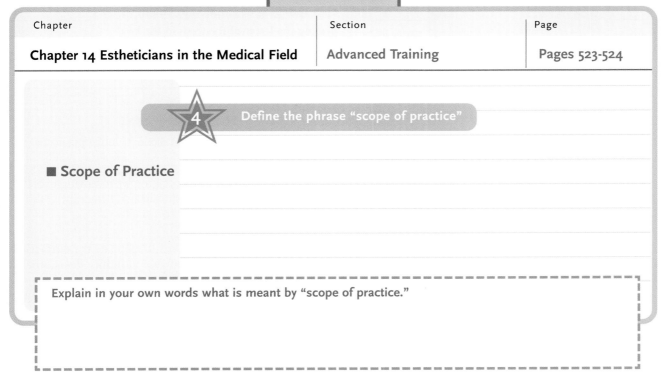

4 Define the phrase "scope of practice"

■ **Scope of Practice**

Explain in your own words what is meant by "scope of practice."

LEARNING **CONNECTION** — Networking

Continuing education can be obtained through a network of different places. For each of the places listed below give an example of how you could obtain continuing education from them.

Medical Facilities ➤➤➤

Product Manufacturers ➤➤➤

Professional Associations ➤➤➤

Medical Esthetics Courses ➤➤➤

| 1 | 2 | 3 | 4 | 5 | 6 | 7 |

Match the term from Column A with the corresponding description in Column B by placing the letter of the term in the box provided in front of the description.

Column A		Column B
A. Chemical peel		Performed for aesthetic and reconstructive purposes
B. Fat injections		Can improve visible signs of aging by removing excess fat, tightening underlying muscles and re-draping the skin of the face and neck
C. Dermabrasion		The use of chemical solutions to exfoliate the surface of the skin, promote cell turnover and induce desquamation
D. Plastic surgery		Process in which fat is removed with a syringe from a "donor site" and injected into the area to be treated
E. Blepharoplasty		Removes the affected portion of the epidermis to heat the papillary dermis, which regenerates collagen
F. Rhytidectomy		Surgery to reshape the nose
G. Ablative laser		Clinical term for bruising of the skin
H. Rhinoplasty		An extremely contagious bacterial infection that affects the membrane that lines the eyelids
I. Conjunctivitis		Surgical procedure that improves uneven skin textures due to acne, facial scars and fine wrinkles
J. Ecchymosis		Develops when microbes invade an injured, open or wounded part of the body
K. Erythema		Characterized by a break in the continuity of the skin that is caused by trauma to the tissue
L. Keratolytic medications		The least severe type of burns that only damages the epidermis
M. First-degree burn		Crèmes or ointments used to promote rapid cell turnover and exfoliation
N. Bacterial infection		Clinical term for redness of the skin
O. Wound		Eyelid surgery to remove excess fat, skin or muscle from the upper and lower eyelids

TALKING POINTS

Your next challenge is to be ready to talk about some of the important ideas in this chapter. Follow the directions listed next to each box and practice talking about your ideas.

1. Skin Care & Surgery

Discuss, with a partner, the possible role of a skin care specialist in the pre- and post-operative treatments of a patient who is going to have a Blepharoplasty surgery.

2. Post-op Observations

Estheticians who work in almost any medical setting need a basic knowledge of post-operative surgical concerns and possible complications.

Discuss, with a partner, any post-operative complications you have already experienced or have witnessed firsthand.

3. Ongoing Training

It is in the best interest of estheticians in the medical field to find ways of gaining additional and advanced training in the field.

Discuss, with a partner, sources where you can find additional and advanced training.
.

| 1 | 2 | 3 | 4 | 5 | 6 | 7 |

Now it's time to see how well you know your new material. First answer these questions. Then use the Memory Box that follows to check yourself. Look up each answer on the corresponding page in the *Salon Fundamentals™ Esthetics* textbook. Check "got it" for all correct answers and "not yet" for all incorrect responses. Using the "Know Chart," record all of your correct responses in the "I Know" column. After correcting incorrect answers, record all of your corrected responses in the "I Need to Study" column. That way you know exactly what to review before continuing in this Guide.

Directions: Identify whether questions 1 and 2 are True or False by circling TRUE or FALSE. You can earn an extra point for each false statement you appropriately correct. Question 3 requires you to write in an answer in the blank provided. Answers to the questions found in questions 4 through 10. may be selected by circling a, b, c, or d, below each statement to indicate your choice.

1. TRUE FALSE   A chemical peel is the use of chemical solutions to exfoliate the surface of the skin, promote cell turnover and induce desquamation.

2. TRUE FALSE   Medium-Depth Peels use the strongest of the chemical peel solutions

3. _____ is a naturally occurring protein that is a component of human skin, joints, bones and ligaments.

4. What is the primary purpose for the surgical procedure called dermabrasion?
   a. adds fullness to lips
   b. plumps up facial skin
   c. lifts drooping eyelids
   d. improves uneven skin textures

5. Which of the following can improve visible signs of aging by removing excess fat, tightening underlying muscles, and re-draping the skin of the face and neck?
   a. rhinoplasty
   b. rhytidectomy
   c. blepharoplasty
   d. laser resurfacing

6. Which of the following terms characterizes a break in the continuity of the skin that is caused by trauma to the tissue?
   a. wound
   b. conjunctivitis
   c. blepharoplasty
   d. bacterial infection

7. The clinical term for redness of the skin is referred to as:
   a. scarring
   b. erythema
   c. blepharoplasty
   d. first-degree burn

8. What is used to treat inflammatory conditions such as dermatitis?
   a. antibiotics
   b. keratolytic medications
   c. antibacterial medications
   d. anti-inflammatory medications

9. Which of the following is used to promote rapid cell turnover and exfoliation?
   a. antibiotic
   b. antihistamine
   c. antibacterial medication
   d. keratolytic medication

10. The procedures that may be legally performed, as defined by a regulatory agency, are referred to as the:
    a. network
    b. scope of practice
    c. esthetics procedures
    d. professional procedures

MEMORY BOX

1.	page 510	☐ got it ☐ not yet
2.	page 512	☐ got it ☐ not yet
3.	page 513	☐ got it ☐ not yet
4.	page 514	☐ got it ☐ not yet
5.	page 516	☐ got it ☐ not yet
6.	page 519	☐ got it ☐ not yet
7.	page 520	☐ got it ☐ not yet
8.	page 521	☐ got it ☐ not yet
9.	page 521	☐ got it ☐ not yet
10.	page 524	☐ got it ☐ not yet

KNOW CHART

I know...

I need to study...

SHOW YOU KNOW...

Contact an esthetician who works with a medical practice. Discuss the relationship between esthetics and approved health practices and procedures. Also discuss what is expected of estheticians who work in a medical environment. Compare your results with your classmates.

Start at the top of the Knowledge Grid and work your way down, answering each question to check your understanding Chapter 14, Estheticians in the Medical Field. The questions found here will help you deepen your understanding, build self-confidence and increase your awareness of different ways of thinking about the subject.

KNOW

Describe what is meant by a fat injection.

COMPREHEND

What is the difference between dermabrasion and microdermabrasion?

APPLY

Explain how the dermaplaning procedure works.

ANALYZE

Compare the desired results of collagen or fat injections with Botox® cosmetic injections.

SYNTHESIZE

Create a catchy phrase that shows the differences between the three types of burns.

EVALUATE

What is your opinion of performing cosmetic surgery on patients?

| 1 | 2 | 3 | 4 | 5 | 6 | 7 |

Multiple choice. Circle the correct answer.

1. A physician specializing in diagnosing and treating diseases of the skin and nails is known as a(n):
   a. dentist
   b. obstetrician
   c. dermatologist
   d. plastic surgeon

2. What is the maximum percentage of acid that the EMDA allows estheticians to use in AHAs?
   a. 10%
   b. 20%
   c. 30%
   d. 40%

3. The EMDA does NOT allow estheticians to use an AHA with a pH lower than:
   a. 1.0
   b. 2.0
   c. 3.0
   d. 4.0

4. Which type of peel uses trichloroacetic acid (TCA)?
   a. light
   b. medium-depth
   c. medium/deep-depth
   d. deep

5. Which type of peel uses phenol, the strongest of the chemical peel solutions?
   a. light
   b. deep
   c. medium-depth
   d. medium/deep-depth

6. A fat injection is also called a(n):
   a. rhinoplasty
   b. dermabrasion
   c. laser resurfacing
   d. microlipoinjection

7. Which of the following is a naturally occurring protein that is a component of human skin, joints, bones and ligaments?
   a. fat
   b. phenol
   c. collagen
   d. bovine collagen

8. All of the following are side-effects of collagen or fat injections EXCEPT:
   a. swelling
   b. nausea
   c. mild redness
   d. excess fullness

9. Which procedure is used to treat sunken cheeks, laugh lines, skin depressions or indentations, forehead wrinkles or to enlarge lips?
   a. fat injection
   b. chemical peel
   c. Botox® injection
   d. cosmetic surgery

10. All of the following statements are true about dermabrasion EXCEPT:
    a. requires client to be anesthetized
    b. must be performed by a physician
    c. ointment may be prescribed to ease tightness
    d. is not as invasive as exfoliation

11. Normal activities may be resumed after what period of time following a blepharoplasty procedure:
    a. immediately
    b. 2 – 3 days
    c. 4 – 6 days
    d. 7 – 10 days

12. The surgical procedure that improves uneven skin textures, due to acne, facial scars and fine wrinkles, by mechanically scraping off the top layers of skin is called:
    a. fat injection
    b. dermabrasion
    c. Botox® injection
    d. collagen injection

13. Which of the following is NOT a side-effect of dermabrasion?
    a. redness
    b. excess fullness
    c. formation of milia
    d. lightening of treated skin

14. What is the term for aesthetic and reconstructive procedures?
    a. dermabrasion
    b. chemical peel
    c. Botox® injection
    d. cosmetic surgery

15. The procedure performed to restore the functioning of body parts or to correct a deformity that may be the result of a birth defect, burn, injury or trauma to the skin, tissue, nerves or muscles is known as:
    a. dermabrasion
    b. chemical peel
    c. Botox® injection
    d. reconstructive surgery

16. Which of the following is known as eyelid surgery and is used to remove excess fat, skin or muscle to form the upper and lower eyelids?
    a. rhinoplasty
    b. rhytidectomy
    c. blepharoplasty
    d. laser resurfacing

17. Which type of cosmetic surgery is recommended for individuals whose face and neck have begun to sag but still have some facial skin elasticity and good bone structure?
    a. rhytidectomy
    b. chemical peel
    c. blepharoplasty
    d. laser resurfacing

18. Results of rhytidectomy include all of the following EXCEPT:
    a. reduction of jowls
    b. making loose neck skin more taut
    c. improvement of sagging facial skin
    d. improvement of irregularities from acne scars and wrinkles

19. Which type of cosmetic surgery uses a beam of highly focused light to vaporize the upper layers of damaged skin at specific and controlled levels of penetration?
    a. rhytidectomy
    b. dermabrasion
    c. blepharoplasty
    d. laser resurfacing

20. Which of the following types of lasers removes the affected portion of the epidermis to heat the papillary dermis to regenerate collagen?
    a. ablative
    b. non-ablative
    c. carbon monoxide
    d. short pulsed erbium

21. Which type of laser penetrates the epidermis, usually without affecting it, to treat the papillary dermis below?
    a. ablative
    b. non-ablative
    c. carbon dioxide
    d. long pulsed erbium

22. All of the following are side-effects of laser resurfacing EXCEPT:
    a. excessive tearing
    b. temporary swelling
    c. lightening of treated areas
    d. increased sensitivity to sun and makeup

23. Approximately how many weeks should a laser resurfacing patient wait before returning to normal activities?
    a. one week
    b. 2 weeks
    c. 3 weeks
    d. 4 weeks

24. Cosmetic surgery to reshape the nose is referred to as:
    a. rhinoplasty
    b. rhytidectomy
    c. blepharoplasty
    d. laser resurfacing

25. The six signs of infection include pain, swelling, redness, local fever, throbbing and:
    a. pus
    b. itching
    c. burning
    d. sallowness

26. Which type of post-operative complication develops when microbes invade an injured, open or wounded part of the body?
    a. conjunctivitis
    b. yeast infection
    c. herpetic infection
    d. bacterial infection

27. A superficial infection that occurs on moist areas of the skin is called a(n):
    a. conjunctivitis
    b. yeast infection
    c. herpetic infection
    d. bacterial infection

28. An extremely contagious bacterial infection that affects the membrane that lines the eyelids is known as:
    a. ecchymosis
    b. conjunctivitis
    c. yeast infection
    d. herpetic infection

29. Which of the following is a highly contagious viral infection that is triggered when the body or skin is placed under extreme stress?
    a. ecchymosis
    b. conjunctivitis
    c. yeast infection
    d. herpetic infection

30. The clinical term for bruising of the skin is known as:
    a. scarring
    b. erythema
    c. ecchymosis
    d. conjunctivitis

31. Which of the following description of care would be recommended for a first-degree burn?
    a. apply butter
    b. apply aloe vera
    c. break the blister
    d. perform skin graft

32. To care for second-degree burns, the burned area should be:
    a. treated with aloe vera
    b. treated with an ointment
    c. immersed in cool water
    d. covered tightly with sterile gauze

33. A procedure that takes a section of healthy skin from an unburned area of the body and surgically reattaches it, covering the burned area to try to re-grow skin is referred to as:
    a. rhinoplasty
    b. ecchymosis
    c. rhytidectomy
    d. skin grafting

34. The most severe of the burns, the one that damages or destroys underlying tissue, exposes nerve endings and burns fat, muscle and bone, is known as:
   a. first-degree burn
   b. second-degree burn
   c. third-degree burn
   d. fourth-degree burn

35. Which type of medication is frequently used to relieve skin from itching and hives?
   a. antibiotics
   b. keratolytic
   c. antibacterial
   d. antihistamine

36. An example of a systemic medication would be:
   a. keratolytic
   b. antibiotic
   c. antibacterial
   d. anti-inflammatory

37. Which of the following is NOT an example of a systemic medication?
   a. accutane
   b. antibiotic
   c. keratolytic
   d. antihistamine

38. Which of the following is NOT considered a topical medication?
   a. antibiotic
   b. keratolytic
   c. antibacterial
   d. anti-inflammatory

39. Extended use of which of the following medications may cause skin dryness and dehydration?
   a. keratolytic
   b. antibacterial
   c. antihistamine
   d. anti-inflammatory

40. The procedures that may be legally performed, as defined by a regulatory agency, are referred to as the:
   a. network
   b. scope of practice
   c. esthetic procedures
   d. professional procedures

Write Your Own Ticket! For numbers 41, 42, and 43, write your own questions and answer them. Your questions can be true/false, multiple choice or fill-in-the-blank. The only parameter is that your questions cannot already be found on this test. Earn one point each for writing your way to success.

41.   Q: _____   A: _____

42.   Q: _____   A: _____

43.   Q: _____   A: _____

BONUS QUESTION!
Question 44 is the ultimate question. To earn two points, design a question for your class. If you stump the class, and no one can answer the question within an agreed upon time (between you and the teacher), you earn a BONUS OF FIVE ADDITIONAL POINTS.

44. _____

ESSAY QUESTION:
45.   A maximum of five additional points is possible by selecting one of the following essay questions to answer.

45a.   Describe three different types of medical procedures performed by physicians that are related to the esthetics profession.

_____

_____

_____

_____

_____

45b.   In your opinion, what is the most important fact to remember when working under your esthetics license?

_____

_____

_____

45c.   Identify various ways to gain additional and advanced training to become qualified to work in a medical setting.

_____

_____

_____

FINAL REVIEW

Check your answers as you did before. Place a check mark next to the page number for any incorrect answer. On the lines to the right, jot down topics that you still need to review.

1.	page 510
2.	page 511
3.	page 511
4.	page 511
5.	page 512
6.	page 513
7.	page 513
8.	page 513
9.	page 513
10.	page 515
11.	page 516
12.	page 514
13.	page 515
14.	page 510
15.	page 510
16.	page 515
17.	page 516
18.	page 516
19.	page 517
20.	page 517

21.	page 517
22.	page 517
23.	page 517
24.	page 518
25	page 519
26.	page 519
27.	page 519
28.	page 519
29.	page 519
30.	page 520
31.	page 520
32.	page 520
33.	page 520
34.	page 520
35.	page 521
36.	page 521
37.	page 521
38.	page 521
39.	page 521
40.	page 524

NOTES TO MYSELF — *My Reflections About Estheticians in the Medical Field*

Experts agree that it is important to summarize your feelings and reactions about what you are learning. Note especially things that surprised you, things you found difficult to learn, and suggestions and ideas you received from friends that helped make learning this chapter easier and more enjoyable.

| 1 | 2 | 3 | 4 | 5 | 6 | 7 |

A

Abducent (ab-**DEW**-sunt) **nerve** – Also known as the sixth cranial nerve; motor nerve that controls motion of the eye

Abductor (ab-**DUK**-tor) **muscles** – Muscles of the hand that allow fingers to spread apart and separate

Ablative laser – Laser that removes the affected portion of the epidermis to heat the papillary dermis, which regenerates collagen

Accessory (ack-**SES**-uh-ree) **nerve** – Also known as the eleventh cranial nerve; motor nerve that controls motion of neck muscles

Acupressure – Advanced massage technique that involves applying pressure to specific points on the body

Acupuncture – Medical treatment in which specific body areas are pierced with fine needles to relieve pain or produce regional anesthesia

Accutane® – Medication, also known as **Isotretinoin**; derivative of Vitamin A prescribed for severe, disfiguring cases of acne and certain other skin diseases

Acid – Solution containing positively charged ions

Acid balanced – Measurement indicating balance within the **acid** range of 4.5 to 5.5

Acid mantle – Protective barrier of the skin formed by a mixture of **sebum** and sweat combined with lipids, minerals and moisture

Acne – Skin condition caused by overactivity of sebaceous glands; characterized by the presence of blackheads, whiteheads, papules and pustules; generally occurs in adolescence

Acne treatment – Topical therapies and medications, oral medications and various other treatments, all of which can be done individually or in conjunction with each other

Acoustic (uh-**KOOS**-tik) **nerve** – Also called the auditory (**AW**-di-tor-ee) or eighth cranial nerve; controls sense of hearing

Acquired Immunodeficiency Syndrome (AIDS) – See **AIDS**

Actinic keratosis (**AK**-tin-ec **CAR**-a-toe-sis) – Irregularly shaped, scaly, red-pink skin growths that feel rough to the touch and occur on sun-exposed areas

Active electrode – Electrode held by the skin care specialist during a treatment

Active ingredients – Chemicals, such as alkaloids or glucosides, that give plants their healing properties

Active listening – Listening strategy that involves the whole body—ears, eyes and intellect

Active stage – Also known as the vegetative stage; the stage of rapid bacterial growth and reproduction

Acute – Term used to identify conditions that are intense and severe; implies a rapid onset

Adductor (ah-**DUK**-tor) **muscles** – Muscles of the hand that draw the fingers together

Adipocyte (**AD**-ih-poe-site) **cells** – Cells containing fat used for energy production; found in the subcutaneous layer of the skin

Adipose (**AD**-eh-poz) **cells** – Cells providing insulation from and absorption of mechanical forces; located in the subcutaneous layer of the skin

Advertising – Marketing strategies that incorporate all activities that attract attention to your skin care center and create a positive impression; projects an image and tells the public about the skin care center – the services offered, the quality of service and any other reasons that clients should patronize the center

Aerosol – Product packaged under pressure and blended with a propellant (gas) inside a container, usually a can

Affusion therapy – Also known as Vichy shower treatment, Scotch hose treatment or jet blitz treatment; treatment in which showerheads are positioned along the spine and the client is sprayed with water, seawater or mineral water, any of which may be infused with herbs or essential oils

Agreement – Phase three of Client Consultation in which the esthetician summarizes and makes sure that the client agrees with the recommended treatments

AIDS *abbr.* **Acquired Immunodeficiency Syndrome** – Highly infectious disease caused by HIV, which interferes with the body's natural immune system and causes it to break down

Airbrushing – Method of makeup application in which pigment is applied by a stream of air that pushes pigment out of a gun-like implement with the use of a compressor; creates a flawless, smooth appearance and is regularly used for theatrical performances, high-fashion runways, art form designs, and high-definition television

Albinism (AL-bin-izm) – Congenital disease that results in the failure of the skin to produce melanin

Algotherapy – Therapeutic treatment that uses marine plants to cleanse and revitalize the skin and body

Alkaline – Solution of negatively charged ions

Alkaloid – Organic compound with medicinal attributes

Allergen – Substance or ingredient likely to cause an allergic reaction

Allergy – Physical condition causing sensitivity to develop from contact with normally harmless substances, such as fragrances or colorings; symptoms may include itching, redness, swelling and/or blisters

Alpha hydroxy acid (AHA) – Chemical ingredient with the carboxyl group located on the first carbon atom of the organic **acid** chain

Alternating current – Rapid oscillating cycle that alternates back and forth, allowing electrons to flow first in one direction, then in the other

Amino acid – Compound consisting of carbon, oxygen, hydrogen and nitrogen that join together in chains to form proteins

Amp – Short for ampere; unit of electric strength

Amp rating – Measurement indicating the number of electrons flowing through a particular line

Anabolism (ah-NAB-oh-lizm) – Process of building up larger molecules from smaller ones

Anagen – First and longest phase of hair growth; phase in which the hair actively grows

Analgesic oil – Medicinal oil used to help deaden surface pain

Analogous color scheme – Art principle that uses three colors adjacent to each other on the color wheel; often used for daytime makeup design

Anaphoresis – Skin treatment that allows an **alkaline** solution to enter the skin when assisted by **Galvanic Current** and the negative pole of an electrode

Anatomy – Study of the organs and systems of the body

Androgen – Male hormone present in both men and women

Angular artery – Artery supplying blood to the sides of the nose

Anhidrosis (an-heye-DROH-sis) – Body condition that identifies a lack of perspiration caused by failure of the sweat glands

Anode – Positively charged electrode

Anterior (an-TEER-ee-er) – Term that means front, in front, in front of

Anterior auricular artery – Artery that supplies blood to the **anterior** part of the ear

Anterior dilatator naris – One of four muscles of the nose; helps control contraction and expansion of the nostrils

Antibacterial – Ingredient that destroys **bacteria** that can cause undesirable effects, such as acne or other infections

Antibacterial medication – Topical medication applied to kill **bacteria** and prevent them from reproducing

Antibiotic – Systemic medication used to treat a variety of conditions; primarily used to kill or prevent the growth of **bacteria**

Antigen – Foreign substances, such as **bacteria**, **viruses**, parasites or toxic materials that provoke an immune response in the body

Antihistamine – Systemic medication prescribed to relieve uncomfortable skin conditions, such as itching and hives

Anti-inflammatory medication – Topical medication used to treat inflammatory conditions, such as **dermatitis**

Anti-inflammatory oil – Oil used to reduce inflammation and soothe swollen muscles

Antimicrobial – Kills a wide range of harmful bacteria, fungi and viruses

Antioxidant – Ingredient used in certain types of treatment products to prevent skin inflammation and damage due to free radicals

Antioxidant oil – Oil that helps fight skin-ravaging free radicals

Antiseptic – Solution that assists in preventing the growth of **bacteria** on the skin

Antiseptic oil – Oil that helps destroy **bacteria** and heal skin eruptions

Antiseptic preparation – Sanitizing solution used on the skin prior to service; removes buildup on the body from deodorants, body lotions and oils

Apocrine gland – Sweat gland located under the arm, in the genital area and the nipple; secretes an odorless substance, which is triggered by emotions rather than hormones

Aponeurosis (ap-o-noo-**ROH**-sis) – Tendon that connects the frontalis muscle and the occipitalis muscle to form the epicranius

Apprentices – Term describing new estheticians that assist experienced staff members until they attain a satisfactory level of performance with procedures and practices within the skin care center

Aromatherapy – Therapeutic treatment that involves the use of essential oils

Aromatherapy oil – Essential oil that is highly fragranced for specific outcomes

Artery – Tubular, elastic, thick-walled branching blood vessel that carries oxygenated blood away from the heart through the body

Artificial eyelashes – Strip or individual lashes for the eye; used to create a more dramatic makeup design or add density to sparse lashes

Ask, Analyze and Assess – Phase two of Client Consultation; guided dialogue that invites clients to share their expectations as well as their reasons for requesting services

Asset – All the property a person owns

Asteatosis (as-tee-ah-**TOH**-sis) – Also called **xerosis**; dry, scaly skin caused by reduced **sebum** production

Astringent – Skin care product used to help further cleanse the skin while properly balancing the pH; also called **toner** or skin refiner

Astringent oils – Skin care product that temporarily tightens tissue and reduces secretion

Asymptomatic carrier – Person that carries disease-producing **bacteria** or **viruses** with no recognizable symptoms of the disease

Atom – Smallest complete unit of an element

Atomic number – Number of protons in a single atom of an element

Atomizer – Also referred to as a spray machine; an automated spraying device used to achieve a more thorough cleansing or toning

Atopic dermatitis – Hereditary rash or an inflammation of the skin characterized by dry, sensitive, irritated skin

Attitude – Feeling or emotion toward something or someone; person's manner or disposition

Auricularis (aw-rik-ya-**LA**-ris) **anterior muscle** – Muscle located in front of the ear

Auricularis (aw-rik-ya-**LA**-ris) **posterior muscle** – Muscle located behind the ear

Auricularis (aw-rik-ya-**LA**-ris) **superior muscle** – Muscle located above the ear

Auriculo temporal (aw-**RIK**-u-lo **TEM**-po-ral) **nerve** – Nerve extending from the ear to an area from the top of the head to the temple

Autoclave sterilizer – Pressurized, steam-heated piece of skin care equipment that sterilizes objects with high pressure and heat, or pressurized steam, killing all microorganisms

Autologous fat transplantation – Also called **fat injection** or **microlipoinjection**; a procedure in which fat is removed with a syringe from a "donor site," such as the patient's abdomen, thigh or buttock, and injected into the area to be treated

Autonomic nervous system – One of the three subsystems in the nervous system; controls the respiratory, digestive, circulatory, excretory, endocrine and reproductive systems; governs all involuntary body functions, such as breathing, blinking, sweating and digesting

Axons (**AK**-sonz) – Also called processes; threadlike, fibrous part of a nerve extending from the cell

Ayurveda – An ancient science of health and medicine that utilizes aromatic massage oils

Azaleic acid – **Acid** that promotes drying and cell turnover

B

Bacilli (ba-**SIL**-eye) – The most common form of bacterial cells; bar or rod-shaped cells that can produce a variety of diseases including tetanus, bacterial influenza, typhoid fever, tuberculosis and diphtheria

Bacteria – Also called germs or microbes; one-celled microorganisms that are either disease-producing or non-disease producing

Bacterial infection – Disease developed when microbes invade an injured, open or wounded part of the body

Bacteriology – The study of **bacteria**

Barba – Thick, coarse hair that grows on the face to form a beard

Barbae folliculitis – Also called ingrown hair; a hair that grows from underneath into the surrounding tissue rather than through the follicle out to the surface of the skin, resulting in a bump or inflammation; can occur when the hair curls and continues growing back into the skin

Basal (**BAY**-zel) **cells** – Cells that divide and produce new cells to replace skin cells that have been shed

Basal cell carcinoma (car-sin-**O**-ma) – Common malignant lesion that tends to appear translucent, has irregular borders and tiny blood vessels running through it

Base – A chemical solution that releases negatively charged hydroxide ions

Belly – The midsection of the muscle, between the two attached sections

Benefit – A result that an ingredient delivers to enhance the appearance or improve the condition of the client's skin

Benign growth – Also called **mole**; regularly shaped skin growth; harmless collection of pigmented cells; can be raised or flat

Benzoyl Peroxide – Ingredient used to dry and exfoliate

Beta hydroxy acid – Ingredient with the carboxyl group located on the second carbon atom of the chain

Bicep (**BI**-sep) – Primary muscle in the front of the upper arm; raises the forearm, bends the elbow and turns the palm of the hand down

Bikini wax – Waxing service that removes unwanted hair that appears along the panty line, but does not include the pubic area

Biochemistry – Study of chemical reactions, such as growth, reproduction and respiration, that occur within a living organism

Blackhead – Open follicle with a black surface plug, which has been oxidized and discolored due to the **sebum**'s contact with the air

Blend method – Method of electrolysis that combines Galvanic and short-wave current

Blepharoplasty (BLEF-a-row-PLAS-tee) – Eyelid surgery to remove excess fat, skin or muscle from the upper and lower eyelids

Blood – Sticky, salty fluid that circulates through the body, bringing nourishment and oxygen to all body parts and carrying toxins and waste products to the liver and kidneys to be eliminated

Bloodborne pathogen – **Bacteria** or **virus** that flow through the blood or body fluids and cause infectious diseases

Bloodborne Pathogen Standard – Regulation that should be followed for all tools and implements that have come into contact with blood or body fluids; requires the use of an EPA-registered, hospital-level disinfectant that is labeled as effective against HIV and HBV or tuberculocidal

Blood platelets (**PLATE**-lets) – Also called thrombocytes (**THROM**-bo-sites); cells that begin the process of coagulation, or clotting, when exposed to air or trauma in the skin tissue, such as bruising

Blood vessel – Any vessel through which blood circulates in the body

Blush – Cosmetic product sometimes referred to as rouge or cheek color; used to add color to the face, especially to the cheek area

Body scrub – Mechanical exfoliant used to remove dead skin cells and produce smooth, soft, healthy skin

Body wrap – Popular body treatment that creates temporary tightness due to absorption and compaction; when wrapped tightly, body sweats, which in turn causes the skin to lie flatter against underlying muscles

Boil – Also called a **furuncle**; painful infection of a hair follicle and adjacent subcutaneous tissue that appears as a firm nodule with a central, hard, pus-filled core

Bones – Body's hardest structures with a composition that is two-thirds mineral matter and one-third organic matter

Botanical – Cosmetic ingredient; general classification for a wide variety of natural or naturally derived ingredients extracted from plants

Brazilian wax – Waxing service; removes all pubic hair entirely

Broad-spectrum disinfectant – Formerly known as a hospital-level disinfectant; germicidal, fungicidal, pseudomonacidal and virucidal and must be effective against HIV and HBV or tuberculocidal

Bromidrosis (broh-mih-**DROH**-sis) – Sometimes called **osmidrosis**; a foul-smelling perspiration caused by the yeast and **bacteria** that break down the sweat on the surface of skin

Bronchi (bron-**KEE**) – Also called bronchial tree; deliver air directly to the lungs

Brush – Implement used to apply makeup; specific to product types

Brush cleaner – Makeup supplement that cleanses, sanitizes and maintains brushes

Buccal (BUK-al) branch – Branch of facial nerve that extends to the muscles of the mouth

Buccinator (BUK-si-na-ter) – Muscle located between the jaws and cheek; compresses the cheek to release air outward, as in blowing

Bulla (BOO-la) – Lesion similar to a vesicle, but larger, found above and below the skin; contains a clear watery fluid; also known as a blister

Burn – Damage or injury to the skin by fire, heat, radiation, electricity or a caustic agent, such as a chemical

Burr – Tool with an abrasive rotating attachment used to scrape away the surface of the skin

Business card – Card printed with a company logo, name, address and phone number given to current and potential clients

Business plan – Central company document that owner and employees use to make decisions

C

Calibration – Adjustment of settings on a piece of equipment so that it operates safely according to the manufacturer's instructions and within tolerances set forth by state law

Calorie – Unit measuring energy found in food

Camouflage makeup – Makeup application used to normalize the appearance of clients who have experienced disfigurement from surgery, an accident, disease or a congenital condition

Candida (kan-deed-ah) – Also known as **yeast infection**; superficial infections that occur on moist areas of the skin

Candida albicans (kan-deed-ah ALL-be-kanz) – Common skin infection caused by yeast

Caninus (kay-NEYE-nus) – Also known as the **levator** anguli oris; muscle located above the corners of the mouth; raises the angle of the mouth, as in snarling

Capillary – Small vessel that takes nutrients and oxygen from the arteries to the cells and takes waste products from the cells to the veins

Capilli – Hair that grows on the scalp

Carbohydrate – Major energy source found in whole grains, vegetables, fruits, legumes, nuts and seeds; should account for 45 to 65% of daily nutrient intake; used in body to store energy

Carbonic gas spray – A high-powered spray that results in a deep pore cleansing for oily and acne-prone skin; commonly used after extraction or suction

Carbuncle (KAR-bun-kel) – Sebaceous gland disorder; group of boils; very painful acute bacterial infection characterized by inflammation that involves several hair follicles and the adjacent subcutaneous tissue

Cardiac muscle – Muscle of the heart itself and the only muscle of its type in the human body; functions involuntarily

Cardiovascular system – Also known as the blood vascular system; includes the heart, arteries, veins and capillaries; circulates the blood

Carpals (KAR-pels) – Eight small bones held together by ligaments to form the wrist or carpus

Carpal Tunnel Syndrome – Condition caused by tendonitis in which the tendons swell, pinch the nerve in the carpal tunnel making the hand numb and weak

Carrier oil – Neutral oil, most often grape seed, almond, apricot kernel, jojoba or olive; used to dilute an essential oil

Cartilage – Connective tissue that lines the parts of the bones that would otherwise rub against each other in joints

Catabolism (kah-TAB-oh-lizm) – Process of breaking down larger molecules or substances into smaller ones

Catagen – Transitional and shortest phase of hair growth cycle; phase in which the hair begins to destroy itself as it disconnects from the papilla

Cataphoresis – Type of **phoresis** that allows an acidic solution to enter the skin when assisted by **Galvanic Current** and the positive pole of an electrode

Cathode – Negatively charged electrode

Cell – Body structure considered the basic unit of life

Cell membrane – Outer surface and enclosing structure of the cell

Cellulite – Deposit of fat, water and waste materials trapped between skin fibers

Cellulite massage treatment – Skin treatment used to reduce the appearance of cellulite by increasing circulation

Cellulite wrap – Skin treatment that softens or eliminates the appearance of cellulite by increasing circulation and making skin look firmer; encourages the body to release toxins and excess fluids that may be trapped in the tissues

Central nervous system – Also called the cerebrospinal nervous system; composed of the brain and spinal cord; controls all voluntary and involuntary body action

Cerebellum (ser-e-**BEL**-um) – Structure of the brain that regulates motor function, muscle movement and balance; located in the occipital area directly below the cerebrum

Cerebrum (se-**REE**-brum) – Large, rounded structure of the brain that occupies the upper front part of the cranial cavity; center of higher mental functions, such as thought, emotion and memory

Cervical (**SUR**-vi-kal) **branch** – Body structure extending to the muscles on the side of the neck

Cervical cutaneous (**SUR**-vi-kal ku-**TA**-ne-us) **nerve** – Nerve that extends into the side and front of the neck to the breastbone

Cervical vertebrae (**SUR**-vi-kel **VURT**-e-bray) – The seven bones that form the top part of the spinal column

Chamomile – Ingredient that can be used for any skin condition or in any treatment; provides soothing, healing, anti-inflammatory, antiseptic and antimicrobial benefits

Chelating agent – Ingredient added to a product to enhance the effectiveness of the preservative

Chemical behavior – Reactivity of an atom

Chemical bond –Any of several forces or mechanisms by which atoms are bound in a molecule

Chemical burn – Skin condition; burn or burning sensation to a client's skin caused by certain chemicals

Chemical change – Process that occurs in a substance and creates a new substance with different material characteristics from those of the original substance

Chemical depilatory – Painless hair removal method that dissolves the hair at skin level

Chemical exfoliant – Product consisting of a natural substance, such as an enzyme or **alpha hydroxy acid**; works in conjunction with other ingredients to cause a chemical reaction that removes dead skin cells

Chemical exfoliation – Process of using natural substances, such as enzymes or **alpha hydroxy acid** in conjunction with other ingredients to cause a chemical reaction to remove dead skin cells

Chemical peel – Chemical solution used to exfoliate the surface of the skin, promote cell turnover and induce desquamation of the stratum corneum

Chemical symbol – Notation that describes atoms in a molecule

Chemiclave – Machine that sterilizes surgical instruments with high-pressure, high-temperature water vapor, alcohol and formaldehyde vapor

Chemist – Scientist who studies matter, its properties and changes

Chemistry – Scientific study of matter, the physical and chemical changes affecting matter and the energy changes that accompany those processes

Chemotherapy – Radiation treatment that may heighten a client's sensitivity and cause thinning of the skin

Chiaroscuro (key-ar-o-**SKU**-ro) – Art of arranging light and dark so as to produce the illusion of three-dimensional shapes

Chloasma (kloh-**AZ**-mah) – Also called **melasma** (**MEL-AZ**-mah); common skin condition in pregnant women that results in increased pigmentation causing flat, light-to-dark patches to occur on the face

Chronic – Term used to identify conditions that are frequent and continuing, persisting for a period of three months or more

Chucking – Massage manipulation; form of friction used on the arms and body; performed by holding the client's arm in one hand and lifting the skin firmly up and down over the bone with the other hand

Cilia (**SIL**-ee-a) – Hair-like projections found in the cells used to move cells with a wave-like motion; type of hair found in eyelashes

Circuit breaker – Safety device that breaks the flow of current when an overload occurs; contains two pieces of metal that make contact with each other to allow the flow of electric current

Circulatory system – Also known as the vascular system; body system that controls the circulation of blood and lymph through the body

Clavicle (KLAV-i-kel) – Also known as the collarbone; bone that runs across the chest between the shoulders

Clay/Mud mask – Component of a facial procedure; facial mask rich in minerals, clay and mud derived from the earth; absorbs excess oil, tightens and refines the pores and aids in preventing clogging

Cleanser/makeup remover – Solution that removes dirt, makeup and impurities

Cleansing – First step in a daily skin care regimen; designed to remove dirt, oil, makeup and environmental pollutants from the surface of the skin

Cleansing crème – Solution that removes impurities from the skin

Client care – Also known as personal care; method of caring for clients

Client Consultation – Communication exchange in which skin care provider offers expert advise based on the personal needs of the client

Client Consultation Form – Form filled out at the beginning of each visit that helps the esthetician obtain information pertinent to the facial procedure

Clientele – Description identifying client base developed and maintained by an esthetician; consists of both the clients you serve repeatedly as well as those that you try to "recruit" as repeat customers

Client Release Statement – Form that gives the esthetician permission to treat clients based on the information they have provided during consultation; may protect the skin care center, esthetics business owner or individual esthetician from some claims related to accidents in the skin care center or damage that may occur to the client's skin as a result of services provided

Closed Comedo – Also called a **whitehead**; sebaceous gland whose opening is partially plugged or not widely dilated

Closed path – Electrical circuit; path on which the electricity leaves the source and travels to an appliance in order to power it

Closing the sale – Selling strategy that involves presenting a product and asking for a commitment

Cocci (KOK-sigh) – Spherical or round-shaped bacterial cells that appear singularly or in groups

Co-Enzyme Q-10 – known as ubiquinone; powerful antioxidant that occurs naturally in human cells

Cold sore – Highly contagious viral infection triggered when the body or skin is placed under extreme stress, such as a laser treatment

Collagen – Fibrous protein substance that forms bundles that strengthen and give structure to components of the human body, including skin, joints, bones and ligaments

Collagen injection – Injections of collagen into a treatment site using a fine needle inserted at several points

Coloring agent – Vegetable, mineral or pigment dye added to products to enhance their appearance

Color wheel – Circular diagram in which the 12 colors, (three primary, three secondary and 6 tertiary), are positioned in a circle; position on the wheel demonstrates the relationship of each color to the primary colors

Combination skin – Skin type that displays both dry and oily areas; most common skin type

Comedogenic – Ingredient likely to block or clog pores and contribute to pimples

Comedogenicity – Tendency to clog

Comedone extractor – Metal implement used to ease the removal of comedones

Commission – Employee compensation based on a percentage of the dollar income the individual esthetician generates by serving clients and selling products

Common carotid (kah-ROT-id) **arteries (CCA)** – Arteries located on either side of the neck; supply blood to the head, face and neck; split into the internal carotid artery (ICA) and the external carotid artery (ECA)

Communicable disease – Also known as contagious illness; condition capable of being transmitted from person to person as well as from animal to human; communicable by casual contact

Communication – Exchange of thought, verbally or nonverbally

Comparison shopping – Process of visiting competitors to compare their business practices to your own

Compensation – Earnings paid to an employee; **compensation package** includes benefits

Complementary color scheme – Art principle that uses colors directly across from each other on the color wheel to achieve the greatest amount of contrast; often used to enhance eye color

Completion – Final phase of Client Consultation in which the esthetician solicits feedback, recommends a home care regimen and retail products, schedules the client's next appointment and expresses appreciation while saying goodbye

Complimentary consultation – Brief 15-minute interview that allows the opportunity to become familiar with a potential new client, discover what his or her skin care needs are and share options available to make a difference on the client's skin

Compound – Combination created by chemically uniting two different elements

Concealer – Makeup product that includes crème, liquid, stick and pot formulations used to correct particular facial imperfections

Conchae (KONG-kee) – Mucus membrane that warms inhaled air as it passes through the nasal passages

Conduction – The transfer of heat via direct contact

Conductor – Material through which electricity can flow easily

Conjunctivitis – Also known as **pink eye**; extremely contagious bacterial infection that affects the membrane that lines the eyelids

Connective tissue – Tissue that supports, protects and holds the body together

Consultation – A meeting with the client to determine the client's needs and expectations and to explain what will be best for the skin and its appearance

Contact dermatitis – Rash caused either by an allergic reaction from contact with substances, such as dyes, detergents, nickel, fabrics or plants, or by non-allergic irritation from contact with these substances

Contagious – Disease that is communicable by contact; also known as a communicable disease

Contaminated – Term that identifies objects containing pathogens; not free from dirt, oil and/or microbes

Continuing education credits (CEUs) – Required number of educational credits earned each year as a part of the licensure agreement

Contour – Process of creating an outline, especially of a curving or irregular figure or shape

Contraction – Tightening movement of a muscle in which the insertion of the muscle moves while the origin remains fixed

Contraindication – Condition signaling that it is inadvisable to perform an esthetics procedure

Convection – Transfer of heat via liquid or gas

Converter – Instrument used to change **direct current** to **alternating current**

Cool color – Color tone classification containing blue undertones; generally categorized in the blue and green half of the color wheel

Cool undertone – Color tone classification that contains blue/violet or reddish/red-violet undertone

Co-op promotion – Advertising technique combining one's own business promotional efforts and dollars with non-competitive businesses, shops and stores into a single campaign

Corporation – Type of business ownership in which a group of people form a legal entity, separate from its members, formed under legal guidelines; has a charter describing the purposes of the corporation and the structure of the company, owned by its shareholders

Correspondence – Marketing strategy in which the professional sends thank-you cards to clients after appointments, calls new clients after first visit to follow up, mails out reminder notes a week prior to appointments or calls the day before an appointment to offer a friendly reminder

Corrugator (KOR-e-gat-er) – Muscle located under the eyebrows; causes eyebrows to draw in and downward

Cosmetic – Descriptive term for articles intended to be rubbed, poured, sprinkled or sprayed on or introduced onto or otherwise applied to the human body or as part thereof for cleansing, beautifying, promoting attractiveness or altering the appearance, and articles intended for use as a component of any such articles; except that such a term shall not include soaps; as defined by the FFDCA

Cosmetic ingredient allergen – Color and fragrance that can cause an allergic reaction

Cosmetic surgeon – Also known as a **plastic surgeon**; medical doctor who specializes in cosmetic and/or reconstructive surgery

Cosmetic surgery – Also called **plastic or reconstructive surgery**; medical procedure performed for aesthetic and reconstructive purposes

Couperose – Skin condition that displays fine dilated capillaries; most frequently found on the cheeks and corner of the nose

Covalent bond – Chemical term that identifies the sharing of electrons by two atoms

CPR *abbr.* **cardiopulmonary resuscitation** – Emergency first aid used to restart the heart once it has stopped

Cranial nerves – Twelve pairs of nerves that connect the brain directly with other parts of the body, specifically the face, head and neck

Cranium – Anatomy term used to describe the eight bones that enclose and protect the brain and primary sensory organs

Crème – Most common cosmetic product type on the market; used to impart emolliency and moisturization on the skin; has a heavier consistency and is used when additional coverage is desired

Crème mask – Component of a facial procedure that uses a rich and creamy-textured product ideal for dry skin types; generally rich in moisturizers, humectants and other nutrient-rich ingredients, such as vitamins

Crème-to-powder – Also known as powder, "one-step" or "dual-finish"; cosmetic product that combines makeup base and powder in one and provides minimum coverage and creates a natural effect

Critical objects – Highest level of **infection control**; required for objects coming in contact with sterile tissue or the vascular system

Cross-contamination – Spread of **bacteria** by contaminated equipment, surfaces or food

Cross-selling – Strategy used in the marketing or recommending of a product that complements another product the client has already purchased

Crust – Dried mass that is the remains of an oozing sore

Customer service – Process of personal attention to meet the needs of the client by displaying a willingness to show concern for a client's personal well-being

Customizing – Strategy for finding the appropriate product to fit the needs of the client

Cyclomethicone – Non-comedogenic emollient that gives products a silky feel

Cyst (sist) – Skin condition that describes an abnormal membranous sac containing a gaseous, liquid or semi-solid substance

Cytoplasm (**SI**-to-plazm) – Anatomy term that describes the production department of the cell, where organelles are found

D

Decoctions – Mixtures created by boiling loose herbs in water

Décolleté (dek-o-**LAH-TAY**) – Term that identifies the upper chest area

Decontaminated – Term that identifies objects from which pathogens have been removed; free from dirt, oil and/or microbes

Deep peel – Medical treatment that uses phenol to remove dead skin cells; performed by a medical doctor; affects the dermis more intensely than medium-depth peel because it uses stronger products

Dehydration – Term that identifies a loss of fluids; lack of moisture in the skin characterized by superficial dryness, flakiness and lines

Delivery – Phase four of Client Consultation; also called the "feature/benefit" phase; goals of this phase are to ensure client comfort, educate the client, explain what is taking place and attain results that satisfy the client's needs and wants

Deltoid (**DEL**-toid) – Triangular-shaped muscle covering the shoulder; lifts the arm or turns it

Demand-release chlorine dioxide – Agent that sterilizes after six hours

Dendrites (**DEN**-dritz) – Short fibers extending from the nerve cell

Depressor (de-**PRES**-er) – Muscle that draws down or depresses

Depressor septi – One of the four muscles located inside the nose; helps control contraction and expansion of the nostrils

Dermabrasion – Skin treatment using a motorized rough wire brush or a burr to scrape away the surface of the skin; can reach as deep as the dermis

Dermaplaning – Surgical procedure using a dermatome to remove the surface of the skin that has grown higher around scarred or wrinkled areas; levels the skin

Dermascope – An elaborate magnifying mirror/light that incorporates a black light; also called a **skin scope**

Dermatitis – Inflammatory disorder of the skin

Dermatitis Venenata – Allergic reaction to certain cosmetics or chemicals; form of contact dermatitis that frequently occurs on the skin of professionals working with wet product

Dermatologist – Physician who specializes in diagnosing and treating diseases of the skin, hair and nails

Dermatology – Study of the skin, its structure, functions, diseases and treatment

Dermatome – Oscillating blade

Dermis – Second layer of the skin; also called the dermal layer, derma, corium, cutis or true skin

Desincrustation – Process that unblocks clogged pores, making it easier to remove debris

Desincrustation facial treatment – Treatment that utilizes **Galvanic Current** in conjunction with an **alkaline** solution to force the solution deep into the skin

Desincrustation solution – Highly **alkaline** solution that liquifies **sebum**

Desmosomes (**DEZ**-ma-sohms) – Intercellular connections that interconnect keratinocytes

Desquamation – Process in which skin sheds, peels or comes off in scales

Diabetes – Medical condition; clients with this condition may often have a decreased sensitivity in their hands and feet and may not fully experience sensations

Diagnosis – Identification of a disease based on the presence of certain characteristics

Diamond facial shape – -The diamond-shaped face is identified by predominant width through the cheekbones that is contrasted by a narrow forehead, chin and jaw area

Diaphragm – Muscular organ that separates the chest cavity from the abdomen

Digestive system – Body system that breaks food down into simpler chemical compounds that can be easily absorbed by cells or eliminated from the body as waste

Digital nerve – Nerve of the hand that extends into the fingers of the hand

Dilator (**DI**-la-ter) – Muscle that opens, enlarges or expands

Dimethicone – Silicone oil used to give products lubricity or "slip"

Dimethicone Copolyol – Silicone ingredient that makes products feel soft, especially sunscreens

Diopter – Measurement of the degree of magnification

Diplococci (dip-lo-**KOK**-sigh) – Bacterial cells that grow in pairs and are the cause of certain infections, including pneumonia

Direct current – Constant current in which electrons move at an even rate and flow in only one direction

Direct Faradic Current treatment – Method of application in which the esthetician places both electrodes on the client's skin, being certain that the electrodes never touch

Direct High Frequency Current treatment – Method of application in which a skin care specialist uses an electrode in direct contact with the client's skin to deliver antibacterial and drying benefits to the skin

Direct mail advertising – Advertising technique that involves sending postcards or flyers to prospective clients encouraging them to try a new service

Disaccharides – Term describing two saccharides linked together; carbohydrate or table sugar

Disc – Body structure located between each pair of vertebrae and filled with a jelly-like substance; offers flexibility to the neck and back

Discretionary income – Money available to be spent freely

Disinfection – Process of eliminating **bacteria**, **viruses** and most organisms on inanimate non-porous surfaces

Display – Floor space allocated to exhibit retail merchandise; visual sales tool that lets you be creative

Disposable facial sponge – Sponge that removes product from the face and neck

Distributor – "Middleman" who maintains contracts to sell professional products or equipment; acts as a link between the manufacturer and the skin care center

Dome brush – Also called a large fluff or powder puff; brush used for the application of powder

Drug – Product intended to treat symptoms or cure medical conditions, including altering the function and/or structure of parts of the human body

Dry skin – Type of skin lacking adequate **sebum** production; exhibits heightened sensitivity; prone to fine lines and wrinkles

Dyschromia – Abnormal pigmentation

E

Ecchymosis – Clinical term for bruising of the skin

Eccrine glands – Sweat glands located throughout the entire body; most abundant on the forehead, the palms of the hands and soles of the feet; open directly onto the skin's surface through pores not associated with hair follicles

Ecology – The scientific study of the relationship of organisms to each other and to their environment

Eczema – Skin condition characterized by dry or moist lesions, an eruption of small vesicles and watery discharge

Edema – Skin condition involving the swelling of tissue or skin caused by an excessive accumulation of fluid in the tissue

Efficacy – Ability to produce results or effectiveness

Efficacy label – Label required on all disinfectants to inform the user about what organisms the product is effective against

Effleurage (ef-lure-AH-jh) – Massage movement involving a light, relaxing, smooth, gentle, stroking or circular movement carried out with the pads of the fingertips or the palms of the hands

Elastin – Fibrous protein, similar to collagen; basis of what forms elastic tissue

Electrical burn – Burn that occurs when flesh comes into contact with a flow of electrical current; usually the result of faulty equipment or improper use of equipment

Electrical shock – Human contact with an electric current

Electric current – Flow of electricity along a conductor; also known as **modality**

Electricity – Form of energy that produces light, heat, magnetic and chemical changes

Electric mask – Component of a facial procedure that produces warm moist heat at a comfortable temperature; used to help soften the skin to aid in deeper pore penetration of products

Electric pulverizer – Unique atomizer that allows for the application of various herbs, extracts or astringents to the skin in a very fine mist

Electric treatment mittens and booties – Electrically heated hand and foot covers used to penetrate a product deeper into the skin

Electrochemical effect – Effect on the skin of the passage of electric current through a water-based solution and onto the body

Electrocution – Severe electric shock that occurs when the current passes through the nervous system, causing the heart and breathing to stop; also called **general shock**

Electrode – Conductor used to bring current from an appliance to the client's skin

Electrologist – Person specializing in electrolysis

Electrolysis – Method of hair removal that requires the technician to insert a small needle into each hair follicle, at the angle of the follicle and alongside the hair, until it reaches the root

Electromagnetic radiation – Wave patterns of electrons created when heat energy is transferred by radiation

Electromagnetic spectrum – The range of all the wavelengths that can be produced by radiant energy

Electron – Tiny, negatively charged particle that enables atoms to unite with other atoms to form bonds

Electrotherapy – Application of electrical currents during treatments to the skin

Element – Basic unit of matter; cannot be broken down into simpler substances by any chemical reaction

EMDA *abbr.* **Esthetic Manufacturers and Distribution Alliance** – Association that establishes procedural guidelines to ensure safety and consistency in the use of **alpha hydroxyl acids** for chemical peels

Emollient (ee-**MAHL**-ee-ent) – Oil and oil-soluble substance used to condition and soften the skin by providing an occlusive barrier

Emulsifier – Binding substance used to slow down the destruction of the product

Emulsifying agent – Chemical structure with polar and non-polar ends allowing compatibility with both water and oil due to chemical structure of a polar and non-polar end; binds ingredients together

Emulsion – Mixture of two or more nonmixable substances, such as oil and water, united by small droplets of a binder or gum-like substance

Endocrine gland – Gland that releases secretions into the blood; known as a ductless gland

Endocrine system – Group of specialized ductless glands that regulates and controls the growth, reproduction and health of the body

Energy – The ability to do work to accomplish some change

Enfleurage – Process of steeping material in odorless oils or fats, which in turn absorb the material's fragrance

Environmental allergens – Substances, including pollen, animals and food, that cause increased sensitivity to products and stimulation of the skin

Environmental Protection Agency (EPA) – Organization in charge of approving the efficacy of products used for infection control

Enzyme – Ingredient designed to dissolve keratin proteins on the surface of the skin, resulting in exfoliation and softer, smoother skin; material that breaks down large molecules into smaller ones; secretions from the salivary glands that break down food during digestion

Enzyme exfoliator – Product designed to dissolve dead skin cells; can often tingle or itch

EPA Standards – Guideline requiring efficacy labels on all disinfectants to inform the user about what organisms the product is effective against

Epicranium (ep-i-**KRA**-nee-um) – Scalp

Epicranius (ep-i-**KRA**-nee-us) – Broad muscle covering the scalp or **epicranium**

Epidermis – Outermost layer of the skin; also referred to as cuticle, scarf skin or epidermal layer

Epilepsy – Medical condition; clients with this condition should not have any services using **electrical current**

Epithelial (ep-i-**THE**-lee-el) (ep-eh-**THEE**-lee-el) **cells** – Cells that cover and protect the inside of the body

Epithelial (ep-i-**THE**-lee-el) **tissue** – Tissue covering and protecting body surfaces and internal organs

Ergonomics – Science that studies the relationship between people and their work environment

Erythema – Redness of the skin caused by dilation or congestion of the capillaries; **rash**

Esophagus (e-**SOF**-ah-gus) – Passage between the pharynx and the stomach

Essential fatty acid (EFA) – Nutrient that produces hormones and helps protect against heart disease, cancer, autoimmune diseases and skin diseases

Essential oil – Natural cosmetic ingredient distilled from plant materials

Ethics – Rules that determine right and wrong conduct in relationships with others

Ethmoid (**ETH**-moid) **bone** – Spongy bone between the eyes that forms part of the nasal cavity

Ethyl Alcohol (70%) – Anti-bacterial, anti-fungal and antiviral alcohol; but does not destroy bacterial spores

Ethylene Oxide Gas – Sterilization method ideal for porous or difficult-to-clean, narrow, channeled implements

Etiology – Study of the cause of diseases, disorders or conditions

Eucalyptus oil – Essential oil used to treat stiff, sore muscles or to boost circulation; has stimulating, analgesic, antiseptic, antimicrobial and anti-inflammatory properties

Evening makeup – Type of makeup that tends to be more dramatic; colors are often deeper and more intense; these colors help enhance the definition of facial features in dimmer evening light without creating a look that is too severe

Excoriation (ek-score-ee-**AY**-shun) – Mechanical abrasion of the **epidermis** that occurs when insect bites, scabs or acne breakouts are scratched

Excretory system – System that eliminates solid, liquid and gaseous waste products from the body

Exercise – Activities that develop and sustain muscle tone and help stimulate blood circulation and metabolism, allowing the body to function at optimal performance

Exfoliation – Process of removing dead skin to stimulate new cell growth

Exfoliator – Makeup product used to remove excess surface skin cells

Exhalation – Respiratory process of breathing out to eliminate oxygen's toxic by-product, carbon dioxide

Exocrine gland – Gland that releases secretion into a duct that deposits the glandular secretion onto the surface of the skin

Expansion – Relaxing movement of a muscle

Expression – Method of obtaining essential oil by squeezing out an ingredient's fragrant oils

Extensor radialis (eks-**TEN**-sor ray-dee-**AHL**-is) – Muscle located mid-forearm, on the outside of the arm; straightens the fingers and wrists

External carotid artery (ECA) – Artery branching into smaller arteries, supplying blood to the skin and muscles of the head

External jugular (**JUG**-u-lur) **vein (EJV)** – Vein that returns blood to the head, face and neck

External maxillary (**EKS**-tur-nal **MAK**-si-ler-ee) **artery** – Also known as the **facial artery**; supplies blood to the lower portion of the face, including the mouth and nose

External parasites (**PEAR**-uh-sights) – Organisms that grow and feed on other living organisms, contribute nothing to their host and cause contagious diseases

Extraction – Procedure using a chemical solvent, such as petroleum or ether, to leach the aromatic component from an ingredient

Extrinsic aging – Also known as skin deterioration; aging factor caused by external factors within an individual's control, sun exposure, smoking and alcohol

Eyebrow pencil/powder – Makeup product that fills in, defines and/or corrects shape of the eyebrows

Eyebrow shaping – Technique removing excess or unwanted hair from the eyebrow area; essential part of grooming

Eyebrow tinting – Process involving darkening the eyebrows with a semi-permanent tint product

Eyebrow wax – Process of removing eyebrow hair using wax to shape and improve the look of the entire face

Eye contact – Nonverbal gesture that demonstrates undivided attention and personal confidence

Eye crème – Product that supports, moisturizes and cushions tissue around the eyes

Eyelash/eyebrow tinting – Technique involving the darkening of the eyebrows and eyelashes with a semi-permanent tint product

Eyeliner – Product used in makeup application to accent and emphasize the shape and size of the eyes and to enhance the thickness of the lashes; comes in liquid, pencil and powder; usually applied at the lashline, below the lashes or above the lashes on the eyelid

Eye shadow – Product used to highlight and accentuate the color and shape of the eyes; can be used to create more contour or to exaggerate areas, such as the crease; comes in many forms, including crayon, gel, powder and pencil

F

Facial (**FAY**-shul) **artery** – Also known as the **external maxillary**; artery that supplies blood to the lower portion of the face, including the mouth and nose

Facial chair – Specialized piece of equipment that allows client to be positioned at proper height and angle for service

Facial nerve – Also known as the seventh cranial nerve; chief motor nerve of the face that controls the motion of the face, scalp, neck, ear and sections of the palate and tongue

Facial steamer – Also known as a facial vaporizer or atomizer; electrical device that sprays a lukewarm, diffused vapor mist onto the surface of the facial skin; expands pores for cleansing and softens dead skin cells for easier removal

Fan brush – Brush used to apply product on face or neck

Faradic Current – An alternating current (AC), which is interrupted to produce a mechanical, non-chemical reaction

Fat injection – Also called **autologous fat transplantation** or **microlipoinjection**; type of injection removing fat with a syringe from a "donor site," such as the patient's abdomen, thigh or buttock and injecting it into the area to be treated

Fats – Source of concentrated energy that provides the body with necessary fatty acids; a healthy diet includes approximately 30% unsaturated fat

Fatty acid – Cosmetic ingredient derived from plant and animal sources; used as an ingredient to assist in keeping crèmes and lotions easy to apply

GLOSSARY

Fatty alcohol – Fatty acids that have been exposed to hydrogen

Feature – The product's characteristics, such as the size of the container, the aroma or a specific ingredient that makes it effective

Fibroblast (FI-bro-blast) cells – type of cells responsible for the formation of fibers; aid in the production of collagen and elastin

First-degree burn – Minor burn that affects the outer layer of skin (**epidermis**); accompanied by pain, swelling and redness; does not produce blisters; least severe type of burn

Fissure (FISH-er) – Crack or line in the skin that may penetrate as deep as the dermis

Fitzpatrick Scale – Phototype scale shows how different skin types react to UV radiation

Fixative – Oily ingredient that adds a warm, musky odor and also prevents a fragrance from quickly evaporating

Fixed cost – Cost that does not change from month to month for at least one year; includes the rent or mortgage payment, salaries and insurance

Fixed rent – Set dollar amount paid each month to the lessor; allows renter to predict monthly expenses

Flagella (flah-JEL-ah) – Hair-like projections that move the cells using a wave-like motion

Flat bones – Plate-shaped bones located in the skull, the scapula, hip bone, sternum, ribs and the patella

Flexor ulnaris (FLEX-er uhl-NAR-is) – Muscle located mid-forearm, on the inside of the arm; bends the wrist and closes the fingers

Floor plan – Drawing or blueprint depicting the various areas, fixtures and operations of the skin care center

Floral – Fragrances that smell strongly of a single flower, such as gardenia, orchid, rose, jasmine, orange blossom, tuberose or freesia

Floral bouquet – Fragrances made up of several floral scents

Fluorescent light – An economical and long-lasting light source that can create "blue" tones or "cool" casts in objects it lights

Follow-up – Service necessary in order to guarantee client satisfaction

Fomentation – A treatment that involves soaking a clean towel in a liquid and applying it to a specific area of the body

Forest blend fragrance – Also known as wood blend; encompasses many men's fragrances; combination of woods, such as sandalwood, pine, eucalyptus, cedar, rosewood or even tobacco

Foundation – Cosmetic product that evens out skin color and creates a smoother skin texture; used to correct undesirable skin tones and conceal imperfections; often used to achieve the effects of facial contouring/shading

Fragrance – Complex blend of many essential oils and other compounds used to create unique scents

Fragrance-free – Term denoting a product with less than 1% fragrance added or no added fragrance at all

Franchise – Operating license; agreement in which a fee is paid to a parent corporation in exchange for fixtures, promotion, advertising, education, management techniques and name

Free electron – Electron in atom's outermost orbit that is easily moved from its orbit

Free radical – Chemically unstable molecule, caused by environmental pollutants and UV exposure; creates a chain reaction with other components in the skin, causing damage and inhibiting proper functioning within the skin

Frequency – Number of times electrons alternate direction per second

Friction (FRIK-shun) – Circular or wringing massage manipulation with no gliding; usually performed with the fingertips or palms of the hands

Frontal artery – Artery that supplies the forehead with blood

Frontal bone – Bone that extends from the top of the eyes to the top of the head and forms the forehead

Frontalis (frun-TAL-is) muscle – Muscle that extends from the forehead to the top of the skull; raises the eyebrows or draws the scalp forward

Fruit blend fragrance – Fresh, often sweet, fragrance concocted with the aroma of common and uncommon fruit, such as citrus, apple, melon, pear, berry or pomegranate

Fulling – Massage movement; form of petrissage most frequently used during a hand and arm massage

Furuncle (fu-**RUN**-kel) – Also called a **boil**; a painful infection of a hair follicle and adjacent subcutaneous tissue that appears as a firm nodule with a central, hard, pus-filled core

Fuse – Safety device that prevents electrical wires from overheating

G

Galvanic Current – Also known as **ionization**; the only constant direct current (DC) of low voltage and high amperage that produces an electrochemical effect; used to force water-soluble skin care products into the **epidermis**

Galvanic electrolysis method – Also called the "multiple needle" process; permanent hair removal method that destroys the hair by passing a low level of current into a needle, resulting in a chemical reaction that decomposes the papilla; 12 to 14 needles are inserted into individual follicles at a time

Gases – Matter with definite weight, but indefinite volume and shape

Gel – A product that has been formulated with a thickening agent to increase its viscosity

Gel mask – Component of a facial procedure applied directly to the skin and designed for a wide variety of purposes depending upon the ingredients used

General infection – Also called systemic infection; medical description of an interference in the body's normal state; occurs when the circulatory system carries **bacteria** and their toxins to all parts of the body

General shock – Term describing **electrocution**; passes through the nervous system and causes the heart to stop, breathing to cease and the muscles to convulse

Generator – Machine that converts mechanical energy into electrical energy

Gift-with-purchase – Promotional strategy; also called gift-with-service; clients purchase a treatment or a product at full price and receive a free gift or service or a discounted product or service

Glossopharyngeal (glos-o-fa-**RIN**-jee-ul) **nerve** – Also called the ninth cranial nerve; controls sense of taste

Glucoside – Organic compound with medicinal attributes

Glutaraldehyde-based formulations (2%) – Disinfectants; lower levels of glutaraldehyde phenate are not considered high-level disinfectants and must be used at 2%

Glycolic acid – Cosmetic ingredient; form of **alpha hydroxy acid** that is an excellent source of skin renewal and exfoliation since it has the smallest molecular structure of all AHAs and can penetrate the skin quickly

Gomage – Exfoliating treatment in which a layer of crème is applied to the skin, allowed to dry and then rubbed away

Grade 1 acne – Mild chronic inflammatory skin disorder; consists of open and closed comedones scattered over less than half of the areas of the face or back

Grade 2 acne – Moderate chronic inflammatory skin disorder; consists of an increased number of open and closed comedones as well as an occasional papule or pustule

Grade 3 acne – Moderately severe chronic inflammatory skin disorder; characterized by numerous open and closed comedones, papules, pustules and occasional cysts

Grade 4 acne – Severe chronic inflammatory skin disorder; consists of numerous papules and pustules as well as a large number of cysts on the face, chest and/or back

Greater auricular – Nerve extending into the side of the neck and external ear

Greater occipital – Nerve extending up the back of the scalp to the top of the head

Greeting – Service strategy; Phase one of Client Consultation; gesture of respect; phase in which the professional tries to make positive personal impressions when greeting clients

Gross anatomy – Study of body structures that can be seen with the naked eye

Ground fault circuit interruptor (GFCI) – Safety device consisting of an outlet installed in any area where water and electricity could come in contact; can sense current leakage in an electrical circuit and will interrupt power if there is contact with water, preventing electrical shock

Grounding wire plug – Safety device designed to protect the user during the operation of appliances, especially those in metal cases; contains two rectangular prongs and one circular prong

H

Habit – A learned behavior reinforced through events in the environment

Hacking – Massage manipulation that resembles a chopping movement using the edge of the hands

Hair follicle – Opening that contains the root of a hair; originates in the dermis; rooted in the dermal papilla bulb and nourished by the capillaries

Hair growth retardant – Skin care product that slows the growth of hair after waxing

Hair lightener (bleach) – Chemical solution used to lighten the hair by removing the pigment, making it less obvious; softens the hair, but does not remove hair

Halitosis (hal-eh-**TOH**-sis) – Bad breath

Hand-held exfoliators – Devices used on dry skin to apply cleanser to a particular area of the face or body; include loofahs, body brushes, sponges and washcloths

Hard keratin – Form of hard protein (keratin) that makes up the fingernails

Hard water – Water that contains salts, such as calcium and magnesium

Hard wax – Skin care product warmed in a heated wax pot, applied with a spatula in a thick layer to the skin, allowed to harden and then lifted with the fingers at one end and removed

Healing oil – Oil used to promote cell regeneration for skin repair

Heart facial shape – A wider forehead with a narrow jaw and chinline characterize the heart-shaped face

Heat sterilization – Sterilization method using dual purpose autoclaves/sterilizers used for steam (moist heat) or dry heat ranging from 320° to 375°; takes about 30 minutes to sterilize

Heimlich Maneuver – Emergency technique using abdominal thrusts on a person that is choking

Hemidesmosome (heh-me-**DEZ**-ma-sohm) – Specialized cellular connection located in the lower layer of the stratum germinativum that attaches it to the basement membrane

Hemoglobin (**HEE**-mo-glo-bin) – Protein in the red blood cells that attracts oxygen molecules through oxygenation

Hepatitis B Virus (HBV) – Highly infectious disease that affects the liver

Herpes Simplex (**HER**-peez **SIM**-plex) – Highly contagious viral infection that lies dormant between outbreaks; causes an eruptive, blister-like cluster that is typically found on the mucous membranes or skin around the mouth, nose or genital area

Herpes Simplex lesion (cold sore) – Highly contagious viral infection that causes a blister-like outbreak

Herpes Zoster (**HER**-peez **ZOS**-tur) – Condition caused by the Varicella-Zoster virus, which is a relative of the herpes family that causes chickenpox; also called shingles

Herpetic infection – Also known as cold sores; highly contagious viral infection triggered when the body or skin is placed under extreme stress, such as a laser treatment

Hertz rating – Term that indicates the number of cycles, per second, that a generator alternates current

High blood pressure – Medical condition; clients with this condition should avoid treatments that utilize electrical current, increase body temperature or promote circulation

High Frequency Current – Also referred to as **Tesla Current**; an alternating (or oscillating) current that can be adjusted to different voltages to produce heat or germicidal effects

Hirsutism (**HER**-se-tizm) – Condition typically affecting women; causes dark hair to grow in areas of the body where men usually grow more hair, such as the face, arms, legs and back; heavy growth of hair, often in abnormal distribution

Histology – Study of structures too small to be seen except through a microscope

HIV *abbr.* **Human Immunodeficiency Virus** – Life-threatening viral disease

Hives – Allergic reaction that produces an eruption of **wheals**; also referred to as urticaria

Holiday promotion – Advertising technique capitalizing on yearly celebrations to sell products by running a promotion

Homeostasis (ho-mee-oh-**STAY**-sis) – Body's state of balance

Hormone – Chemical substance manufactured by glands in the endocrine system

Hormone replacement therapy (HRT) – Estrogen or estrogen/progestin medication taken to relieve the symptoms of hormone depletion associated with the natural aging process

Hue – Another term for color

Humectant (hue-**MEK**-tent) – Organic ingredient that binds water and deposits it onto the skin

Humerus (**HU**-mur-us) – Largest bone of the upper arm; extends from the elbow to the shoulder

Hydrochloric (hi-dro-**KLO**-rik) **acid** – **Acid** that breaks down food in the stomach

Hydrotherapy tub treatments – Also called balneotherapy; use of fresh water treatments

Hydroxy acid – Organic **acid** extracted from a variety of natural sources, including fruits, sugar and milk

Hydroxy acid allergens – Alpha and beta hydroxy acids that promote cell turnover and exfoliation; may cause irritation, redness and increased sensitivity, as in an allergic reaction

Hygiene – Applied science that deals with healthful living

Hyoid (**HI**-oid) **bone** – U-shaped bone at the base of the tongue that supports the muscles of the tongue.

Hyperhidrosis (hy-per-hy-**DROH**-sis) – Condition involving an over-production of perspiration caused by excessive heat or general body weakness

Hyperkeratosis – Skin condition involving an excessive amount of keratin cell production on the stratum corneum, or horny layer of the skin

Hyperpigmentation – Skin condition involving excess production of melanin resulting in darker patches

Hypertrichosis (hi-per-tri-KOH-sis) – Condition that causes excessive hair growth; genetically determined; can occur anywhere on the body in both men and women

Hypertrophic scar – Thick, raised scar caused by excessive amounts of collagen

Hypoallergenic – Term describing products less likely to provoke an allergic reaction

Hypoglossal (high-po-**GLOS**-ul) **nerve** – Also known as the twelfth cranial nerve; motor nerve that controls motion of the tongue

Hypopigmentation – Skin condition producing light or white patches resulting from a lack of pigmentation or melanin production

I

I-9 form – Document required by the U.S. Department of Justice, Immigration and Naturalization Service to verify an employee's identity and eligibility to work in the United States

Immersion time – Length of time implements need to be soaked in a disinfecting agent

Immiscible – Solvents that do not mix easily with each other

Immune system – Body's defense mechanism that fights infection

Immunity – Body's ability to destroy infectious agents that enter it

Impetigo (em-**PET**-e-go) – Highly contagious bacterial infection caused by the Staphylococcus Aureus or Streptoccocus A organism

Improvement cost – Amount of money that must be spent to meet a skin care center's unique needs; does not include separate expenses for skin care equipment

Inactive electrode – Electrode held by the client during a treatment

Inactive stage – Inactive, spore-forming stage **bacteria** enter in unfavorable conditions

Incandescent light – Kind of light provided by an ordinary light bulb that creates the closest substitution for natural sunlight; composed of red and yellow light

Income – Also referred to as revenue; all payments received from clients for services performed and home care products purchased

Income tax – Tax paid on the profits or earnings of a business; tax on personal income

Indirect High Frequency Current treatment – Method of application in which current is used to relax the client, aid in the penetration of product and assist in massage for mature skin; during the treatment, the client holds an electrode and the skin care specialist's hands are in direct contact with the client's skin; most frequently used application of Faradic Current

Individual eyelashes – Artificial lashes that are more natural-looking than strip eyelashes; suitable for daytime or evening makeup designs

Infection – Medical term that describes the entry of **pathogenic bacteria** or **viruses** into the body or skin and multiplying to the point of interfering with the body's normal state

Infection control – Prevention of the spread of infectious agents among estheticians and clients

Infectious disease – Disease caused by **bacteria** or **viruses** that can be transmitted from person to person; communicable by invasion of the body

Inferioris (in-**FEER**-ee-or-es) – Term that describes something located below or smaller than

Inferior labial artery – Artery that supplies the lower lip with blood

Inflammation – Body's defense mechanism against harmful **bacteria**; reaction of tissue to irritation characterized by redness, pain, swelling or increased temperature

Infraorbital nerve – Nerve that extends to the lower eyelid, side of the nose, upper lip and mouth

Infrared lamp – Piece of skin care equipment that provides soothing heat that penetrates into the tissues of the body; relaxes the client and softens the skin to allow for penetration of product

Infrared light – Also known as **ultraviolet light**; light that produces heat; benefits include increased circulation and skin gland secretions; relaxes muscles and stimulates cell and tissue activity

Infrared ray – Invisible ray slightly longer than the wavelengths that produce the visible light ray; seen as the color red

Infusion – Phytotherapy method that involves steeping an herb in a container, such as a tea ball or tea bag in boiling water

Inhalation – Respiratory process of breathing in; intake of oxygen to be absorbed into the blood

Inorganic chemistry – Study of the elements in the periodic table and their compounds, excluding the compounds based on carbon

Insertion – Portion of the muscle joined to movable attachments, such as bones, movable muscles or skin

Insulator – Material that does not allow the flow of electric current

Insurance – Protection for the owner of the business from financial difficulties that can follow the unexpected loss of property, income, health and/or life

Integumentary system – The skin and its layers; a basic body system

Intensity – Term that refers to the vibrancy of a color

Intercellular cement – Substance that binds, adds structural strength and mediates biochemical interactions between cells

Internal carotid artery (ICA) – Artery that supplies blood to the brain, eyes and forehead

Internal jugular (JUG-u-lar) **vein (IJV)** – Vein that returns blood to the head, face and neck

Internal Revenue Service (IRS) – Agency that establishes the criteria for reporting a business's profit and loss

Intrinsic aging – Skin's natural aging process

Inventory – All products and items purchased by the skin care center owner for use during services and selling of retail products; itemized list or record of such products

Inventory control – Procedures used in the skin care center to ensure that products are accounted for from the time they are added to the inventory until they are sold or used

Invisible light – Range of light not visible to the human eye

Involuntary muscle – Also known as a non-striated muscle; muscle that responds automatically to control various body functions, including those of the internal organs

Iodophor germicidal detergent solution – Iodine solution that relieves skin irritation and is antiseptic

Ion – Charged atom that attracts or repels another based on charge

Ionic bond – Chemical union of positive and negative ions

Ionization – Also known as **Galvanic Current**; the only constant direct current (DC) of low voltage and high amperage that produces an electrochemical effect

Iontophoresis facial treatment – Skin treatment that utilizes **Galvanic Current** to deeply penetrate nourishing, hydrating and firming ingredients deep into the skin

Irregular bones – bones found in the wrist, ankle or spinal column (the back)

Irresistible close – Term used for moment when client witnesses or experiences the benefits that a product offers making it more difficult to go home without it

Isopropyl Alcohol (90%) – Anti-bacterial, anti-fungal, and antiviral alcohol; does not destroy bacterial **spores** or inactive hydrophilic **viruses**

Isotretinoin – Medication; also known as Accutane®; derivative of Vitamin A prescribed for severe, disfiguring cases of **acne** and certain other skin diseases

J

Jacquet movements – Massage technique that uses gentle kneading and pinching movements designed to force excess **sebum** from the pores

Jessner's Solution – Mixture of salicylic **acid**, resorcinol, lactic **acid** and ethanol, which is used both for superficial and **medium-depth peels**, depending upon the concentration of **acid**

Job description – Written description that serves as an outline of the tasks and responsibilities needed in a new employee and a checklist for future job performance reviews and promotions

Joint – Connective tissue that gives the neck and back flexibility; located between each vertebrae

Joint replacement – Condition that is a contraindication for the use of any electrical equipment

K

Keloids – Thick raised scars caused by excessive amounts of collagen

Keratin – Primary component of skin cells made up of a protein substance; contains several chemical elements, such as carbon, nitrogen, hydrogen, oxygen and sulfur

Keratinization – Chemical conversion of living cells into dead protein cells

Keratinocyte (**CARE**-a-tin-o-site) – Skin cell located throughout the **epidermis**; consists of keratin

Keratohyalin – Specialized proteins

Keratolytic medication – Crème or ointment used to promote rapid cell turnover and exfoliation

Keratosis – Build up of skin cells on the **epidermis**

Kilowatt – Another measurement for watts; 1,000 watts equal one kilowatt; rate at which energy used is measured in **kilowatt hours**

Kinetin – Essential growth factor that slows age-related changes in cultured skin cells; believed to partially reverse clinical signs of photo-damaged facial skin

Krause's end bulb (krow-siz **END** bulb) – Pressure and pain receptor within the dermal layer of the skin

L

Lacrimal (**LAK**-ri-mal) **bones** – Smallest two bones of the facial skeleton; form the front part of the inner, bottom wall of the eye socket

Langerhans (**LANG**-er-hanz) **cells** – Cells found in the stratum spinosum layer of the skin; help protect the body from infection

Lanugo – Soft, downy hair found on the body at birth

Large intestine – Also known as the colon; part of the digestive system that stores the waste for eventual elimination through the anal canal

Larynx (**LAR**-ngks) – Part of the respiratory system that contains the vocal cords and connects the pharynx to the trachea

Laser hair removal – Removal method using wavelengths of light to penetrate and diminish or destroy hair bulbs

Laser resurfacing – Technique using a beam of highly focused light to vaporize the upper layers of damaged skin at specific and controlled levels of penetration

Latex sponge – Makeup implement used to apply foundation and concealer blend and/or clean up

Latissimus dorsi (lah-**TIS**-i-mus **DOR**-si) – Muscle covering the back of the neck and upper back that draws the head back; controls the shoulder blades and swinging motion of the arms

Lavender – Substance used in many facial and body treatments, as well as products; has antiseptic, antimicrobial, soothing, stimulating and healing properties

Law of color – Law that states that, out of all of the colors in the universe, only three are pure

Lawyer – Advisor on the legal obligations of business ownership, borrowing money, signing rental (lease) agreements and assuming tax responsibilities

Lease – Rental agreement

Left atrium (AY-tree-um) – Upper chamber of the heart; commonly referred to as the left auricle

Left ventricle (VEN-tri-kel) – Lower left chamber of the heart

Lentigo (len-**TEE**-goh) – Also known as a freckle; small yellowish or brownish spot on the skin, particularly on the face, hands or neck

Lesion – Wound, injury, infected or diseased patch of skin; change in the structure of the skin tissue; most often caused by injury, damage or skin conditions and diseases

Lesser occipital nerve – Nerve that extends into the muscles at the back of the skull

Leukoderma (loo-ko-**DUR**-mah) – Congenital disorder that occurs when the skin lacks pigmentation (hypopigmentation) due to a decrease in melanocyte activity

Levator (le-**VA**-ter) – Muscle that lifts up

Levator palpebrae (pal-**PEE**-bray) **superioris** – Muscle located above the eyelids; opens the eyelids

Liability – All the money a person owes

Ligament – Dense, strong band of fibrous tissue that holds bones to other bones

Lightener – Ingredient used in skin treatment products in order to bleach or lighten areas of hyperpigmentation

Light therapy – Treatment producing beneficial effects on the body through the use of light rays or waves

Line of credit – Reserve of cash from bank that person can draw upon to meet operating expenses during a slow month or two

Lip brush – Brush used to apply lip color

Lip gloss – Cosmetic product that imparts a shiny appearance and can also be used as highlighter over a lipstick shade

Lipid – Complex substance synthesized by the body; used in many important biological functions, among them the formation of components that fill the intercellular spaces in the skin

Lip liner – Cosmetic product applied to the outer edge of the lips to define the shape of the lips and to prevent lipstick from "bleeding" onto the skin around the mouth

Liposuction – Cosmetic surgery procedure that removes cellulite permanently

Liquid – Matter with definite weight and volume, but no shape

Liquid foundation – Most common form of foundation; offers sheer, natural coverage and is easy to apply and blend

Liquid tissue – Tissue that carries food, waste products and hormones

Load – Technical term for any appliance that requires electricity in order to work

Local infection – Type of infection present in a small, confined area often indicated by a pus-filled boil, pimple or inflammation

Local shock – Type of shock that passes through a small part of the body; can cause burns and muscle contractions

Logarithmic – Scale in which each step or number increases by multiples of 10

Long bone – Type of bone found in the arms and legs

Loss – Financial outcome that occurs when operating expenses are greater than income

Lotion – Along with crème, the most common product type on the market; used to impart emolliency and moisturization to the skin

Loupe – Also referred to as a **magnifying lamp**; tool used to provide light and magnification to determine skin type and condition

Lower leg wax – Hair removal procedure using wax from the top of the knee to the ankles, from the top of the thigh to the ankles or on the tops of the feet and the toes

Lower respiratory tract – Part of the respiratory system that includes the trachea, bronchi and lungs

Lucas spray – A unique atomizer that allows for the application of various herbs, extracts or astringents to be applied to the skin in a very fine mist

Lupus – Autoimmune disease in which the body's immune system is impaired or begins to fight against itself; person with lupus may be contraindicated for waxing services

Lymph – Colorless liquid produced as a by-product of plasma; passes nourishment to capillaries and cells; circulates through the blood system via muscular contraction, carries away cellular waste before it becomes toxic to the body

Lymph node – Gland that filters out toxic substances, such as **bacteria**

Lymphobiology – Skin care treatment that uses machines to increase the rate of lymphatic drainage

Lymphocyte (**LIM**-fa-site) – Medical term that describes a cell that carries lymph

Lymph vascular system – Also referred to as the lymphatic system; system that circulates lymph through lymph glands, lymph nodes and vessels

M

Maceration – Technique used in aromatherapy that involves plunging a substance into hot oil or fat, which then absorbs the ingredient's fragrance

Macrophage (**MAK**-ro-fay-je) – White blood cells that surround and digest foreign substances in the bloodstream and tissues

Macule (**MAK**-yool) – Skin disorder; discoloration on the skin's surface

Magnetic effect – Effect on the skin produced by electricity similar to the repulsion (push) and attraction (pull) exhibited by magnets; also called **mechanical effect**

Magnifying lamp – Also called **loupe**; piece of skin care equipment that provides light and magnification to determine skin type and condition

Makeup chair – Specialized piece of skin care equipment that allows client to be positioned at proper height and angle for makeup application/service

Makeup implement – Hand-held tool, which must be disinfected or discarded after each use

Malignant growth – Cancerous growth that must be diagnosed by a physician and treated immediately

Malpractice insurance – Coverage that protects the skin care center owner from financial loss that can result from an employee's negligence while performing skin care services on clients

Mandible (**MAN**-di-bl) – Lower jaw bone; largest bone of the facial skeleton

Mandibular (man-**DIB**-u-lur) **branch** – Main nerve branch to the lower 1/3 of the face that divides into the auriculo temporal and the mental nerve

Manipulation – Massage movement; actual action or movement performed during the massage treatment

Manual exfoliant – Cosmetic product that contains a granular substance with a slightly grainy or rough texture; the abrasion of the rough texture against the face causes a scraping effect to remove dead skin cells

Manual lymphatic drainage (MLD) – Massage treatment that uses a gentle pumping technique to help eliminate toxins, waste and excess water that can leave the face and body looking puffy and fatigued

Marginal mandibular nerve – Extends to the muscles of the chin and lower lip

Mascara – Cosmetic product that defines, lengthens and thickens the eyelashes

Mask – Facial procedure designed to provide the skin with necessary and desired benefits

Massage – Skin care procedure that involves a systematic, therapeutic method of manipulating the body by rubbing, pinching, tapping, kneading or stroking with hands, fingers or an instrument

Massage #1 – Cleansing process using massage techniques

Massage #2 – Application and deep penetration of massage crème to a client during a relaxing massage

Massage crème/oil – Product that reduces friction and provides "slip" to the skin during massage

Massage therapist – Trained professional that uses touch to provide relaxation, stress reduction, health promotion, pain management and injury recovery

Masseter (**MAS**-se-ter) – Muscle that covers the hinge of the jaw and aids in closing the jaw, as in chewing

Mast cell – Cell that releases histamines in response to allergic reactions

Mastication muscle – Muscle that controls the opening and closing of the jaw, enabling chewing and talking

Material Safety Data Sheet (MSDS) – Form required by OSHA that provides information on specific products regarding ingredients, associated hazards, combustion levels and storage requirements

Matter – Scientific term that describes anything that occupies space

Mature/Aging skin – Skin type that displays loose, thin, crepe-like skin and apparent fine lines and wrinkles; lacks elasticity and firmness

Maxillae (mak-**SIL**-e) – Two bones of the upper jaw

Maxillary (**MAK**-si-ler-e) **branch** – Main nerve branch to the middle 1/3 of the face that divides into the zygomatic nerve and the infraorbital nerve

Mechanical effect – Effect on the skin produced by electricity similar to the repulsion (push) and attraction (pull) exhibited by magnets; also called **magnetic effect**

Mechanical exfoliation – Process of physically removing dead skin cells by using an abrasive action combined with a product

Mechanoreceptor (ma-**CAN**-o-re-sep-ter) – Cells that sense stretching, compression or twisting of the skin

Median nerve – Nerve that extends down the mid-forearm into the hand

Medical history – Part of the **Client Consultation Form** pertaining to the past treatments the client may have received and his or her personal medical history

Medium-depth peel – Type of peel using trichloroacetic **acid** (TCA) and beta hydroxy acids, such as salicylic **acid**, to affect the dermis

Medulla oblongata (me-**DOOL**-ah ob-long-**GA**-ta) – Body structure that governs respiration, circulation, swallowing and certain other body functions; connects parts of the brain to the spinal column; located just below the pons

Meissner's corpuscle (**MY**-snerz **COR**-pus-el) – Touch receptor within the dermal layer of the skin that reports cold, fine touch, light pressure and low frequency vibrations

Melanocyte (**MEL**-en-o-site) – Cells that produce melanin to give skin its color; not found in thick skin, such as the palms of your hands and the soles of your feet

Melanoma (mel-a-**NO**-ma) – Most dangerous skin growth that evolves from flat or raised pigmented lesions anywhere on the body; pre-cancerous growths that, if untreated, will change in color, size and shape and, over time, will become malignant

Melanosome – Intracellular vesicle that holds melanin

Melasma (**MEL**-AZ-mah) – Also called **Chloasma**; a common disorder in pregnant women that results in increased pigmentation (hyperpigmentation) causing flat, light to dark patches to occur on the face

Mentalis (men-**TAL**-us) – Muscle located at the tip of the chin; pushes the lower lip up and/or wrinkles the chin, as in expressing doubt

Mental nerve – Nerve extending to the lower lip and chin

Merkel (**MUR**-kul) **cell** – Touch receptor, or sensory cell, that is only found in thick skin in the stratum germinativum

Meridian – Specific point on the body to which pressure is applied during an acupressure treatment

Metabolism (me-**TAB**-e-lizm) – Chemical process by which cells receive nutrients for growth and reproduction

Metacarpals (met-ah-**KAR**-pels) – The five long, thin bones that form the palm of the hand

Microbiology – Study of small living organisms called microbes

Microdermabrasion – Superficial resurfacing of the skin that removes a portion of the stratum corneum and requires 6 to 12 treatments to achieve noticeable improvement; recommended for lines, wrinkles, hyperpigmentation and superficial scarring

Microdermabrasion machine – A machine used to achieve a light resurfacing of the **epidermis**

Microlipoinjection – Also called **fat injection** or **autologous fat transplantation**; a procedure in which fat is removed with a syringe from a "donor site," such as the patient's abdomen, thigh or buttock and injected into the area to be treated

Microphage (**MIKE**-ro-fay-jez) – Cell that fights infection

Microscopic – Term used to describe objects that can be seen only with the aid of a microscope

Middle temporal artery – Artery that supplies the temples with blood

Milia (**MIL**-ee-uh) – Pearly white enclosed cyst; also referred to as "baby acne"

Miliaria Rubra (mil-ee-**AY**-re-ah **ROOB**-rah) – condition characterized by an acute burning, itching rash caused by excessive heat

Milliampere – $1/1000^{th}$ of an amp; unit used to measure the power that skin care equipment emits

Milliamperemeter – Instrument used to measure the electrical current used in skin care equipment

Mineral – Organic substance essential for normal growth and activity

Miscible – Solvents that easily mix together

Mitosis (my-**TOE**-sis) – Also known as indirect cell division; process in which human cells reproduce by dividing in half

Mixture – Two or more compounds blended together physically, rather than chemically, creating a new overall product but still retaining the separate chemical characteristics of the components being blended

Modality – Also known as **electric current**; the flow of electricity along a conductor, which is equal to the ratio of voltage to resistance

Modeling mask – Component of a facial procedure that delivers the benefits of the ingredients it contains and also seals the skin, locking in moisture and creating a firm, taut feeling after removal

Modern blend fragrance – Fragrance concocted from several different scents, including fruit, floral, spicy and wood; may also feature food scents, such as chocolate, coffee, caramel, licorice, mint or almond

Modified Brazilian wax – Type of waxing service performed by removing hair along the outside of a g-string; leaves a strip of pubic hair that is about an inch in width

Moisturizer – Skin care product used to replenish and balance moisture and oil as well as protect the skin

Moisturizing oil – Product used to soften dry or flaky skin

Molecular weight – Measurement listed on the Periodic Table of Elements and determined by adding neutrons and protons together

Molecule – Smallest particle of a compound that has all the chemical properties of that compound; two or more atoms joined together by one or more chemical bonds

Mole – Skin condition also called a **benign growth**; has a regular/symmetrical shape; harmless collection of pigmented cells; can be raised or flat

Monochromatic color scheme – Art principle that involves using the same color with variations in value and intensity throughout the entire makeup design

Monomer – Basic building-block molecule that connects with another to form larger, more complex compounds

Monosaccharide – A single saccharide

Motor nerve – Also called efferent nerve; nerve that carries messages from the brain to the muscles

Multi-Function Machine – Machine consisting of a steamer, vacuum, toner spray and rotating brush that offers four or more electrical treatment options during facial treatments

Muscle – Fibrous tissue that, when stimulated by messages carried by the nervous system, contracts to produce movement

Muscular system – Body structure that supports the skeleton, produces body movements, contours the body and is involved in the functions of other body systems

Muscular tissue – Tissue that contracts, when stimulated, to produce motion

Muslin –Fabric pre-cut into strips of various sizes used to remove wax and hair

Myology (mi-**OL**-o-jee) – The study of the structure, function and diseases of the muscles

N

Nasal (**NA**-zel) **bones** – The two bones that join to form the bridge of the nose

Nasalis – One of the four muscles located inside the nose; helps control contraction and expansion of the nostrils

Nasal nerve – Nerve extending to the tip and lower side of the nose

Natural immunity – Partially inherited natural resistance to disease

Nephrons (**NEF**-rons) – Small, tubelike kidney structures that filter waste products and water from the blood system, allowing usable nutrients to be reabsorbed into the blood

Neroli – Product used to treat oily and acneic skin; known for its antimicrobial and antiseptic qualities, as well as for being very soothing

Nerve cells – Also known as neurons (**NU**-rons); cells with axons that are responsible for sending messages in the form of nerve impulses

Nerve tissues – Tissues that carry messages to and from the brain and coordinate body functions

Nervous system – Body structure that coordinates and controls the overall operation of the human body by responding to both internal and external stimuli

Networking – Developing relationships with individuals who can put you in contact with potential customers or employers

Net worth – Person's or company's assets minus liabilities; what you own minus what you owe on assets

Neurology – Study of the nervous system

Neutral solution – Solution with an equal number of positive hydrogen and negative hydroxide ions

Neutral undertone – Color classification that contains brown/gray undertones

Neutron – Subatomic particle with no electric charge

Nevus (NEE-vus) – Birthmark or congenital mole

Nodular cystic acne – Skin condition characterized by inflammatory hard **lesions** found deeper in the skin at the point where the hair follicle becomes plugged with dead skin cells

Nodule (NOD-yool) – Solid mass within the skin; also called a **tumor**

Non-ablative laser – Laser that penetrates the **epidermis**, usually without affecting it, to treat **the papillary dermis** below

Non-comedogenic – Products less likely to clog pores

Non-critical objects – Lowest level of **infection control**; objects that come into contact with intact skin need only be sanitized

Nonpathogenic bacteria – Non-disease-producing **bacteria**; harmless and can be beneficial

Nonverbal communication – Also called body language; type of communication in which the exchange of messages takes place without speaking

Normal skin – Skin type that contains sufficient moisture and **sebum** production; displays few breakouts and clogged areas

Nucleus (NU-kle-us) – Core of an atom or a living cell; dense core of protons and neutrons at the center of the atom; control center of cell activities that is vitally important for cell reproduction

Nutrition – Process of converting raw materials in the form of carbohydrates, fats and proteins into energy

O

Objective symptom – Signs of illness visible to the eye, such as papules, pustules and redness

Oblong (long) facial shape – The oblong (rectangular) face shape tends to be long, narrow and angular; an elongated oval

Occipital (ak-SIP-et-el) artery – Artery that supplies blood to the back of the head, up to the crown

Occipital (ak-SIP-et-al) bone – Bone that forms the back of the skull, indenting above the nape area

Occipitalis (ok-sip-i-TAL-is) muscle – Muscle located at the nape of the neck; draws the scalp back

Occipito-frontalis (ok-SIP-ih-to-frun-TAL-is) – Also called the epicranius; a broad muscle that covers the epicranium or scalp

Occlusive barrier – Emollient that seals moisture into the skin

Occupational disorder – Health condition created or influenced by the employment environment

Occupational Safety and Health Administration (OSHA) – Regulating agency under the Department of Labor that enforces safety and health standards in the workplace

Oculomotor (ock-yoo-lo-MO-tur) nerve – Also called the third cranial nerve; nerve that controls motion of the eye

Ohm – Unit of electric resistance

Ohm's rating – Measure of resistance to the motion of electrons through a **conductor**

Oil-in-water (O/W) – Cosmetic product type in which oil is equally distributed throughout a water base

Oily skin – Skin type that displays excess **sebum** production; appears thick and shiny; prone to breakouts and clogged areas

Ointment – Anhydrous (without water) cosmetic substance based on a mixture of oils and waxes, normally having the texture of a paste, thick cream or salve; also made from the combination of herbs and petroleum

Olfactory (ol-FACK-tur-ee) nerve – Also called the first cranial nerve; nerve that controls sense of smell

Open circuit – Break in the path of **electricity**

Operating capital – Reservoir of cash needed to stay ahead of creditors

Operating expense (OE) – All the costs incurred in the day-to-day running of the skin care center

Ophthalmic (of-**THAL**-mik) **branch** – Main nerve branch to the top 1/3 of the face that divides into the supraorbital, supratrochlear and the nasal

Opponens (uh-**POHN**-nenz) – Muscles located in the palms of the hands that cause the thumbs to move toward the fingers, allowing the hands to grasp or make fists

Optic (**OP**-tik) **nerve** – Also known as the second cranial nerve; nerve that controls sense of sight

Oral antibiotic – Medication taken by mouth; can create dryness and increased sensitivity

Oral hygiene – Good dental care

Orbicularis oculi (or-bik-ye-**LAR**-es **AK**-yu-le) – Muscle that circles the eye socket and closes the eyelid

Organ – Separate body structure that performs a specific function; composed of two or more different tissues

Organelle – Basic body structure that performs most of the cell's activities; stores food for growth, as well as repairs and restores the cell; structure or component that performs specific functions for each cell

Organic chemistry – Study of all matter now living, that was alive at one time, or that contains carbon

Oriental fragrance – Category of full-bodied, warm, often heavy aromas typically composed of woods, spices, exotic florals and musk

Origin – Nonmoving (fixed) portion of the muscle attached to bones or other fixed muscles

Oris orbicularis (**O**-ris or-bik-ye-**LAR**-es) – Muscle that circles the mouth, contracts, puckers and wrinkles the lips, as in whistling

Osmidrosis – Sudoriferous gland disorder; also called **bromodirosis**; foul-smelling perspiration caused by the yeast and **bacteria** that break down the sweat on the surface of the skin

Osteology (as-tee-**AL**-e-jee) – Study of bones

Oval facial shape – The oval facial shape is generally the most symmetric and balanced; considered ideal because it can be visibly divided into equal thirds

Overload – Problem that occurs when too many appliances are put on one circuit and operated at the same time because more current flows through the line than it is designed to carry

Overtone – Mismatch between a person's tone of voice, inflection, expressions and reactions and his/her spoken words

Oxidation – Chemical reaction in which a substance loses an electron and gains oxygen; opposite of **reduction**

Oxidation-reduction reaction – Process taking place any time a chemical reaction occurs

Oxygen – Most abundant element in the earth's crust; second most abundant in atmosphere

Oxygenation (ok-si-je-**NAY**-shun) – Process by which **hemoglobin** attracts oxygen molecules

P

Pacemaker – Surgically implanted electronic heart device; person with such a device may be contraindicated for the use of any electrical equipment

Pacinian corpuscle (pa-**SIN**-ee-en **COR**-pus-el) – Deep pressure and pain receptor within the dermal layer of the skin

Pain receptors (**PAYN** re-**SEP**-ters) – Free nerve endings not associated with cells; detect extreme temperatures, mechanical surface injury and application of chemicals

Pancake – Also called pan-stick or greasepaint; oil-based foundation product that provides maximum coverage

Papillary dermis – Layer of the **dermis** directly under the **epidermis** that is rich in blood vessels and capillaries; provides nutrients to the upper layer; also houses touch receptors

Papule (**PAP**-yool) – Small elevation of the skin, usually inflamed, that does not contain pus

Paraffin heating unit – Electric container that melts blocks of paraffin wax for use in face, hand, foot and body treatments

Paraffin mask – Component of a hand or facial procedure; in facial procedure, paraffin wax is applied over a thin piece of gauze and allowed to harden as it cools; benefits include increased circulation and penetration of ingredients applied beneath mask; recommended for dry, mature skin

Parasitic disease – Skin condition caused by animal or vegetable parasites, such as pediculosis (lice) or ringworm

Parasympathetic nervous system – Sub-system of the autonomic nervous system; slows the heart rate, dilates blood vessels and lowers blood pressure

Parietal (pah-**RI**-e-tal) **artery** – Artery supplying the crown and the sides of the head with blood

Parietal bone – Bone forming the crown and upper side of the head

Partnership – Business owned by two or more persons that share all costs of opening, operating and maintaining the business

Passive (acquired) immunity – Type of immunity that occurs through vaccination, or the injection of an antigen, which stimulates the body's immune response

Pasteurization – Heating process that kills microorganisms in food and beverages

Patch test – Test usually performed on the inside of the arm or behind the ear that provides a basis for judging the sensitivity level of each client's skin

Pathogenic bacteria – Disease-producing **bacteria** that causes infection and disease; some produce toxins

Pathogens – Microorganisms, such as **viruses**, **bacteria**, protozoa and fungi, that cause infection within the body

Pathology – Study of diseases and disorders, their causes, processes, development and consequences

Pear facial shape – A pear-shaped face has a narrow forehead and a wide jawline

Pectoralis (pek-toe-**RAL**-us) **major and minor** – Muscles that extends across the front of the chest and assist in swinging the arms

Pellon® – Fabric pre-cut into strips of various sizes used to remove wax and hair

Pelvic tilt – Bending of knees slightly and pulling in abdominal muscles when reaching up to prevent arching backward

Pepsin – Enzyme responsible for the breakdown of protein into polypeptide molecules and free amino acids

Peptide bond – Bond uniting two amino **acid** groups

Performance review – Opportunity to discuss job performance with a manager at regular intervals throughout employment

Pericardium (per-i-**KAR**-dee-um) – Membrane that encases the heart; contracts and relaxes to force blood to move through the circulatory system

Peripheral (pe-**RIF**-ur-al) **nervous system** – Central nervous subsystem composed of sensory and motor nerves that extend from the brain and spinal cord to the voluntary muscles of the body and to the surface of the skin

Peristalsis (per-i-**STAL**-sis) – Twisting and turning motion of the esophagus

Permanent hair removal methods – Techniques designed to damage the papilla of the hair, inhibiting the hair's ability to grow back; include electrolysis, laser hair removal and photo-epilation; requires use of electrical equipment and specialized training and licensing

Permanent makeup – Separate specialty within the field of tattooing; involves the placement of colorants into the skin for the purpose of cosmetic enhancement, medical correction and/or esthetic restoration as defined by the American Academy of Micropigmentation

Personal ethics – Personal system of moral principles and values

Personal financial statement – Statement listing a person's assets, liabilities and net worth

Personal hygiene – Individual system for maintaining cleanliness and health

Personality – Complex set of characteristics that distinguishes individuals from others; the outward reflection of inner feelings, thoughts, attitudes and values

Personal Service Workers (PSW) – Nurses, doctors, teachers, cosmetologists and estheticians who work with the public and are often asked to take precautions against all **viruses** but, in particular, HBV and HIV

Petrissage (pet-tree-**SAH**-jh) – Massage manipulation involving light or heavy kneading, pinching and rolling of the muscles

pH adjuster – **Acid** or base used to adjust the product pH level to a desired level

Phalanges (fah-**LAN**-jees) – Fourteen bones that form the digits or fingers

Pharynx (**FAR**-ingks) – Passageway to the stomach and lungs; part of the digestive system

pH balanced – Measurement indicating balance somewhere within the pH scale but not necessarily at 4.5 to 5.5 (the average pH range of the skin)

pH measurement scale – Scientific tool that ranges from zero to fourteen; used to describe the degree of acidity or alkalinity of a solution

pH number – Number indicating amount of **acid** or **alkali** in a water-based solution

Phenolic germicidal detergent solution – Disinfectant option; three percent phenolics are not considered high-level disinfectants due to their inability to inactivate bacterial spores, mycobacterium tuberculosis and fungi

Phoresis – Process of forcing a water-based solution into the skin by applying **Galvanic Current** to the solution

Photo-damaged skin – Light-damaged skin due to external influences from the sun

Photo-epilation – Permanent hair removal method; intense pulsed light beam creates a burst of energy used to destroy hair bulbs with minimal scarring; also called pulsed light; uses principle similar to lasers but not considered to be a laser light

Physical change – Change in the physical form of a substance without creating a new substance possessing a distinct material composition

Physiology – Study of the functions body organs and systems perform

Phytocosmetics – Phytotherapy preparations used for cosmetic purposes

Phytohormones – Concentrated source of trace elements, mineral salts, essential amino acids, polysaccharides, vitamins, enzymes, helpful **bacteria**, natural antibiotics and plant hormones

Phytotherapy (FIGHT-oh-thare-ah-pee) or (FEE-toh-thare-ah-pee) – Advanced therapy process; medicinal use of plants

Pink eye – Also known as **conjunctivitis**; extremely contagious bacterial infection that affects the membrane that lines the eyelids

Pityriasis versicolor (pit-i-**REYE**-ah-sis **VUR**-si-color) – Commonly known as tinea versicolor; non-contagious infection that produces hypopigmented areas, usually on the neck, chest, back and arms

Plasma – Fluid part of the blood in which red and white blood cells and blood platelets are suspended; composed of about 90% water

Plastic surgeon – Also called a **cosmetic surgeon**; medical doctor specializing in cosmetic and/or reconstructive surgery

Plastic surgery – Also called **cosmetic or reconstructive surgery**; performed for aesthetic and reconstructive purposes

Platysma (plah-**TIZ**-mah) – Muscle that extends from the tip of the chin to the shoulders and chest; depresses the lower jaw and lip, as in expressing sadness

Podiatrist – Also known as a chiropodist; foot doctor

Polarity – Term describing the opposite, negatively or positively charged poles in an electric current

Polarity changer – Switch on electrotherapy machines that changes current from negative to positive or positive to negative

Poly hydroxy acid – Molecule that contains several carboxyl groups in the same chain

Polymers – Chemical bond; groups of monomers that bond together

Polypeptide chain – Chemical bond; thousands of amino acids connected lengthwise to form a chain

Polysaccharides – Carbohydrates; hydrate, revitalize and infuse the skin with nutrients

Pons (**PONZ**) – Prominent band of nerve tissue that connects other parts of the brain to the spinal column; located below the cerebrum and directly in front of the cerebellum

Pore – Skin opening; tiny opening or "passageway" that allows sweat or **sebum** (oil) to pass through the surface of the skin

Posterior (pos-**TEER**-ee-er) – Term meaning behind or in back

Posterior auricular (pos-**TEER**-ee-or aw-**RIK**-u-lur) **artery** – Artery; supplies blood to the scalp above and behind the ears

Posterior auricular (pos-**TEER**-ee-er aw-**RIK**-u-lur) **branch** – Nerve tissue; extends to the muscles behind and below the ear

Posterior dilatator naris – One of the four muscles located inside the nose; helps control the contraction and expansion of the nostrils

Post Inflammatory Hyperpigmentation (PIH) – Pigmentation disorder that results from trauma to tissues from acne, burns, injury or some skin rashes, such as dermatitis or psoriasis

Posture – Position of the body while standing, sitting and moving

Potential hydrogen (pH) – Unit of measurement that indicates whether a substance is acidic, neutral or **alkaline**

Poultice – Cosmetic mixture of crushed herbs and hot liquid to form a paste

Powder – Cosmetic product; finely ground solid evenly mixed with additional ingredients, which in some cases include oils; used to "set" the foundation, concealer and other makeup products, so they don't fade, streak or rub off

Pre-malignant (pre-ma-**LIG**-nent) **growth** –Skin growth; can be flat or raised and irregular in shape and border

Premise insurance – Also known as **property insurance**; Policy that covers the actual skin care center equipment and physical location in case of natural disasters, fire, theft or burglary, or accidents occurring at the business

Preservative – Ingredient included in cosmetic products to maintain microbiological integrity or product quality during manufacturing, storage and use by the consumer

Preservative-free – Products containing less than 1% preservative ingredients

Pressure receptor (**PRESH**-er re-**SEP**-ter) – Sensory cell that reports the degree of mechanical distortion and the amount of weight felt on the skin

Primary colors – Three pure colors in the universe, red, yellow and blue

Primary lesion – Change in the structure of the skin during the early development of a skin condition

Prism – Three-sided glass object; if white light passes through it, wavelengths are separated and become visible to the eye as seven colors (red, orange, yellow, green, blue, indigo and violet)

Procerus (pro-**SER**-us) – Muscle located between the eyebrows across the bridge of the nose; draws brows down and wrinkles the area across the bridge of the nose

Product liability insurance – Insurance offering protection from a client's misuse of products recommended, sold or produced by the skin care center

Product statement – Explains what a product will do and why; describes features and benefits of a product.

Professional ethics – Study and philosophy of human conduct that deals with proper conduct in relationships with the employer, co-workers and clients

Professional product – Product that is only available through special retail outlets, such as a skin care center or a doctor's office

Profit – Financial gain or benefit from using a particular type of product; taking in more money than paid out

Prognosis – Medical term predicting the probable course and outcome of a condition, disorder or disease

Pronator (**PRO**-nat-or) – Muscle that runs across the front of the lower part of the radius and the ulna; turns the palm of the hand downward and inward

Property insurance – Also known as **premise insurance**; insurance policy that covers the skin care center equipment and physical location in the event of natural disaster, fire, theft or burglary, or accidents occurring at the business

Propionibacterium – Known as P. acnes bacteria; **bacteria** that plugs hair follicles and causes acne

Prosthetics – Artificial devices, such as metal plates, pins, dental braces or any device used to replace a missing body part; person with such a device may be contraindicated for the use of any electrical equipment

Protein – Body's building block used to construct and renew itself; a good diet includes approximately 10% to 35% protein that is low in cholesterol and saturated fats

Proton – Atomic particle with a positive electrical charge; identifies the atom as, for example, a hydrogen atom or an oxygen atom

Protoplasm (**PRO**-to-plazm) – Colorless gel-like substance that contains water, salt and nutrients obtained from food

Pruritus – Inflammation in the skin that causes severe itching; usually found on undamaged skin

Psoriasis – Inheritable disease that can be triggered by environmental factors in persons genetically predisposed to the disease

Public hygiene – Also referred to as public health; science and practice of protecting and improving the health of a community

Public relations (PR) – Ability to create a favorable relationship with the public; methods and strategies used to establish and sustain such a relationship

Pulmonary (**PUL**-mo-ner-e) **artery** – Artery that carries blood from the right ventricle to the lungs where it is oxygenated

Pulmonary circulation – Body system in which blood travels through the pulmonary artery to the lungs where it is oxygenated

Pustule (**PUST**-yool) – Primary lesion; next step in the progression from a **papule**; filled with bacterial fluid and pus

Pyrolysis – Skin condition; thermal breakdown of the skin

Q

Quadratus labii inferioris (kwod-**RA**-tus la-be-i in-feer-ee-**OR**-es) – Also known as the depressor labii inferioris; muscle located below the lower lip; pulls the lower lip down or to the side, as in expressing sarcasm

Quadratus labii superioris (kwod-**RA**-tus la-be-i soo-peer-ee-**OR**-es) – Also known as the levator labii superioris; muscle located above the upper lip and consisting of three parts; raises both the nostrils and the upper lip, as in expressing distaste

Quaternary ammonium germicidal detergent solutions – Anti-fungal, antibacterial and antiviral disinfectants; not sporicidal or tuberculocidal

R

Radial nerve – Nerve that extends down the thumb side of the arm into the back of the hand

Radiation – Transfer of heat energy through empty air space (vacuum)

Radius (**RAD**-ee-us) – Small bone on the thumb side of the lower arm or forearm

Rash – Skin condition visible on the surface of the skin; includes small red bumps, urticaria, blisters, scales and **erythema**

Rebooking – Scheduling a client's next appointment in advance before he/she leaves the skin care center

Receptionist – First person to greet the clients as they arrive; performs many duties in the skin care center

Receptor – Nerve cell located in the papillary layer of the **dermis** that reacts to outside stimulation by sending a sensory message to the brain

Recommended Dietary Allowances (RDA) – Appropriate nutrient intakes for people in the U.S. established by the U.S. government; also Recommended Daily Allowances

Reconstructive surgery – Also called **plastic or cosmetic surgery**; surgery performed for aesthetic and reconstructive purposes

Record keeping – Technique used for keeping accurate and detailed records essential for tax purposes; used to ensure the general well-being of the business; essential for evaluating a client's reaction to a product and monitoring his or her progression through treatment

Rectifier – Special instrument used to change **alternating current** to **direct current**

Red blood cell (RBC) – Also called erythrocyte (e-**RITH**-ro-site) or red corpuscle; carries oxygen throughout the body; contains a protein called **hemoglobin**

Reduction – Chemical reaction in which a substance gains an electron and loses oxygen; opposite of **oxidation**

Referral – Client-building strategy; client sent to the esthetician on recommendation of another client

Reflective listening – Communication strategy; act of repeating out loud what was heard and processed inside the listener's head

Reflex action – Medical term that describes the interaction of sensory and motor nerves

Reflexologist – Trained professional who practices reflexology

Reflexology – Technique that uses pressure on specific points of the feet, hands and sometimes the ears to influence certain body conditions

Rental agreement – Lease; promise to pay rent and use the property according to the agreement

Repeat business – Client-building strategy; key to building a strong client base and ensuring that appointment books are full from week to week and month to month

Reproductive system – Body system that allows a living organism to procreate

Request – Client-building strategy in which clients call the skin care center and ask for a specific esthetician to perform the service

Respiratory system – Body system that maintains the exchange of oxygen and carbon dioxide in the lungs and body tissues

Retailing – Selling strategy involving recommending and providing the best products for client purchase

Retention hyperkeratosis – Skin lesion; accumulation of keratinized skin cells that adhere to hair follicle

Reticular dermis – Skin layer; lowest layer of the dermis; contains the collagen and elastin fibers that provide the skin with its strength and flexibility

Retin-A®– Medication prescribed for acne, hyperpigmentation, premature aging and rosacea; can cause dryness, increased sensitivity and irritation; contains Tretinoin, a powerful derivative of Vitamin A that dries the skin and promotes rapid exfoliation

Rheostat – Electrical device found in skin care equipment that indicates the amount of current flowing through the equipment and regulates the amount with a dial

Rhinophyma – Skin condition; more severe form of rosacea that causes the tissue of the nose to swell and enlarge

Rhinoplasty (RYE-no-PLAS-tee) – Cosmetic surgery to reshape the nose

Rhytidectomy (RYE-ti-DECK-toh-mee) – Cosmetic surgery; a facelift that can improve visible signs of aging by removing excess fat, tightening underlying muscles and re-draping the skin of the face and neck

Rib – One of twelve bones of the chest that aids in the protection of the heart, lungs and other internal organs

Right atrium (AY-tree-um) – Heart chamber; commonly known as the right auricle; upper chamber of the heart

Right ventricle (VEN-tri-kel) – Heart chamber; lower right chamber of the heart

Risk management – Insurance involving several types of coverage to protect you from the financial difficulties that can follow the unexpected loss of property, income, health and/or life

Risorius (re-SOR-e-us) – Muscle located at the corner of the mouth; draws the mouth up and out, as in grinning

Rosacea (ro-ZA-shee-ah) – Skin condition; chronic inflammatory condition of the face in which the small capillaries of the face become dilated and inflamed; vascular disorder characterized by flushed redness and small red bumps

Rose – Aromatherapy ingredient; incorporated into facial and body treatments for antiseptic properties and ability to soothe and moisturize

Rotating brush machine – Features a handheld attachment with a small round brush suitable for the face and body; used to slough dead skin cells and deeply, thoroughly cleanse the skin

Round facial shape – The round face is circular; appears to be short and wide rather than long and narrow; often called a full face; characterized by a rounded hairline and chinline

Ruffini's corpuscle (roo-FEE-neez COR-pus-el) – Sensory cell; heat receptor within the dermal layer of the skin sensitive to long-term pressure

Ruptured disc – Health condition; pain in the neck, back, arms or legs caused when the jelly-like substance leaks out of the disc

S

Salary-plus-commission – Compensation that guarantees the employee a certain amount of money on a regular basis and provides additional income when the esthetician meets a predetermined benchmark or goal

Sales tax – Taxes paid on products and services

Salicylic acid – Beta hydroxy acid that mildly dries and promotes cell turnover by producing a mild keratolytic action

Salivary (SAL-i-ver-ee) **gland** – Gland that secretes enzymes to break down food

Sandalwood – Fragrance used in therapies aimed at treating sore muscles; may also be used in facial treatments for acne or irritated skin

Sanitation – Infection control involving low-level destruction of surface **bacteria**

Saponification – Liquification of **sebum** in **desincrustation** procedure

Saprophytes (SAP-ro-fights) – **Nonpathogenic bacteria** that live on dead matter

Saturation point – Point at which a **solute** will no longer dissolve evenly in the **solvent**

Sauna – Treatment using warm steam to induce relaxation, expand pores and promote sweating

Scabies – Parasitic animal that causes contagious diseases

Scale (skayl) – Process of shedding dead skin cells of the uppermost layer of the **epidermis**

Scalp – The epicranium

Scapula (SKAP-yu-lah) – The two large, flat bones extending from the middle of the back upward to the joint where they attach to the clavicle; also called shoulder blades

Scar (skar) – Type of lesion, also called cicatrix; formation resulting from a lesion that extends into the dermis or deeper; part of the normal healing process

Scope of practice – Esthetics practices that may be legally performed, as defined by the local regulatory agency

Seasonal disease – Skin condition or disorder that is influenced by the weather or seasonal changes

Seasonal promotion – Advertising technique capitalizing on yearly celebrations to sell products by running a promotion

Sebaceous (si-**BAY**-shus) **gland** – Also called oil gland or duct gland; part of the integumentary system that secretes into canal-like structures, or ducts, and deposits its contents on the surface of the skin; not located on the palms of the hands and the soles of the feet

Seborrhea (seb-oh-**REE**-ah) – Skin condition caused by excess secretion of the sebaceous gland; commonly associated with oily skin types

Seborrheic dermatitis – Common skin rash with redness and scaly, pinkish-yellow patches that have an oily appearance

Sebum – Complex mixture of fatty substances that keeps the skin soft, supple and pliable

Secondary colors – Orange, green and violet; colors produced when primary colors are mixed together in varying proportions

Secondary lesion – Skin lesion that appears as a condition or disease progresses and requires treatment by a physician

Second-degree burn – Burn affecting both the **epidermis** and underlying dermis; accompanied by pain, swelling and redness; does cause blisters; damage penetrates to the dermis

Self-appraisal – Act of accessing personal skills carefully to pinpoint strengths and weaknesses

Selling – Often called "the art of persuasion" or the "technique of recommendation"; term that describes recommending products and services to provide quality home maintenance or service

Semi-critical objects – Midlevel of **infection control**; objects that come in contact with mucus membranes or broken skin; require **disinfection**

Semi-permanent eyelash tinting – Procedure involving darkening the eyelashes with a semi-permanent tint product

Sensory-motor nerve – Also called a mixed nerve; large nerve that performs both sensory and motor functions

Sensory nerve – Also called afferent nerve; nerve that carries messages to the brain and spinal cord and provides our sense of smell, sight, touch, hearing and taste

Serotonin – Neurotransmitter involved in normal perception and emotional control

Serratus anterior (ser-**RA**-tus an-**TER**-e-er) – Muscle located under the arm that helps in lifting the arm and in breathing

Shade – Color hue with black added

Shareholder – Stockholder; owner of a corporation

Sharps container – Red, puncture-resistant containers labeled with the biohazard symbol and the words "Sharps waste" or "biohazard"

Shaving – Technique performed by the client at home with an electric shaver, clipper or razor; removes hair from the surface of the skin

Short circuit – Break in an electrical circuit; any time a foreign conductor comes in contact with a wire carrying current to a load (appliance)

Sinusoidal Current – Alternating current (AC) that produces a mechanical effect, similar to the way Faradic Current produces muscle contractions

Skeletal muscle – Muscle attached to bone

Skeletal system – Physical foundation of the body that consists of 206 bones of different shapes and sizes, each attached to others at movable or immovable joints

Skin – The body's largest organ, which forms the external protective layer of the body

Skin graft surgery – Medical procedure in which a section of healthy skin is taken from an unburned area of the body and surgically reattached, covering the burned area to try to re-grow skin

Skin histology – Microscopic study of the skin's tissue

Skin physiology – Study of the skin's functions

Skin scope – Elaborate magnifying mirror/light that incorporates a black light; also called a **dermascope** or skin scanner

Skin tag – Small, elevated growth that can easily be removed by a physician

Skin tone – Skin color classification that identifies the warmth or coolness of the skin color

Skull – Also referred to as the skeleton of the head or facial skeleton; bone that encloses and protects the brain and primary sensory organs

Small intestine – Part of the digestive system that begins the breakdown of nutrients

Social Security – A planned savings/retirement fund for every worker in the United States

Sodium Hypochlorite – Liquid chlorine disinfectant found in household bleach that has a wide range of antimicrobial activity, is inexpensive and fast-acting

Soft keratin – Form of protein (keratin) that makes up the skin and hair

Soft water – Water containing very few minerals

Soft wax – Also known as classic wax; a skin care supply used in majority of professional waxing services; melted in a heated wax pot, applied to the skin in a thin layer with a spatula and covered with strips of material, such as muslin or Pellon®; material is then lifted off the skin, removing wax and hair

Sole proprietorship – Type of business ownership; owned by one person who is in complete control of the business, receives all profits from the business and is responsible for all debts and losses

Solid – Chemical mixture; matter with definite weight, volume and shape

Solute – Dissolved part of a chemical solution

Solution – Chemical mixture of two or more chemicals in which each component is evenly distributed in the mixture to form a complete and homogeneous dispersion

Solvent – Liquid part of a chemical solution

Soothing lotion – product that calms the skin after waxing

Soothing oil – Aromatherapy oil that helps reduce irritation, e.g., chamomile, aloe and lavender

Sparking – Also known as spark gap; technique that involves using the narrow space between the electrode and skin to provide germicidal, healing and drying effects during either Direct or Indirect High Frequency treatments

Spatula – Skin care implement used to remove product from containers

SPF *abbr.* **Sun Protection Factor** – Degree of exposure, or time, in sun before skin starts to burn

Sphenoid (SFEE-noid) bone – Bone located behind the eyes and nose; connects all the bones of the cranium

Spice blend – Fragrance made from several spicy aromas, such as vanilla, cinnamon, pepper, nutmeg, ginger or clove

Spinal cord – Long nerve fibers that originate in the base of the brain and extend to the base of the spine; holds 31 pairs of spinal nerves that branch out to muscles, internal organs and skin

Spirilla (spi-**RIL**-uh) – Spiraled, coiled, corkscrew-shaped bacterial cells that cause highly contagious diseases, such as syphilis and cholera

Spores – **Bacteria** that form hard protective coatings that encase their key parts to survive

Spore test strips – Biological monitoring systems designed for use with the type of sterilization being used

Spray machine – Also referred to as an atomizer; automated spraying device used to achieve more thorough cleansing or toning; assists in removing clay masks

Squamous (SQUAW-mus) cell – Cell found in the **stratum lucidum** (hands and soles of the feet) with the main function of protection of the skin

Squamous cell carcinoma – Malignant cell growth; an irregular, crusted, red papule that occurs in sun-exposed areas and may be an **actinic keratosis** that went untreated; these lesions are dangerous and need to be removed

Square facial shape – The square facial shape is usually characterized by a broad, straight forehead and hairline, with a broad, square jawline; very angular and somewhat masculine

Stabilized hydrogen peroxide (6%) – Antibacterial, antiviral and anti-fungal disinfectant

Stable atom – Atom not missing any electrons in the outer shell

Staphylococci (staf-i-lo-**KOK**-sigh) – Pus-forming bacterial cells that form grape-like bunches or clusters and are present in abscesses, pustules and boils

Steam bath – Treatment using warm steam to induce relaxation, expand pores and promote sweating

Steam distillation – Phytotherapeutic method in which steam percolates through plant material, pulling off volatile oils, which are then condensed

Steatoma (ste-ah-**TOH**-mah) – Also called a **wen**; harmless sebaceous cyst filled with **sebum**; considered to be a tumor of the sebaceous gland

Sterilization – Procedure that eliminates all living organisms on non-porous surfaces, including bacterial spores that adhere to surgical instruments in medical treatment rooms

Sternocleido mastoideus (stur-no-**KLI**-do mas-**TOID**-e-us) – Muscle that extends along the side of the neck from the ear to the collarbone and moves the head from side to side and up and down, as in nodding "yes" or "no"

Sternum – Bone of the chest that aids in the enclosure and protection of the heart, lungs and other internal organs

Steroid – Medication that, when used, will thin the skin and increase its sensitivity

Stick – Hard, low-level water or anhydrous product applied to the skin by rubbing the product directly on the desired area

Stimulating oil – Aromatherapy oil that boosts circulation to the skin

Stock – Total merchandise kept on supply for future use by a merchant, commercial establishment, warehouse or manufacturer

Stratum corneum (**KOHR**-nee-um) – Toughest layer of the **epidermis**

Stratum germinativum (jur-mih-nah-**TIV**-um) – Also known as the basal layer; lowest layer of the **epidermis** containing basal cells that continually divide through mitosis to replace the cells that are lost from the stratum corneum

Stratum granulosum (gran-yoo-**LOH**-sum) – Layer of the **epidermis** below the stratum lucidum and above the stratum spinosum in which the cells become more regularly shaped and look like many tiny granules

Stratum lucidum – Transparent layer that lies between the stratum corneum and stratum granulosum

Stratum spinosum (spin-**OH**-sum) – Spiny layer that provides strength and support between cells

Streptococci (strep-to-**KOK**-sigh) – Pus-forming bacterial cells, which form in long chains and can cause septicemia (sometimes called blood poisoning), strep throat, rheumatic fever and other serious infections

Stress – Tense, "tied-up-in-knots" feeling caused when life's circumstances become challenging or ambiguous

Strip (band) eyelashes – Cosmetic accessory that creates a more intense look to the eyes, making them appear wider or "doe-like"

Subcutaneous layer – Bottom layer of the skin that insulates and acts as a shock absorber to protect the bones and help support other delicate structures; also called the subdermis or subcutis

Subjective symptom – Symptom that can be felt by the client but is not visible to others, such as itching and burning

Sublimation – Process of a solid or gas changing states without becoming a liquid

Submental artery – Artery that supplies the chin and the lower lip with blood

Suction machine – Machine that acts like a miniature vacuum cleaner to help in deep pore cleansing, drawing out dirt, impurities and grease from the skin

Sudoriferous (soo-dohr-**IF**-er-us) **gland** – Also called a duct gland; gland that secretes into canal-like structures, or ducts, that deposits its contents on the surface of the skin; produces sweat, a mixture of water, urea, electrolytes and lactic **acid**

Sugaring – Hair removal technique that originated in Egypt; a paste made primarily of sugar is applied to the surface of the skin in a rolling motion; when removed, it takes the hair along with it

Sunscreen – Also called **UV absorbers** or **UV blockers**; skin care product that protects the skin from the harmful **UVA rays** and **UVB rays** projected from the sun

Sunscreen allergen – Ingredient in sunscreens that is a common **allergen**

Supercilia – Eyebrow hair

Superficial chemical peel – Facial treatment; light chemical peel that uses **alpha hydroxyl acid**, glycolic acid or lactic acid and affects only the **epidermis**

Superficial temporal (su-pur-**FI**-shul **TEM**-po-ral) **artery** – Artery supplying blood to the sides and top of the head; branches into five smaller arteries that supply more precise locations

Superioris (su-peer-ee-**OR**-es) – Term that means located above or larger than

Superior labial artery – Artery supplying the upper lip and septum with blood

Superior vena cava – Vein that carries oxygen-poor blood to the right auricle

Supinator (SU-pi-nat-or) – Muscle that runs parallel to the ulna and turns the palm of the hand up

Supraorbital nerve – Nerve that extends to the skin of the upper eyelid, eyebrow, forehead and scalp

Supratrochlear (soo-pra-TRO-klee-ur) nerve – Nerve that extends to the skin of the upper side of the nose and between the eyes

Surfactant (sur-FAC-tent) – Large category of ingredients with the ability to bind a wide variety of organic and inorganic matter to water

Suspension – Cosmetic product category; the even dispersion of a solid substance in a liquid base

Sympathetic nervous system – Sub-system of the autonomic nervous system that accelerates the heart rate, constricts blood vessels and raises blood pressure

Synapses (SI-nap-ses) – Junctions across which nerve impulses pass

System – Group of organs that, together, perform one or more vital functions for the body

Systematic medication – Medication taken orally; travels through the body in the bloodstream

Systemic circulation – Also known as general circulation; process in which blood travels from the heart throughout the body and back to the heart

Systemic disease – Disease that is active internally throughout the body system

T

Tabbing – Method of applying individual eyelashes

Tact – Term used to describe the ability to be truthful without being offensive

Tactile (TAK-tile) receptor – Sensory cell that senses gentle touch, pressure or vibration

Tapotement (tah-pot-e-MAHNT) – Also known as percussion; a message manipulation; light tapping or slapping movement applied with the fingertips or partly flexed fingers

T-cell – Immune cell that recognizes antigens displayed in **Langerhans cells** to assist in destroying them

Tea Tree – Aromatherapy ingredient used in treating acne; has antiseptic and antimicrobial benefits perfect for treating problem skin

Telangiectasia – Skin condition marked by dilated capillaries that indicate damage to the skin and possible heightened sensitivity; should be treated with gentle massage and soothing, mild products

Telogen – Third phase of hair growth cycle during which hair sheds and the follicle rests and prepares to resume the anagen phase

Temporal (TEM-poh-ral) bone – Bone located on either side of the head, directly above the ear and below the parietal bone

Temporal (TEM-po-ral) branch – Nerve that extends to the muscles of the temple, the side of the forehead, the eyebrow, eyelid and upper cheek

Temporalis (tem-po-RA-lis) muscle – Muscle located above and in front of the ear that opens and closes the jaw (as in chewing, or mastication)

Temporary hair removal – Hair removal classification that includes procedures, such as shaving, the use of chemical depilatories, tweezing and waxing

Tendon – Fibrous cord of connective tissue that links muscles and bones

Tendonitis – Medical condition that occurs when tendons become inflamed

Terminal – Thicker, pigmented hair that grows on areas of the body after puberty

Tertiary colors – Color classification; the six colors that result when primary colors are mixed with their neighboring secondary color in varying proportions

Tesla Current – Also known as **High Frequency Current**; electrical current; an alternating (or oscillating) current that can be adjusted to different voltages to produce heat

Thalassotherapy – Any treatment using sea products, such as seawater, sea mud, sea sand and sea plants

Thermal effect – Effect on the skin of warmth created by the friction generated from resistance to the flow of electricity

Thermal energy – Heat energy; involves movement of heat from a warmer body to a cooler body; can be transferred from one object to another by conduction, convection or radiation

Thermolysis – Permanent hair removal method that involves inserting a single needle into the follicle, current travels to the papilla for less than a second, resulting in a coagulation of the cells that destroys the papilla; also called High Frequency/short wave electrolysis method

Thermoreceptor (THUR-mo-re-sep-ter) – Sensory nerve located in the dermis that responds to temperature changes

Thermoregulation – Body function that lowers body temperature

Thickener – Cosmetic ingredient that helps increase the density in emulsions and gel-type products; allows for suspension of small particle solids in a base by creating enough of a supporting structure to prevent settling

Third-degree burn – Type of burn that destroys all layers of the skin and damages underlying tissue, including nerves

Thoracic (tho-RAS-ik) vertebrae – Also known as the spine; one of the bones of the thorax that encloses and protects the heart, lungs and other internal organs

Thorax – Also known as the chest; bony cage composed of the spine, the sternum and 12 ribs that encloses and protects the heart, lungs and other internal organs

Threading – Ancient method of hair removal that originated in the Middle East and is still used frequently in India and Pakistan; technique utilizes a 100% cotton thread that is twisted and rolled along the surface of the skin, entwining the hair in the thread and then lifting it from the follicle

Thyroid – Primary hormonal gland that regulates the human body; overactive thyroid can result in excess **sebum** production, while an underactive thyroid can result in a lack of **sebum** and dryness

Tincture – Commercial extraction that requires soaking an herb in alcohol to extract the active ingredient from the plant

Tinea (TIN-ee-ah) – Medical term for ringworm; contagious fungal disease characterized by a red circular patch of blisters; caused by fungal vegetable parasite

Tinea corporis (TIN-ee-ah KOR-pur-is) – Fungal infection affecting the trunk, legs or arms; characterized by a pink to red rash and itching

Tinea versicolor (VUR-si-color) – Commonly known as Tri-Color Yeast infection or Pityriasis versicolor; a noncontagious infection that produces hypopigmented areas, usually on the neck, chest, back and arms

Tint – Color hue with white added

Tissue – Group of similar cells that act together to perform some specific function within the body

Tone – Refers to the warmth or coolness of a color

Toner – Skin care product that assists in cleansing skin and returns normal to dry skin to a normal pH

Topical antibiotic – Medication prescribed by a physician to dry the skin and kill the **bacteria** that causes acne, rosacea and other skin conditions; will heighten sensitivity and dryness; may be a possible contraindication for exfoliation treatments and waxing

Topical medication – Medication applied directly to the skin

Touch – One of the five primary senses; the most personal of the five senses; lowers blood pressure, relieves stress, stimulates circulation and promotes feelings of security and comfort

Touch receptor (TUCH re-SEP-ter) – Sensory nerve cell that reports shape or texture; also called a sensory cell

Trachea (TRAY-kee-ah) – Component of the respiratory system; pathway through which air flows

Transdermal penetration – Process of absorption into the skin

Transverse artery – Artery that supplies masseter with blood

Trapezius (trah-PEE-zee-us) – Muscle that covers the back of the neck and upper back and draws the head back; controls the shoulder blades and swinging motions of the arms

Treatment record – Skin care form; last section of Client Consultation Form to be filled out by the esthetician; used as a reference at the time of each appointment

Triadic color scheme – Art principle that uses three colors located in a triangular position on the color wheel

Triangularis (tri-an-gu-LAR-us) – Also known as the depressor anguli; muscle located below the corners of the mouth; draws the corners of the mouth down, as in expressing sadness

Tricep (TRI-sep) – Muscle that extends the length of the upper arm posteriorly; controls forward movement of the forearm

Tricuspid (tri-**KUS**-pid) **valve** – Pathway for blood pumped from the right auricle to the right ventricle

Trifacial (trye-**FAY**-shul) **nerve** – Also called the trigeminal (trye-**JEM**-i-nul) nerve or fifth cranial nerve; chief sensory nerve of the face that controls sensations of the face, tongue and teeth

Trochlear (TROCK-lee-ur) **nerve** – Also called the fourth cranial nerve; motor nerve that controls the motion of the eye

Tuberculosis (too-**BUR**-cu-lo-sis) – Contagious, and potentially fatal, infection caused by airborne **bacteria** that first affect the lungs

Tumor (too-mer) – Solid mass within the skin that may be soft or hard, fixed or freely moving; also called a **nodule**

Tweezer – Implement used to shape eyebrows, remove stray hairs and apply artificial eyelashes

Tweezing – Technique used to remove unwanted hair from smaller areas, such as the eyebrows, chin or around the mouth; an individual hair is grasped with the tweezers and removed in the direction of the hair growth, effectively extracting it from beneath the skin's surface

Two-way communication – Type of communication describing the act of listening and asking questions to gather information

U

Ulcer (UL-ser) – Open lesion visible on the surface of the skin that may result in the loss of portions of the dermis and may be accompanied by pus

Ulna (UL-nah) – Bone located on the little finger side of the lower arm

Ulnar nerve – Nerve extending down the little finger side of the arm into the palm of the hand

Ultraviolet light – Also referred to as UV; skin care equipment that produces positive or negative effects on the skin, depending on the exposure time

Ultraviolet (UV) light sterilizer – Machine that utilizes UV light to kill bacteria in a dry setting

Ultraviolet rays – Also known as actinic or cold rays; invisible rays slightly shorter than the wavelengths that produce the visible light ray seen as the color violet

Underarm wax – Waxing technique removing the hair from underneath the arms

Underwriter's Laboratory (UL) rating – Government-approved agency that shows an appliance has been certified to operate safely under the conditions specified in the instructions

Universal precaution – Safety measure using the same infection control practices with all clients

Upper respiratory tract – Nose, mouth, pharynx and larynx

Urea (u-**REE**-ah) – Converted and neutralized ammonia from the circulatory system

Ureter (U-re-tur) – Tube through which waste products travel to be eliminated from the body

UVA ray – Longest of the ultraviolet rays; most frequently used in tanning booths

UVA/UVB absorber – Sunscreen ingredient that absorbs the sun's rays and deflects them throughout the layers of skin

UVA/UVB blocker – Sunscreen ingredient that blocks the skin by reflecting the sun's rays back off the surface of the skin

UVB ray – Ultraviolet ray that people are exposed to most frequently from the natural sun; referred to as "the burning ray"

UVC ray – Ultraviolet rays that are beyond the ozone; have little effect on the exposure that the skin receives

V

Vaccination – Injection of antigens to stimulate the body's immune response

Vacuum – Machine that creates mild suction, which increases circulation to the surface of the skin

Vagus (VAY-gus) **nerve** – Tenth cranial nerve; nerve controlling motion and sensation of the ear, pharynx, pneumogastric (larynx, heart, lungs and esophagus); helps regulate the heartbeat

Value – Lightness or darkness of a color

Variable cost – Financial term describing cost changes on a monthly basis, including cost of utilities, supplies, promotions, postage and taxes

Variable rent – Type of lease in which renter pays set dollar amount per month plus a percentage of the total monthly income

Varicose (VAR-ih-kose) **vein** – Permanently dilated vein, most commonly occurring in the legs; swollen veins

Vein – Tubular, elastic, thin-walled branching vessel that carries oxygen-depleted blood from the capillaries to the heart

Vellus – Thin, soft, unpigmented hair covering the body

Venule – Small vein that joins capillaries to larger veins

Verbal communication – Type of communication involving level and tone of voice, inflection and rate of speech used to exchange messages

Verruca (VA-roo-kah) – Also called **warts**; viral infections on the top layer of skin caused by the Human Papilloma Virus (HPV)

Vertebrae – Bones that make up the spine

Vesicle (VES-i-kul) – Type of lesion; fluid-filled elevation in the skin caused by localized accumulation of fluids or blood just below the **epidermis**; also known as a blister

Vibration (vy-BRAY-shun) – Shaking massage manipulation achieved when the esthetician quickly shakes his or her arms while the fingertips or palms are touching the client

Vibrissae (vi-**BRIS**-see) – Mucus membranes in the nose that filter out dust, dirt and foreign debris

Villi (**VIL**-i) – Finger-like projections of the intestine walls that absorb nutrients

Virus – Sub-microscopic infectious agent that replicates itself only within cells of living hosts; many are **pathogenic**

Viscosity – Thickness or density of a product

Viscosity modifiers – Ingredients that help increase the density in emulsions and gel-type products; may be organic compounds

Visible light – Portion of the electromagnetic spectrum humans can see

Visualization Close – Strategy that helps the client to visualize using the product, then seeing the results

Vitamin – Ingredient that delivers a variety of benefits to the skin; organic substances essential for normal growth and activity

Vitiligo (VIT-i-**LEYE**-goh) – Acquired skin disease characterized by white patches caused by loss of pigment in melanin cells

Volt – Unit of electric pressure; short for voltage

Voluntary muscle – Also known as the striated (**STRI**-at-ed) muscle; muscle that responds to conscious commands

W

Warm color – Color classification that contains red or yellow undertones

Warm undertone – Color classification that contains light peach, yellow or medium peach

Wart – Viral infection on the top layer of skin caused by the Human Papilloma Virus (HPV); also called **verruca** (VA-roo-kah)

Water – Clear, colorless, odorless, tasteless liquid essential for almost all living things

Water-in-oil emulsion (W/O) – Cosmetic product type in which small water droplets are evenly dispersed in an oil-based solution

Water therapy – Also known as hydrotherapy or aquatherapy; companion therapy that can be used to moisturize, cleanse, rejuvenate and help eliminate toxins

Watt – Measure of how much electrical energy is being used

Wavelength – Measurement from the crest of one wave to the crest of the next

Waxing – Temporary hair removal process that involves applying wax directly to the skin and then removing the wax and hair

Wen – Harmless sebaceous cyst filled with **sebum** that usually appears on the scalp, neck or back; ranges in size from a pea to an orange; also called a **steatoma**

Wheal (weel) – Solid formation above the skin, often caused by insect bites or an allergic reaction

White blood cell (WBC) – Also called leucocyte (**LOO**-ko-site) or white corpuscle; blood cell that helps protect the body by fighting **bacteria** and other foreign substances; increases in number when infection invades the body

Whitehead – Plugged sebaceous gland with an opening that is not widely dilated; also referred to as a **closed comedo**

White light – Also referred to as combination light; visible light that can be broken into its individual wavelengths by a prism

Whorl – Epidermal ridge that gives palms and soles traction

Withholding tax – Tax taken from employee's income; the owner of a skin care center is responsible for keeping a percentage of funds from an employee's income for payment of certain taxes to the government

Word-of-mouth – News that is spread by verbal communication; best form of advertising in any customer service business

Worker's compensation insurance – State-controlled insurance required by law to cover any expense resulting from an injury to an employee while working in the skin care center

Wound – Break in the continuity of the skin caused by trauma to the tissue

Wringing – Massage manipulation; form of friction used on the arms and body; client's skin is grasped several inches apart and twisted in opposite directions

X

Xerosis – Dry, scaly skin caused by reduced **sebum** production; also called **Asteatosis**

Y

Yeast – Type of fungus found naturally in and on the human body

Yeast infection – Also known as **candida**; superficial fungal infection that occurs on moist areas of the skin

Ylang-Ylang – Aromatherapy oil incorporated into body therapies to enhance circulation; has antiseptic and soothing qualities

Z

Zygomatic (zi-go-**MAT**-ik) **bones** – Also known as the malar (**MA**-ler) bones; two bones that form the upper cheek and the bottom of the eye socket

Zygomatic (zi-go-**MAT**-ik) **nerve** – Nerve that extends to the side of the forehead, temple and upper part of the cheek

Zygomaticus (zi-go-**MAT**-ik-us) – Muscle located outside the corners of the mouth; draws the mouth up and back, as in laughing or smiling; consists of zygomaticus major and minor